Greenberg's® Guide To

· 1970 - 1991 ·
Lionel Trains

Volume II

By Roland E. LaVoie
Michael A. Solly,
and Louis A. Bohn

With the assistance of Andrea L. Kraszewski

Copyright © 1991
by Greenberg Publishing Company, Inc.

Greenberg Publishing Company, Inc.
7566 Main Street
Sykesville, Maryland 21784

(410) 795-7447

First Edition
First Printing

Manufactured in the United States of America

Greenberg Publishing Company, Inc. publishes the world's largest selection of Lionel, American Flyer, LGB, Marx, Ives, and other toy train publications as well as a selection of books on model and prototype railroading, dollhouse building, and collectible toys. For a complete listing of current Greenberg publications, please call 1-800-533-6644 or write to Kalmbach Publishing, 21027 Crossroads Circle, Waukesha, Wisconsin 53187.

Greenberg Shows, Inc. sponsors *Greenberg's Great Train, Dollhouse and Toy Shows*, the world's largest of its kind. The shows feature extravagant operating train layouts, and a display of magnificent dollhouses. The shows also present a huge marketplace of model and toy trains, for HO, N, and Z Scales; Lionel O and Standard Gauges; and S and 1 Gauges; plus layout accessories and railroadiana. They also offer a large selection of dollhouse miniatures and building materials, and collectible toys. Shows are scheduled along the East Coast each year from Massachusetts to Florida. For a list of our current shows please call (410) 795-7447 or write to Greenberg Publishing Company, Inc., 7566 Main Street, Sykesville, Maryland 21784 and request a show brochure.

Greenberg Auctions, a division of Greenberg Shows, Inc., offers nationally advertised auctions of toy trains and toys. Please contact our auction manager at (410) 795-7447 for further information.

ISBN 0-89778-273-9 (hardback)
ISBN 0-89778-272-0 (softback)

(Revised for vol. 2)

LaVoie, Roland, 1943-
    Greenberg's guide to Lionel trains, 1970-
1991.

        Rev. ed. of: Greenberg's guide to Lionel
trains, 1970-1988. 2nd. c1989.
        Includes index.
        Contents: v. 1. Motive power and rolling
stock. -- v. 2. [without special title]
        1. Railroads--Models. 2. Lionel Corporation.
I. Solly, Michael A. II. LaVoie, Roland, 1943-
Greenberg's guide to Lionel trains, 1970-1988.
III. Greenberg Publishing Company. IV. Title.
V. Title: Guide to Lionel trains, 1970-1991.
VI. Title: Lionel trains, 1970-1991.
TF197.L22 1991   625.1'9   90-23375
ISBN 0-89778-194-5 (v. 1)
ISBN 0-89778-189-9 (pbk. : v. 1)
ISBN 0-89778-273-9 (v. 2)
ISBN 0-89778-272-0 (pbk. : v. 2)

◆ TABLE OF CONTENTS ◆

SPECIALTY AREAS OF COLLECTING

Cover Photograph, Volume II: 1253 Quicksilver Express set; 12741 intermodal crane; Classics 13104 locomotive and tender, 13413 combination, 13414 parlor, 13415 observation; Large Scale 81007 Disney Magic Express set; TCA Bicentennial Special engine. L. Caponi, R. LaVoie, C. O'Dell, F. Stem and M. Wolf Collections.

Cover Photograph, Volume I: 18006 Reading T-1 and 18009 New York Central Mohawk. R. Kaptur Collection.

ACKNOWLEDGMENTS

*T*his volume represents a compilation of information from many expert readers and contributors. As each edition of a Greenberg's Lionel Guide is created, the accuracy and detail of the data is refined and sharpened. We are grateful for the assistance of our readers in this effort, and particularly for the outstanding contributions of the following individuals:

John Kouba, one of our manuscript readers, provided excellent detail articles on the Lionel Railroader Club series and the Modern Service Station Sets. He also lent quite a few sets from his collection to enhance the photography in this edition. John's enthusiasm and knowledge were critical to this book's production.

We would also like to acknowledge the efforts of Lou Caponi of *Train 99* and Al Rudman of *Sidetrack Hobbies* for their assistance and comments on Lionel Sets and Special Production. Lou also contributed important comments and trains for photographing for *Greenberg's Guide to Lionel, 1970-1991, Volume I*, and both gentlemen opened their stock and collection for some of the great pictures shown in this book. Our thanks to Mike Wolf of *Mike's Train House*; he granted an interview and graciously opened his doors to Greenberg's photography staff.

The cars produced by the Train Collectors Association comprise a large section of this book, and we would have been lost without the contributions and good will of the following TCA members: Raymond Connolly and Dr. Charles Weber of the Atlantic Division; Ron Artelli of the Southern Division; Ted Brahm of the NETCA Division; Richard Mertes from the Great Lakes Division and Detroit-Toledo Chapter; Chris Rohlfing of the Midwest Division; Tom Gibson from the Sacramento-Sierra Chapter; J. P. Neil of the North Texas Chapter; Newton Derby of the Lone Star Division; George Feyh and Joe Francis from METCA; Jon Lundvall of the Gateway Chapter; Dan Danielson of the WB & A Chapter; Gordon Hinkle from the Ft. Pitt Chapter; Larry Rinehart of the Three Rivers Chapter; and Tom Carney from the Pacific Northwest Division.

There are many other Lionel-related train operating and collector organizations throughout the United States and Canada. All their cars are described in this Volume. The accuracy of the data is due to the detailed contributions of the following officers and members: Bill Schmeelk and Bill Button of the Lionel Collectors Club of America. Mr. Schmeelk provided us with some pieces for photography; Mr. Button wrote a wonderful series on the cars for LCCA's *The Lion Roars*, which was an important reference for this book; The National Business Office of the Toy Train Operating Society provided critical data on TTOS production, as did member Mike Stella. Officers Dick Johnson and Geoff Swan of LOTS provided the definitive data on LOTS' interesting convention series. Geoff also collected the data on the series of cars made by the Lionel Collectors Association of Canada, and member Tom Gascoigne helped review the LCAC listings.

We'd like to acknowledge the support of some of the other collector clubs and their officers: Al Schwartz and Rich Williams of the Nassau Lionel Operating Engineers; Bill Mezger of the Virginia Train Collectors; John Link of the Inland Empire Train Collectors Association; and Ernie Knudsen of the Lionel Central Operating Lines.

We have worked closely over the past year and a half with John Newbraugh of Pleasant Valley Process/Newbraugh Brothers Toys. We are delighted to bring to light the many contributions John and Seymour Knight of PVP-NBT have made to the Lionel hobby. The information John provided has cleared up many Lionel mysteries and certainly "completes" the story of many train club cars.

Another fascinating story told in the Special Production chapter is the Guinness World's Record model train run made by Stewart Roberts in 1980. We appreciate Stew's help in telling the tale and in describing the special cars which were produced for the event.

Nor can any work of this magnitude be published without the critical edits and eyes of an army of manuscript readers. These outstanding Lionel experts again contributed their insight to this book, as each of them has many times in the past: Tony Arpino, Bill Beatty, Neil Fagan, Roland LaVoie, Clark O'Dell and Todd Wagner. The collections of Clark O'Dell and Roland LaVoie were used extensively for the new photos found throughout this Volume. Lou Bohn not only generated the new listings and text for the Lionel Large Scale and Classics chapters, but also reviewed the text for the remainder of the book as well. Lou has been an important contributor to Greenberg Guides for many years.

We are also grateful for the support of Mike Braga, Mark Gordon, Deborah Barton and the staff at Lionel Trains, Inc.

Lastly, we have received some wonderful contributions and details from readers over the past two years: Joe Nowaczyk added many new items and factory errors to the Guide; Patrick Guzzi sent us an important letter on the Nabisco set; Herman Hogue sent an interesting note on the True Value and Kay-Bee cars; Joe Alioto pointed out a few discrepancies in our Dash-diesel descriptions; Tom Watson sent an interesting letter on the Costco set; and Kit Walshock added details on the LOTS cars.

Many staff members of Greenberg Publishing Company, Inc. contributed their talents and professionalism to produce this book. Andrea Kraszewski, Greenberg's in-house editor for the project, organized the text, coordinated communications with many readers, directed photography, wrote captions, and supervised the general editorial direction and book compilation. Donna Dove and Andrea were responsible for the updated, contemporary look of this Volume (and Volume I). Maureen Crum designed the layout of and produced the mechanicals for the covers, devised the timeline for Chapter 1, and sized photographs. Donna Price proofread the book for typographical errors, style and consistency. Bruce Greenberg reviewed the text and, together with Brad Schwab, photographed the numerous train collections found throughout the pages of this book. Cindy Floyd and Samuel Baum supervised production.

My deepest thanks to all the apparent and anonymous train enthusiasts who contributed to our efforts.

————————

Michael A. Solly
September 1991

◆ INTRODUCTION ◆
MODERN ERA LIONEL

NUMBERING SYSTEMS

by Michael A. Solly

As a collector and operator, I was somewhat confused when I came to deciphering Lionel's complex numbering systems. Worse, when I joined the train clubs and started reading the for-sale ads in which members would post an item like "9153, $25", and nothing else, I'd start pounding the wall, trying to remember just what a 9153 was, whether I wanted it, and why this person did not put the name of the car in the ad! (The answer, of course, is that the ads are word-limited.)

Well, Greenberg's newest modern era Lionel Guide has come to the rescue. The following tables will guide you in understanding what types of rolling stock fit in which number sequences. These categories are generally accurate, but there are some cases (such as the 9100 and 9200 series) where Lionel would just toss cars in because it ran out of numbers somewhere else, and that was as good a place as any.

It is of interest to note that from 1970 to 1986, Lionel used a large segment of the numbers from 1 to 9999 for its

---

Lionel's Numbering System, 1970-1986

1XXX	Set designators
2XXX	Accessories
4XXX	Transformers
50XX, 51XX	O27 track and related items
55XX, 56XX	O track and related items
57XX	Reefers and bunk cars
61XX	Hoppers and ore cars
62XX	Gondolas and Standard O rolling stock
63XX	Tank cars
64XX	Cabooses and early Amtrak passenger cars
65XX	Flatcars, crane cars, searchlight cars and misc.
69XX	Later cabooses
72XX	Later passenger cars (after 1983)
73XX	Stock cars
74XX	A few boxcars
75XX	Lionel 75th Anniversary Set, reefers, boxcars and bullion cars
76XX	Bicentennial cars
77XX	Tobacco Road-series boxcars
78XX	Soda Pop and special series boxcars
79XX	Short O27 boxcars and operating cars
8"Y"XX	Engines: steam and diesel; "Y" is generally the last digit of the year the engine is produced
90XX	Hoppers, flatcars, cabooses, gondolas, boxcars and misc. (short O27-style rolling stock)
91XX	Vat cars, early hoppers, tank cars, auto carriers, gondolas, flatcars, cabooses and misc.
92XX	Early collector boxcars (early 1970s), hoppers, operating cars, tank cars, gonolas, flatcars, cabooses and misc.
93XX	Same description as for 92XX, but includes some bullion cars
94XX	Collector boxcars, late 1970s/early 1980s
95XX	Passenger cars, through 1983
96XX	Hi-cube boxcars, including Disney set
97XX	Collector boxcars, 1970s
98XX	Reefers and some Standard O rolling stock

Figure 0.1

production. For the most part, Lionel avoided using the numbers assigned to postwar rolling stock — which were principally in the 2000, 3000 and 6000 series — and engines in the 200- to 2000-ranges. Since 1970, Lionel has made far more pieces than the prewar or postwar Lionel Corporation could have ever imagined (see Figure 0.1).

In 1986 when management changed from Fundimensions to Kenner-Parker, and then to Richard Kughn's LTI, Lionel started to use a new five-digit numbering system. Actually, it is a six-digit numbering system, since each piece is technically numbered "6-XXXXX", but most hobbyists ignore the "6". The advantage is that Lionel now has 100,000 numbers from which to pick (90,000, if we omit the first 10,000 it used before 1987). The problem is that the numbers are harder to remember.

There is one major exception to the new numbering policy: Lionel continued stamping "8000-series" numbers on its locomotives — diesel, steam and electric — yet catalogues them in the "18000-series." This means also that there may be occasional duplicate numbers in the future, which has already happened with the 8800 Lionel Lines small steamer and the (1)8800 Lehigh Valley RS-3 diesel. Because Lionel has now divided the 18000 series into *Traditional* and *Collector* steam and diesel subcategories, it no longer uses the system whereby the digit after the "8" designates the year of production.

Lionel uses the term *Traditional* to designate its inexpensive, smaller rolling stock intended for the mass market. These include short (non-scale length) versions of gondolas, hoppers, boxcars, flatcars, tank cars and passenger cars. The term *O27* is often used interchangeably to describe them. This contrasts to *Collector* series (or "O") trains, which are generally longer, closer to true 1/48-scale proportions, and more expensive. The top-of-the-line is occupied by actual Scale models called the "Standard O" series, for which Lionel has now reserved a separate group of numbers (implying more production in that area). Recent years have seen Lionel move closer to scale model railroading in more ways than ever before.

The new numbering system distinguishes between these pieces, and the separation by car type continues under the new Lionel Trains, Inc. management. The engine categories were changed to reflect the division of plastic and die-cast steam engines, and divisions of the various Collector diesel types (F, GG-1, FM, SD, switcher, etc.) into separate number groups.

The company plans to consecutively use the numbering system without gaps, meaning if a number is initially assigned to a piece that is never made, the number will be reassigned to another piece (see Figure 0.2).

Of course, exceptions to these rules occur. Lionel continues an unfortunate policy (for us "historians") of not printing any numbers at all (or using dates such as "1989") on some of its very low-priced equipment. This makes these pieces

Lionel's Numbering System, 1987 to Present

11XXX	Set designators
127XX	Accessories
160XX	Small passenger cars (Traditional)
161XX	Tank cars and stock cars (Traditional)
162XX	Boxcars (Traditional)
163XX	Flatcars, gondolas, ore cars, barrel ramp cars (Traditional)
164XX	Hoppers (Traditional)
165XX	Cabooses (Traditional)
166XX	Operating cars (Traditional)
167XX	Bunk-type cars
168XX	Special Traditional club cars (Lionel RR Club, etc.)
170XX	Standard O two-bay hoppers (Collector)
171XX	Standard O three-bay hoppers (Collector)
172XX	Standard O boxcars (Collector)
173XX	Standard O reefers (Collector)
174XX	Standard O gondolas (Collector)
175XX	Standard O flatcars (Collector)
176XX	Standard O cabooses (Collector)
178XX	Special club cars (TCA, LCCA, LOTS, TTOS)
180XX	Steam engines (Collector)
181XX	Diesel engines: F-type (Collector)
182XX	Diesel engines: SD-type (Collector)
183XX	Diesel and electric engines: FM and GG-1 (Collector)
184XX	Motorized units
185XX	Diesel engines, switchers: GP-series (Collector)
186XX	Die-cast steam engines (Traditional)
187XX	Plastic steam engines (Traditional)
188XX-189XX	Diesel engines (Traditional)
190XX	Passenger cars, plastic (Traditional)
191XX	Passenger cars, aluminum (Collector)
192XX	Boxcars: "Famous Name" (Collector)
193XX	Hoppers and ore cars (Collector)
194XX	Flatcars, gondolas and crane cars (Collector)
195XX	Reefers and stock cars (Collector)
19600-19649	Tank cars (Collector)
19650-19699	Tool cars and bunk cars (Collector)
197XX	Cabooses (Collector)
198XX	Operating cars (Collector)
199XX	Special series cars (Christmas, Toy Fair, I Love, etc.)

If you're wondering what happened to the other 80,000 numbers and what Lionel will do with them, remember that the company no longer makes just O scale trains!:

130XX	Standard Gauge items
21000	Revolver cars
330XX	RailScope items
48XXX	American Flyer S Gauge items
51XXX	O Gauge Classics
8XXXX	Large Scale
9XXXX	Carry-over sets (from pre-1987)

Figure 0.2

harder to track and list. The company does assign catalogue numbers to them for internal use, but does not always publish them. Thus, gaps remain in the number sequence.

At the premium end of the line, some of the train club cars often receive numbers based on real train equipment numbers. These numbers are outside the usual numbering scheme. LOTS does this for all its cars, and LCCA and TTOS have done it on some pieces.

Then there is the wonderful story about the recent TTOS tank car. The designer scribbled a random number on the artwork for the car he sent to Lionel, assuming Lionel would assign a regular catalogue number to it for production. When the car came out, the designer discovered that Lionel had obediently decorated the car with the number he had written, which turned out to be his telephone number!

Lionel has also assigned prototype numbers to many of its top-of-the-line engines, including the 3100 Great Northern and the 1776 Bicentennial engines. The great scale Hudsons follow the 700-number sequence of their original 700E ancestors.

The unusual numbers on these Collector trains are not a problem because the catalogue numbers are generally published and printed on the box.

LIONEL "BUILT" DATES

In the postwar years, Lionel printed "built dates," or "NEW" dates, on its production pieces similar to the way in which real railroads identified their rolling stock. The built dates were typically in formats such as "BLT 4-53". On a real railroad car this would mean that the car was built in April 1953. However, in the Lionel world it may or may not refer to the actual production year, and almost never to the actual month of production.

In the past, Lionel sometimes omitted printing built dates on cars. Recently, in concert with the introduction of its new five-digit numbering system, Lionel established a policy of including built dates on most items it makes (but not all — the handcars still have no numbers). In order to avoid changing the heat stamp or Tampo plates at the last minute, Lionel decided to simply indicate "BLT 1-89" or "BLT 1-90" for items built in those years, regardless of the actual month they were produced. Most of the time these dates will be correct, but sometimes things get confused due to production delays. For example, 1989's "Midnight Shift" Traditional Line set made an appearance as an uncatalogued Toys 'R Us set in 1988 (set 11708), so that all its rolling stock was given "BLT 1-88" dates. In 1989 it appeared as the "Midnight Shift" (also set number 11708) in the Lionel catalogue. However, its rolling stock was still labeled 1988.

There are, as always, exceptions to the general rule. Many of the specialty club cars show specific dates stamped on them, commemorating a convention or other club event. For instance, the recent Lionel Railroader Club searchlight car has "BLT 5-90" on it.

Due to Lionel's continuing manufacture of many Traditional Line pieces of rolling stock, it is not unusual to find cars

with built dates many years earlier than the date the set actually came out. For example, some of the recent low-end Traditional sets or specialty sets use an Atlantic Coast Line small steamer and SP red caboose which are dated 1979!

REPORTING VARIATIONS

By Michael A. Solly

One of the most exciting events that can happen in this hobby (other than running a Hudson at full throttle around a layout), is discovering previously unknown and unreported variations in Lionel trains. We often get letters from readers stating that they have an unusual piece with a feature different than what is called out in our listing.

It is important for every hobbyist to understand how we distinguish factory production variations from post-Lionel factory changes. Many features on Lionel trains are easily switched or altered. The definition of a variation is that it came that way from the factory. Many tinkerers enjoy modifying their trains. Some of the most talented tinkerers work for Lionel's licensed "Service Stations"! Many people paint, rebuild or otherwise alter a unique piece for their own enjoyment and layout, or to meet the request of a customer or fellow hobbyist. Such pieces do not qualify as factory variations, and so should not be expected to fetch any more on the open market than the original piece. This is not to say, however, that an individual will not be willing to pay extra for it because he finds the piece attractive.

Our readers should make an effort to determine if a piece has been altered outside the factory before reporting it as a new variation. The following is a discussion of some of the more common changes we have encountered:

TRUCKS: Trucks (the wheel sets) on most Lionel train cars are very easy to change. Most of the time, an owner or dealer changes the truck because the old one is broken; but on occasion someone changes a car's trucks because he prefers another design, or feels the piece looks better with other trucks, or because he does not have replacement trucks of the same type as the original. Therefore, for variations in truck type, we prefer reports based on mint (new-out-of-the-box) pieces. We ask that you only report truck differences when you have reasonable confidence that the piece has not been changed. In some cases, older cars can be reported if the user can trace its history fully back to its original condition.

COUPLERS: Variations in couplers are troublesome because couplers are easily changed, and many operators prefer two operating couplers on their rolling stock. So one occasionally finds (especially with some of the smaller O27 rolling stock or cabooses) a piece with two operating couplers where only one or no operating couplers were originally present. This may bring a modest premium (in the sense that it improves operations), but should not be considered a true factory variation. This problem has been a source of frustration in determining the original configuration for our Guides.

Photograph courtesy of Artrain; B. Schwab photograph

Uncatalogued 17885 Artrain tank car from 1990 (see Volume I, page 321, for complete description).

REFRIGERATOR ROOF AND ENDS: The roof and end section on a refrigerator car is attached to the sides and bottom by two screws. It is a simple matter to switch roofs between cars. However, this is not a factory-produced variation. This particular change has an innocent motivation, though; for the most part, it is a matter of someone thinking the car looks better with a different color roof than with its own. Lionel Service Stations, and sometimes Lionel itself, would change roof/end pieces, particularly on the refrigerator cars from the early-to mid-1970s. There are some legitimate factory variations in which Lionel used other stock roof and end piece if it ran out of the intended one. This occurred often with the Bicentennial boxcars, for example. It is very difficult to prove that the factory produced a roof/end combination that differs from the usual version. There are reports of some people switching roof/end pieces and seeking a premium price. We recommend that enthusiasts not pay a premium for refrigerator roof and end variations.

CAR FRAMES: The metal or plastic underframes on Lionel's rolling stock, particularly boxcars, are easily altered. So frame style variations do not generally affect the value of an item. But for the purpose of documenting production, we are interested in learning about pieces with non-standard frames assembled by the factory. Frames can also be switched between some types of diesel engines.

BOXCAR DOORS: Although these are very easy to change, some vendors have sold them for a premium. Even if original, it is not reasonable to pay a premium for a door color variation. This is a difficult matter because Lionel did sometimes use stock of different color doors to complete a production run. We are interested in learning of these variations.

SET CONTENTS: One fascinating aspect of Lionel sets is the firm's frequent switching of the cars (and even sometimes of the engines) packaged with lower-end Traditional Line sets. We have received letters from readers indicating that their set contents do not match those published in our book. These are legitimate variations of the set — in fact, Lionel goes so far as to print a notice saying that set contents can vary due to availability.

So a set which normally came with the blue 9035 Conrail O27 boxcar, for example, may be found with the brown 9037 boxcar in place of the blue car — mint and unopened — depending on the availability of the 9035 boxcar when the set was packaged. This often happens when sets are catalogued from one year to the next, and Lionel runs out of a particular piece of rolling stock between years. Still, readers should be aware that set contents can also be switched by owners after they have been opened. Be wary if the seller tries to convince you the set came with an unusual or rare car, and charges you a premium over what the set would typically cost, or conversely argues that a set without a premium car which it normally includes is a complete set.

Also bear in mind that Lionel has released special versions of its regularly catalogued sets with one special car included (in place of a regular-issue one) to sell to individual department or hardware store chains. These are legitimate factory sets, and usually are given a special Lionel set number different from the regular set number. They will not be found in the Lionel catalogues. Examples are the Toys 'R Us sets which appear every year — Lionel uses a regular Heavy Iron set (and Heavy Iron set box) with a special Toys 'R Us giraffe boxcar included in place of the standard O27 boxcar. Since these sets are produced in limited quantities, they command a higher price over normal Traditional Line sets, as do the special cars themselves.

OPERATIONAL FEATURES: Many operators of Lionel trains have specific preferences. Some, for example, favor the old mechanical E-unit device used to reverse Lionel's locomotives in the pre-microcircuit age. These operators do not trust the electronic "magic" of the electronic reverse unit circuit board developed in the last 15 years. And many operators are also incurable tinkerers. So it is not uncommon, for example, to find a recent engine for sale which has had its electronic reverse unit changed to the older-style mechanical E-unit! This would not, of course, be a factory variation; but unless the seller discloses the change, the buyer may not suspect. When it comes to the action and power in Lionel's accessories, engines and rolling stock, there are infinite ways in which things can be altered. And veteran Lionel operators and tinkerers have tried many of them! Smoke units can be added in steam engines where there was none originally, headlights can be installed, interior lights can be installed or changed, sound systems added or changed, even entire motor trucks changed out from one type to another. These sorts of major changes are in the great majority of cases simply post-factory alterations, a fact of which the buyer should be made aware at the time of purchase. If you encounter such a piece, investigate its background before reporting it. If you can substantiate that the factory produced it, then you have an important variation; please write to us about it.

LOADS: Loads carried in such rolling stock as flatcars, gondolas and hoppers are easily changed. In fact, Lionel markets a variety of loads. An ore car, for example, could come with brown or black plastic ore loads. A gondola could be loaded with cable reels, round canisters, or even the strange square radioactive waste canisters, among millions of other household possibilities. Generally, load variations are not considered significant to the value of the car itself. However, we are interested in hearing from readers who encounter mint-in-the-box cars with loads different from those described in the listings.

COLORS: Colors are a consistent source of interest and confusion in Lionel trains, especially when it comes to fine distinctions in shade. We have difficulty determining if a variation reported by a reader is a new color variation unless the reader has directly compared the two versions. Some of the 9700-series boxcars were made in a wide variety of paint and plastic mold colors. Most of these observed variations are legitimate variations due to production methods. However, it is difficult to confirm this unless the reader provides a basis of comparison. If a reader has a question as to the color shade of the paint, plastic or lettering on a car, the best way to report it is to 1) compare it to another version of the same car, and 2) report the color of the variation as compared to the color of another piece pictured in this book. For example, the "royal" blue color of a boxcar variation may be the same shade as one of the quad hoppers pictured here.

In the last few years, Lionel has tightened its production processes, and the number of variations in recent train production has dropped substantially.

DETERMINING VALUES

Toy train values vary for a number of reasons. First, consider the **relative knowledge** of the buyer and seller. A seller may be unaware that he has a rare variation and sell it for the price of a common piece. Another source of price variation is **short-term fluctuation** which depends on what is being offered at a given train meet on a given day. If, for example, four 8100s are for sale at a small meet, we would expect that supply would outpace demand and lead to a reduction in price. A related source of variation is the **season** of the year. The train market is slower in the summer and sellers may, at this time, be more inclined to reduce prices if they really want to move an item. Another important source of price variation is the relative strength of the seller's **desire to sell** and the buyer's **eagerness to buy**. Clearly, a seller in economic distress will be more eager to strike a bargain. Another source of price variation is **regional location**. Not only are trains generally less plentiful in the South and West than they are in the Northeast, but there are regional road name preferences as well. For example, Union Pacific items may be hard to find and expensive in the West due to high collector interest in that road name; yet Reading and Erie, which are more in demand in the East, may be somewhat easier to find in Western regions. A final source of variation is the **personalities** of the seller and buyer. Some sellers like to quickly turn over items and, therefore, price their items to move; others seek a higher price and will bring an item to meet after meet until they find a willing buyer.

Train values in this book are based on *obtained* prices, rather than asking prices. The prices represent a "ready sale," that is, prices most likely to effect a quick sale at most large train meets. They may sometimes appear lower than those seen on trains at meets for two reasons. First, items that readily sell often do so in the first hour of a train meet and, therefore, are no longer visible. (We have observed that a good portion of the action at most meets occurs in the first hour.) The items that do not sell in the first hour have a higher price tag, and this price, although not necessarily representing the actual sale price, is the price found. A related source of pricing discrepancy is the willingness of some sellers to bargain over price.

Another factor which may affect prices is reconditioning done by the dealer. Some dealers take great pains to clean and service their pieces so that they look their best and operate properly. Others sell their items just as they received them, dust and all. Naturally, the more effort the dealer expends in preparing his pieces for sale, the more he can expect to charge for them. This factor may account for significant price differences among dealers selling the same equipment.

From our studies of train prices, it appears that mail-order prices for used trains are generally higher than those obtained at train meets. This is appropriate considering the costs and efforts of producing and distributing a price list and packing and shipping items. Mail-order items do sell at prices above those listed in this book.

On some items, we have indicated **No Reported Sales** (**NRS**) in the value column. This does not necessarily indicate that an item is particularly rare. It simply indicates that inadequate information is available for pricing these items.

CONDITION

For each item, we provide four categories: *Good* (GD), *Very Good* (VG), *Excellent* (EXC), *Mint* (MT). For 1991 and 1992 items, we state *Current Production* (CP).

GOOD — Scratches, small dents, dirty.

VERY GOOD — Few scratches, exceptionally clean, no dents or rust.

EXCELLENT — Minute scratches or nicks, no dents or rust.

MINT — Brand new, absolutely unmarred with no visible signs of handling, in original box.

CURRENT PRODUCTION — Means that the item is either now being manufactured of is currently available from retail stores.

In the toy train field there is a great deal of concern with exterior appearance and less concern with operation. If operation is important to you, ask the seller if the train runs. If the seller indicates that he does not know whether the equipment operates, you should test it. Most train meets have test tracks for that purpose.

We include Mint prices in this edition because of the important trade in post-1970 mint items. However, there is substantial confusion in the minds of both sellers and buyers as to what constitutes "Mint" condition. How do we define mint? Among very experienced train enthusiasts, a mint piece means that it is brand new, in its original box, never run, and extremely bright and clean (and the box is, too). An item may have been removed from the box and replaced in it, but it should show no evidence of handling. A piece is not mint if it shows any scratches, fingerprints, or evidence of discoloration. It is the nature of the market for the seller to see his item in a very positive light and to seek to obtain a mint price for an excellent piece. In contrast, a buyer will see the same item in a less favorable light and will attempt to buy a mint piece for the price of one in excellent condition. It is our responsibility to point out this difference in perspective *and* the difference in value implicit in each perspective. Buyers and sellers will need to settle or negotiate their different perspectives.

We do not show values for Fair or Restored. **Fair** items are valued substantially below Good. We have not included **Restored** because such items are not a significant portion of the market for modern era trains.

As we indicated, prices in this book were derived from large train meets or shows. If you have trains to sell and you sell them to a person planning to resell them, you should not expect to obtain the prices reported in this book. Rather, you should expect to achieve about 50 to 75 percent of these prices. Basically, for your items to be of interest to a buyer who plans to resell them, he must purchase them for considerably less than the prices listed here.

We receive many inquiries as to whether or not a particular piece is a "good value." This book will help answer that question; but, there is NO substitute for experience in the marketplace. *We strongly recommend that novices do not make major purchases without the assistance of friends who have experience in buying and selling trains.* If you are buying a train and do not know whom to ask about its value, look for the people running the meet or show and discuss with them your need for assistance. Usually they can refer you to an experienced collector who will be willing to examine the piece and offer his opinion.

T
◆ CHAPTER 1 ◆
HE LIONEL MARKET

LIONEL: YESTERDAY, TODAY AND TOMORROW

By Bruce C. Greenberg

*F*or most people, the name "Lionel" represents a generic word for toy trains. Most are unaware of the interesting history of the Lionel Corporation, the manufacturer of these delightful and intensely collectable toys.

Today, the original Lionel Corporation no longer makes trains, an odd fact of which the general public is not aware. The Lionel Corporation is primarily in the "leisure" business, marketing toys through its Kiddie City chains.

In the early 1950s, Lionel's market consisted of hundreds of thousands of families buying toy trains at large department stores and small independent toy, hardware and hobby shops. Lionel's 1950s market was for toys, not scale models. From the late 1940s through the mid-1950s, the "traditional" mass toy market likely accounted for 90 percent and more of Lionel's sales. Collectors, buying the glamorous high-priced trains, comprised only a small part of Lionel's total market, and did not become a significant potential market until the mid-1970s.

In the late 1950s, Joshua Cowen retired and his management process and objectives disappeared. During this same time, due to many external forces — recession, race cars, HO and quality control — and internal problems, Lionel O Gauge train sales plummeted. Several Lionel chief executives sought to stem the losses, but demand for Lionel trains substantially declined. In the late 1950s and early 1960s, Lionel attempted to diversify into other product lines. Lionel reduced costs by reducing quality, and sales declines accelerated.

Lionel ceased train production in 1967 at Irvington, New Jersey, and moved to Hagerstown, Maryland in 1968. It moved back to New Jersey in 1969. Then, in late 1969, Lionel ceased production once again in New Jersey and licensed

General Mills to make trains. General Mills moved production to Mt. Clemens, Michigan. The differences in management style and production policy between New Jersey and Michigan were so substantial that historians have marked it as the dividing line between the "modern era" and the "postwar" period.

In the late 1960s, General Mills and other large American corporations diversified their sales by acquiring lines in other fields. The General Mills managers recognized that the Lionel market had shrunk. Initially, General Mills focused on inexpensive and moderately priced trains which were marketed through discount toy stores, department stores, and small retailers.

Starting in 1970, Lionel trains were made by General Mills' Model Products Corporation (MPC) division for three years, and later by the renamed Fundimensions division (1973 to 1986). General Mills first recognized the collector market in 1973, when its Lionel operation, part of the MPC division, marketed the 8359 Gold Chessie GP-7. The successful sale of the 8359 convinced Fundimensions that a large collector market existed.

Lionel's share of the overall train market was probably about 20 percent. It recognized that this market would not accept problem-plagued equipment and wanted new items. MPC introduced modern features into the trains. Although tooling for new body styles was not feasible, MPC produced a wide variety of road names for both locomotives and rolling stock. These items featured bright graphics which were more attractive than many postwar pieces. New ideas were utilized, including modern electronics for electronic whistles and the Sound of Steam. One of the simplest and most important improvements made by MPC was the change from conventional to "fast angle" wheels, which greatly reduced friction and made much longer trains possible. Eventually, Lionel produced new-style engines and rolling stock, appealing to a new generation of hobbyists.

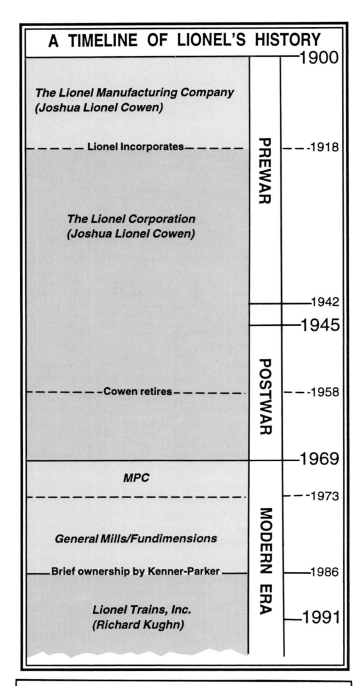

A TIMELINE OF LIONEL'S HISTORY

1900

The Lionel Manufacturing Company
(Joshua Lionel Cowen)

— — — — Lionel Incorporates — — — — —   - -1918

PREWAR

The Lionel Corporation
(Joshua Lionel Cowen)

1942

1945

POSTWAR

— — — — Cowen retires — — — — —   - - -1958

1969

MPC   - - -1973

General Mills/Fundimensions

— Brief ownership by Kenner-Parker —   1986

MODERN ERA

Lionel Trains, Inc.
(Richard Kughn)   1991

Figure 1.1

Through it all, however, there was one constant — the name "LIONEL." The Lionel Corporation recognized the power of its name, and therefore licensed, not sold, the rights to General Mills when it took over their manufacture. There was no market for "General Mills" trains, but many people wanted to buy Lionel trains.

Under MPC and late Fundimensions management, Lionel trains sales volume grew. However, the market was drastically smaller than that of the 1950s, and the company adjusted production quantities to market demands and adjusted prices based on these much smaller runs. Whereas

typical runs of hundreds of thousands were made in the 1950s, only a few thousand would be made. In the 1950s, Lionel offered rolling stock in relatively few road names; in the 1980s Lionel offered many. Lionel expanded its Service Station network and increased the number of dealers marketing its trains. The low-end Traditional sets were primarily sold by the discount mass market toy stores such as Toys 'R' Us. Lionel carefully determined the demand for its sets and cars by planning production based on orders from the New York Toy Fair and from its dealer network. In some cases, the company limited production to pre-orders. The era of the "limited edition" had arrived.

A major upsurge in demand for Lionel trains, and model railroading in general, began in the mid-1980s. It has been fostered by people who enjoyed trains as children in the 1940s and 1950s. In fact, Lionel's current owner, developer Richard Kughn, is a train enthusiast himself. He bought the license and tooling rights in 1986, and changed the company's name to "Lionel Trains, Inc." (LTI).

Although some people experience sticker shock when returning to Lionel, times have not changed so much as our relative wealth and our perception of what is expensive. Given the rates of inflation, the $60 Rail Blazer train sets of today are not relatively more expensive than the same $11 train sets of the 1950s. In fact, the current sets are more colorful and reliable. So, too, the Collector-line Hudsons of today compare favorably at $1100 to the $90 to $100 Hudsons of the 1940s and 1950s.

Therefore, prices appear high in this hobby (for some pieces!). Lionel prices, in part, reflect the small production quantities and the strong demand for these goods.

Good shopping pays dividends, and understanding market forces makes one a better buyer. Prices change in response to changes in consumer preferences.

A classic case today is the Trailers-On-Flat-Cars (TOFCs). For many years, the CP Rail flatcar with trailer was a common piece, selling for $25, because flatcars had little use except as general rolling stock. In the last year, the CP car price jumped to $60. Why? Because demand for trailer-flatcar combinations has surged. When Lionel issued the intermodal crane, it improved the play value of flatcars with trailers. Using the crane, operators have built "industries" which require transferring trailers from flatcars to trucks and vice versa. Lionel has even manufactured standard tractor-trailers which use the same trailers as used on the cars. These tractor-trailers look good near the model factories and on the model roads. Lionel also produced a new single-van TOFC, and a squared-end TOFC (Wabash/Lionel). These new products increased interest in the earlier pieces. Demand for older cars increased and dealers raised their prices.

There is one special TOFC, the Kodak TOFC, which has dramatically appreciated. Although the entire TTOS membership had the opportunity to buy these, only a few hundred cars were produced. Subsequent demand far exceeded supply. The price has skyrocketed. Fortunately, you can always buy something else!

Lionel's limited production runs of some pieces has led to dissatisfaction by some hobbyists. Many collectors have specific areas of interest — certain road names, for example, or certain types of cars, or certain years of production. The

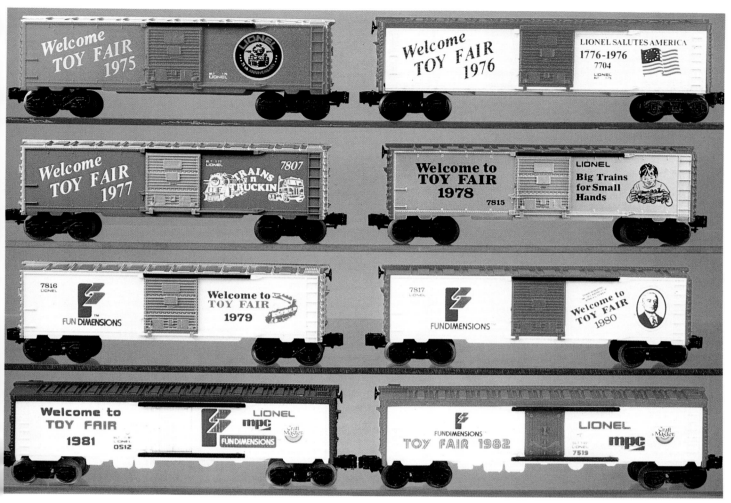

A. Rudman and W. Schmeelk Collections; B. Greenberg photograph

Lionel's first Toy Fair cars, all uncatalogued, marking the annual New York toy show. Lionel had made overstamped cars in 1973 and 1974 (see Volume I for complete descriptions).
Top shelf: 9762 from 1975, no catalogue number on car; 7704 wood-sided boxcar from 1976 (a Canadian version was also made this year).
Second shelf: 7807 boxcar from 1977; 7815 boxcar from 1978.
Third shelf: 7816 from 1979, Fundimensions "F" logo added; 7817 boxcar from 1980.
Bottom shelf: 0512 from 1981, Lionel switched the series to reefers; 7519 reefer from 1982.

problem is, no matter what the area of specialization, there are always one or two pieces (such as the Kodak TOFC) which prove very difficult to find and thus prevent completion of the collection. But this adds to the challenge of collecting and increases the appreciation of the limited run. Lionel is in a balancing act on this one. Lionel's factory setup and use of subcontractors limit how many cars it can produce in one run. Lionel has suffered in the past by overproducing pieces that do not sell well, so it now produces the quantity it believes will rapidly sell. In an expanding hobby, this has produced frequent undersupply. But Lionel management knows that if production runs are too small, hobbyists will be discouraged and may even discontinue collecting. But collectors also want the excitement of watching their last year's purchase increase in value. Also bear in mind Lionel's marketing experience. The higher the ticket price, the fewer Lionel produces, because the market is smaller for high-priced items. Lionel believes it

is better to produce fewer quantities in more varieties than too many of one piece. And collectors enjoy more rapid appreciation of their collection. (You will see summer of 1990 replays where goods are selling below cost. This leads to dealer financial failure and could lead to Lionel failure because dealers do not pay their bills.)

This emphasizes again the most significant development in Lionel trains in the modern era — the entire market is considerably smaller, in terms of numbers produced, than the late postwar era. This can be good if you are an owner or seller, since your pieces have appreciated in value. But it is bad for a new buyer trying to find older pieces from the 1970s and 1980s.

Now that we have summarized the current market, we can speculate on the future: There are signs that the rapid price increases of the last several years may be slowing. The 1990-1991 recession may reduce the rate of appreciation and

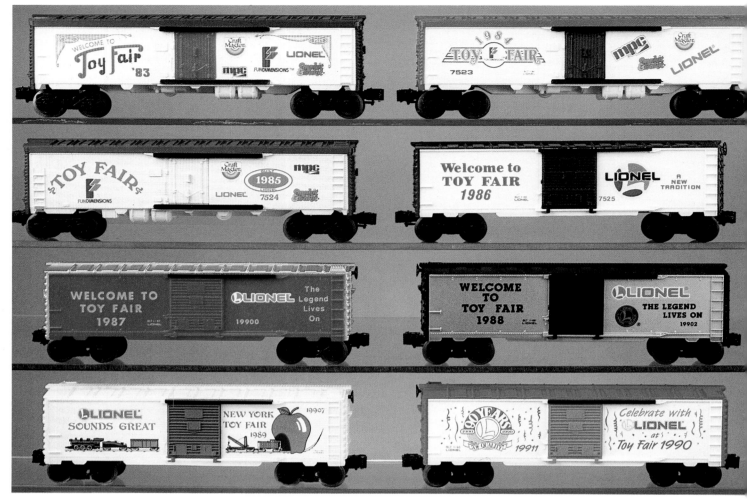

The most recent Toy Fair cars, all hard to find (see Volume I for complete descriptions).
A. Rudman and W. Schmeelk Collections; B. Greenberg photo.
Top shelf: 7521 reefer with extensive graphics, from 1983; 7523 reefer from 1984.
Second shelf: 7524 reefer from 1985; 7525 boxcar from 1986, new logos and slogans signifying Lionel's change in ownership.
Third shelf: 19900 boxcar from 1987; 19902 boxcar from 1988.
Bottom shelf: 19907 boxcar from 1989; 19911 boxcar from 1990.

in some areas reduce prices. Some people in the hobby consider certain pieces substantially overvalued, loudly proclaiming they will not buy them, possibly reducing overall demand. For example, the price of postwar and modern F-3 diesels has skyrocketed in the last few years in part because few were offered for sale. The rapidly increasing prices paradoxically led sellers to hold on to these engines, as a speculative fever swept the market. Collectors believed that these trains would be worth even more in the future. Yet the supply of F-3s is quite large. The F-3s went up much faster then the equally desirable GG-1s and FM Trainmasters.

Another positive sign has been the rapid growth of Lionel product offerings under the leadership of Richard Kughn. Responding to increasing numbers of Lionel hobbyists, the company has embarked on an expansion plan to produce more varieties and greater quantities of most of its line. The average number made of each train item is gradually increasing, and this should moderate price increases.

LIONEL'S MOVE TO SCALE

A significant and positive trend in the train market is Lionel's movement toward scale railroading.

Most model railroaders choose smaller scales rather than Lionel's "O", or 1/48, scale. A majority of model railroaders operate in "HO" (Half-O), or 1/87; some prefer "N" (1/160) or even the smaller "Z" (1/220). The preferences reflect the lower cost of smaller gauge trains and the mistaken belief that larger trains are not realistic, and in particular that the very size of large trains precludes realistic model railroads. In fact, many Lionel enthusiasts believe that high levels of realism are only possible in HO or N. Lionel enthusiasts often fail to recognize that the "realistic" HO and N layouts shown in *Model Railroader* are the works of exceptionally skilled builders and magnificent photography. Most HO and N layouts are highly stylized interpretations of the real world, just as are Lionel layouts.

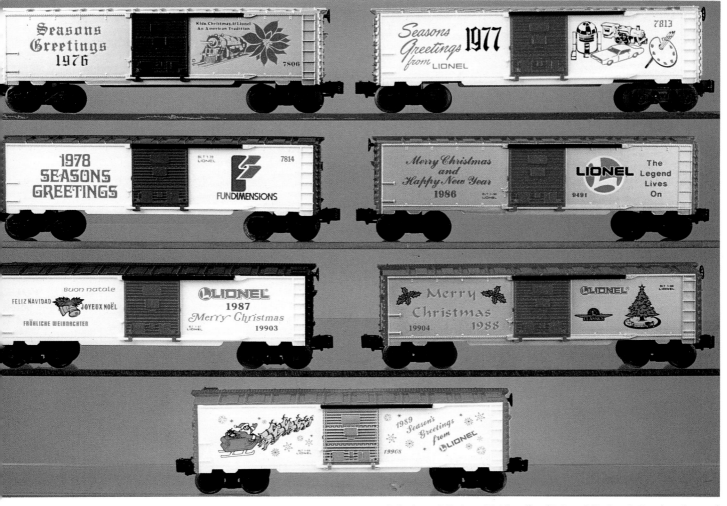

S. Goodman, A. Rudman, W. Schmeelk and F. Stem Collections; B. Greenberg photograph

…el's Season's Greetings boxcars. Pieces from the 1970s are very hard to find. Overstamped cars were made in 1973 and 1974. A car from 1975 is not …own (see Volume I for complete descriptions).

…shelf: **7806 from 1976; 7813 from 1977.**
…nd shelf: **7814 from 1978 (no cars were made from 1979 to 1984; a very rare 9490 from 1985 exists); 9491 from 1986.**
…d shelf: **19903 from 1987; 19904 from 1988.**
…m shelf: **19908 from 1989.**

During the early 1970s, Lionel/Fundimensions recognized that a larger percentage of its market consisted of serious adult model railroaders than in earlier years. These hobbyists were not interested in "toy" products like cop and hobo cars or exploding boxcars. Rather, they sought to model the real railroading world, complete with real timetables, realistic operations, industrial facilities and, most important, scale model trains and accessories.

Some former Lionel modelers have decided to build DC-powered, two-rail model railroads using rolling stock and motive power from small O Gauge manufacturers. These modelers have generally not used Lionel products because they are slightly undersized. They could not use Lionel locomotives, since they are designed to operate on tubular, three-rail track. Lionel has continued with this track because of the great advantages it gives to operators. It greatly simplifies wiring and facilitates the use of track-operated

accessories. Lionel has not made two-rail O Gauge equipment because the market is too small.

Lionel's equipment is very attractive to a fast-growing group of model railroaders — the Hi-Railers. Hi-Railers recognize the operating advantages of Lionel track, but want scale realism. Lionel is now making equipment for these people. In 1976, Lionel produced only seven pieces of rolling stock that are scale-proportioned, about three percent of its total product line. In 1990, Lionel manufactured 20 items (18 percent of its line).

Recently, Lionel has produced four scale-length engine models (the T-1, Northern, B-6 and Mohawk), and introduced scale-sized tank cars in 1990. This followed the introduction of scale-sized two- and three-bay ACF hopper cars in 1986 during and after the B & A Hudson offer.

Since 1973, the company has offered Standard O scale boxcars, refrigerators and gondolas. However, the earliest pieces did not sell well because little compatible equipment (particularly engines) existed with which to run them, and few things look worse than a Standard O boxcar in the same train as an O27 short boxcar. However, as time went on, more cars were released in O Scale size — flatcars, cabooses, and a new scale SD-40 diesel. Now the older Standard O pieces are in considerable demand.

In the mid-1980s, Lionel became bolder in its scale production — the full-length Hudsons reappeared, to the delight of many veteran Lionel railroaders. With the first one came a handsome set of four New York Central Standard O cars. Then, in 1986 came a real breakthrough: In conjunction with the direct mail offer of the 784 Hudson, Lionel produced new scale models of the ACF center-flow hopper car and the wood-side caboose. Because the Hudson direct mail campaign was not successful, the scale cars are highly prized items.

For the last five years, Lionel has included one or two sets of Standard O scale-length cars and engines in each year's catalogue. Examples are the Burlington Northern boxcar unit train from 1985 (a surprising first for modern Lionel), the Chessie hopper unit train in 1988, the CP Rail set from 1989, and the Santa Fe Dash 8 set from 1990. Many scale freight cars are now available: boxcars, refrigerators, hoppers, gondolas, flatcars, cabooses, and now tank cars. The scale Hudsons and the SD-40 diesels head the list of engines to pull them. Will scale-size long passenger cars be next?

Lionel plans to continue its inexpensive Traditional line market, and seeks a 50-50 sales balance between its Collector and Traditional lines. Collectors will pressure Lionel to produce trains and accessories with greater realism, finer detail and better operation. Lionel likely enjoys higher profit margins from its Collector series.

RECOMMENDATIONS FOR THE BEGINNING COLLECTOR

The following are our recommendations for building a quality collection. These suggestions will help you accomplish more with your train budget. Several of these suggestions were discovered the hard way, by not following them and suffering the consequences! Many will be helpful to experienced hobbyists.

1. READ: You have already taken an important first step by obtaining this Guide! Reading books on Lionel is not only fun but will provide you with important information to direct you in your purchases. By studying this book, you will be much better equipped as a buyer.

2. MAKE FRIENDS IN THE HOBBY: You can make lasting friends in the train hobby, people who will be willing to trade with you, enjoy operating your layout, go to meets with you, and even sell pieces to you at reduced prices. This is really one of the greatest benefits of train collecting and one of the best ways to build your collection. The friendships you make can last a lifetime.

3. LOCAL DEALERS: A good local dealer will help you build a collection. He may take pre-production orders, and help you purchase items that are not offered on the open market at a reasonable price.

4. PRE-ORDER: One of the secrets of collecting modern era Lionel is to place early orders for trains with your local shop or a trusted mail-order house. The best time to purchase new items is during the early order period, usually September through November. Prices are usually lower before the trains are produced. However, you take a risk by making non-refundable deposits and buying sight unseen.

5. LOOK FOR UNDISCOVERED GEMS: Do not seek the big-ticket glamour items right away; they are subject to considerable price fluctuation. Look for things other people are not looking for! Concentrate on some of the areas which have not been discovered. There are still many items available at modest prices. Then someday, when your specialty is discovered, you may enjoy substantial appreciation.

6. SHOP AROUND, BE PATIENT, CONTROL YOURSELF! This is the hardest of our rules to follow, but potentially the most important. You will often be tempted to immediately buy a rare or unusual item in excellent condition. You will say: "I may never see the piece again." Almost every collector has made such purchases. Eventually you will find the piece again. Patience is a great virtue. Let your collection build over time, savor the process. Don't try to get everything Lionel ever made all at once. Never let on that you are anxious to buy something, even when you are. Another important hint applies for collectors of the newer Lionel pieces: at many meets, dealers are selling the same trains. This makes for great competition, shopping and deals for you. Do not be afraid to negotiate. Another hint: One of the problems for Lionel dealers is that Lionel requires prepayment by its dealers for its line. Hence the dealers must put up substantial cash. Sometimes you will find dealers offering "fire sales" of older stock at or below cost, to raise cash for new orders. This usually happens around February. The same rules of shopping apply to trains as to anything else.

7. WATCH FOR REGIONAL FLUCTUATIONS: The price of some items varies considerably around the country. If you get to know collectors in various areas, or if you can travel to other locales, you may find that a piece which is nearly impossible to find in your area will often turn up regularly in another. Or you may find the price of an item is quite a bit less (maybe up to 50 percent) in one area than in another. In many cases, this is a matter of local demand. This happens especially with rolling stock. Union Pacific and Southern Pacific are popular names with collectors in the West, and sell well there. Inventories are quickly exhausted, but the same items are sometimes readily available in the East. Conversely, Eastern railroads like Erie-Lackawanna, Lehigh Valley and Reading are popular on the East Coast, and Eastern railroad rolling stock easier to find in the West. These regional differences influence prices, and an astute buyer with the right connections can take advantage of the opportunity.

8. JOIN TRAIN CLUBS: These are an excellent source of Lionel information and potential new friends. You will find club members friendly, interesting and always willing to help.

You may even embark on a few lifelong friendships. Access to club for-sale newsletters is worth the dues charged many times over. Since the sellers are Lionel hobbyists selling to fellow hobbyists, you often find values in the sale listings. But be careful about ordering by mail, as described next:

CAUTIONS:

1. BE CAREFUL ORDERING BY MAIL: Ask your friends about the reputation of a mail-order dealer before ordering for the first time. Most dealers are reliable and fair, but there are a few who are not. Ordering older big-ticket or rare items via the mail involves some risk. Sometimes you may not get what you paid for. If you buy by mail (if you have no local shops, for example, or the local shop does not have the piece), require a written guarantee or your money back if you are not satisfied. If the item sent is not as described, you should return it. Remember that the seller tends to see his piece in a better light than the buyer. With a written understanding, a seller will nearly always accept your return if this is requested. In the rare instance where a seller will not, you can file a complaint with the appropriate train club. Nearly every dealer belongs to one. There is much less risk in buying new pieces advertised as "new in the box" which are less than about 10 years old.

2. DO NOT BUY OLDER "MINT-IN-THE-BOX," until you have gained some market experience. Nearly every train older than 10 years has been out of the box, handled, and even run a little on the track. A sealed box can be opened and resealed. There are very few mint prewar and postwar trains. Many early Fundimensions trains are now hard to find in mint condition. Buying mint pieces may create problems. Lou Bohn, a frequent contributor to our Guides, has reported that some new-from-the-box pieces run poorly and require adjustments or repairs. Some new equipment has been packaged with missing drive rods, bad gears, mis-quartered drivers, shorted track pieces, even boxcars without doors! Bohn recommends that collectors not buy "factory-sealed, never-run" items.

Obviously, the condition of a train is important to you and to the price you pay. There is some difference between "excellent" and "mint." Your choice depends on your plans. If you do not need mint equipment, equipment that has been used and properly cared for can be an excellent value. However, if your purchases are primarily for investment, you should limit your purchases to "like new" and "mint." The rapid price increases of the last five years have applied more to the "mint" pieces than to trains in "excellent" condition.

3. AVOID "VARIATION" COLLECTING, at least until you know the market better. Buying variations often requires expertise to distinguish a highly valued piece from an ordinary piece. Many variations are easy to create. Once you are more knowledgeable, variation collecting can be fun and rewarding.

ADDITIONAL THOUGHTS ON THE SUBJECT:

New collectors can acquire many trains at reasonable prices. There are many undiscovered gems, although most are not as glamorous as those which get most of the attention. Here are a few suggestions:

Fundimensions trains from the early 1970s are not in demand. Prices are starting to creep up as postwar collectors realize that the early Fundimensions pieces are far scarcer than most pieces made between 1945-1969. These items are now thought of as "collector's items." This includes the early accessories, too. One example is the 2494 rotary beacon. The 494 rotary beacon from postwar is common but sells for $60 or so. But the Fundimensions 2494 is extremely hard to find, because not many were made. A related area encompasses the early transition pieces in Type I boxes. You can still find them, but few people seem interested.

Tank cars are still moderately priced, as well as covered hoppers. You can acquire an excellent-looking unit train of tank cars and hopper cars for a reasonable price.

Most of the 9200-series boxcars are relatively inexpensive compared to their postwar 6464 predecessors. Some 9700-series boxcars are expensive, but you can still buy a few for $20 mint-in-the-box. The 9400-series boxcars were made more recently, and some of them are very hard to find. The new 19200-series boxcars represent a good area to collect, too.

Club cars are still attractively priced and just starting to garner attention. But some of them are made in such small quantities that they are impossible to find. The early 9000-series cabooses are attractive and inexpensive.

Another approach is to collect O27 equipment. Generally, experienced collectors ignore these smaller trains, but you can put together a good O27 train for very few dollars. On occasion, a "Traditional" train set will gather some attention — the New York Central Yard Chief set of 1985 was a wonderful group of fun cars.

Finally, you should seriously consider the newer Fundimensions and Lionel Trains, Inc. products. Although more expensive, these trains represent levels of technical innovation and quality that are likely to lead to substantial appreciation. Note that these items are made in relatively small quantities compared with postwar items. The last few years have witnessed an astonishing array of new and unique items: the Northern engines, the Standard O series, and the new RailSounds system. The RailSounds system adds an audio dimension to a Lionel layout only rarely available previously in some of the stationary trackside accessories. While the sound system adds quite a premium to the price (sometimes up to $80), these pieces may enjoy better than average appreciation.

Our conclusion: The great thing about Lionel model railroading is that there is something for everybody, in any price range!

◆ CHAPTER 2 ◆
SPECIAL PRODUCTION

During the modern era, Lionel has made special products at the request of the major train collecting associations in the United States, as well as for special events and organizations such as the 1982 Tennessee World's Fair, the annual New York Toy Fair, the Michigan-based Artrain traveling museum, and many department and retail stores.

Many hobbyists debate what constitutes *special* Lionel production. Some believe that anything not modeled after existing prototype road names or anything not prototypically decorated should be labeled special production. In this view, such items as the Lionel Lines set, the Santa Claus handcar, and the Wanamaker's boxcar, catalogued or not, would be considered special production. For the purposes of this Guide, however, such a view is too restrictive because most collectors, as well as Lionel itself, have categorized such pieces as regular production.

Other train collectors consider anything uncatalogued by Lionel as special production, even if it is a relatively common (or even prototypical) piece such as the 9055 Republic Steel gondola. This illustrates the problem of associating special production with the term uncatalogued. Many of Lionel's products, even though they do not appear in the consumer catalogue, are produced in great quantities and are as readily available as any catalogued piece. This Guide considers them regular production.

Still other hobbyists believe that *anything* made by Lionel should be considered regular production. Anything else is simply not Lionel. The problem here is that such a view does not address the needs of large numbers of people who collect on the basis of car type, roadname, or train club, regardless if the piece was made by Lionel.

A gray area of classification exists for many train pieces which were originally made by Lionel, but were later over-stamped or redecorated by other people for various purposes. A prominent example is the 9754 Pacemaker boxcar, which has been used for many TCA division commemoratives. The original Lionel car has been overstamped (by individual

modelers or professional firms) with a logo for the train club division or event. The result is that far fewer original-condition 9754 Pacemaker boxcars are on the market, thousands having been altered to produce the special cars.

In sum, it is often hard to discern trains made inside the factory from those made or altered outside the factory.

The editors of this Guide studied the many viewpoints when determining how to define these hundreds of special production pieces. It is the editors' opinion that leaving such items out of the book creates a gap in its completeness and in the full story of the Lionel train hobby.

Many train club cars *were* made entirely by Lionel. But many others were not. For example, people who wish to complete a full collection of TCA cars will find an enormous number of division, meet and museum cars that were not made in the Mt. Clemens, Michigan factory. There is a legitimate market for such specialty cars and a growing army of hobbyists who collect them, and it was decided that this edition of the Greenberg Guide should address the interests of these collectors.

The following railroad collecting organizations are represented in this chapter:

1. The Inland Empire Train Collectors Association (IETCA)
2. The Lionel Collectors Association of Canada (LCAC)
3. The Lionel Collectors' Club of America (LCCA)
4. The Lionel Central Operating Lines (LCOL)
5. The Lionel Operating Train Society (LOTS)
6. The Lionel Railroader Club (LRRC)
7. The Nassau Lionel Operating Engineers
8. The Train Collectors' Association (TCA)
9. The Toy Train Operating Society (TTOS)
10. The Virginia Train Collectors (VTC)

The fate of thousands of cars like the 9754 Pacemaker boxcar will help to explain why the market values of the

---

* *Asterisk found in listings indicates that the information within that listing was derived from Lionel catalogue only.*

unmarked originals are what they are. More importantly, the listings here bring to light the important contributions to the Lionel hobby of such artists as Seymour Knight of the Pleasant Valley Process Co. (PVP), Steve Latta of Nostalgia Train Works (NTW), E. C. Kraemer in New England, and some others. And readers will, at last, find some reference to those strange cars they have encountered on dealers' tables over the years.

However, as stated earlier, the concept of special production raises one important question. Namely, how do we distinguish the custom-designed train cars created by artistically-inclined hobbyists from our listings?

Several criteria have been employed: First, the item must have been made in sufficient quantity to constitute a legitimate, marketable, collectable piece. In most cases, at least 50 to 100 items must have been made. Generally, this eliminates the one or two customized trains individual collectors have made for their personal collections. Such pieces, while they may possess interesting and unique aspects, lack general marketability, and therefore are not included in this Guide.

Second, Greenberg's detailed listings include only those pieces made from original Lionel O Gauge cars. The train clubs, particularly the TCA and TTOS, have made convention or meet cars from stock produced by other manufacturers in O and other Gauges — such as K-Line, Williams, McCoy, and Kris Model Trains (KMT). Although this Guide mentions these pieces for the sake of completeness, it does not include details or prices for them. They are the legitimate province of other books on other scales and manufacturers.

The last criterion the editors applied involves the markings. Most of the listings reported here are marked by the manufacturer to avoid any confusion with an original Lionel piece. If there is any doubt as to whether an item was made by Lionel (generally the quality of the paint or lettering will give it away), we do not list the piece. This applies to most of the one- or two-car repaints made by individuals. Professional redecorators such as PVP and NTW take pride in marking their work — on the bottom, on the box or actually on the car itself. In fact, PVP tracks its production (which consists in large part of repainting or overstamping Lionel cars) with a special seven-digit code number.

Because Lionel enthusiasts generally collect these special production cars by year and train club, this chapter has been broken into subheadings for each train club, with the cars produced listed by year. In addition, it includes a report on the Pleasant Valley Process Co., which has done a great deal of work on Lionel cars for the train clubs and others, plus an intriguing article on the Guinness record-length Lionel train run made by Stewart Roberts in 1980. The specially decorated cars used in this train constitute a classic example of special production cars.

The uncatalogued cars and engines made for department stores, hardware stores, food stores, and other retail outlets comprise yet another category of special Lionel cars. While the individual detailed listings of these cars are considered regular production (albeit uncatalogued) and are therefore found in Volume I, tables and discussions are included in the Department Store Specials chapter in this Volume.

All efforts have been made to capture as many known special production pieces as possible. There may be numbers of obscure division or meet cars (particularly from the TCA) which are not listed here. We welcome reader comments to aid us in expanding our knowledge in this area.

THE INLAND EMPIRE TRAIN COLLECTORS ASSOCIATION

The Inland Empire Train Collectors Association is a small group of primarily Lionel model railroaders based in Redlands, California, just east of Los Angeles, founded by the late Guy Liggan in 1979. Despite its name, which has caused some confusion in the past, the group is not associated with the TCA. The IETCA consists of about 50 or 60 local members who meet monthly to discuss various aspects of model and prototype railroading, plan for displays of its modular railroad, and work on articles for its newsletter, *The Smokestack*.

The group comes to our attention because of its annual series of Lionel-based cars, which the club calls *anniversary cars*, produced between 1979 and 1986. The club designed these cars to publicize itself and provide the members with a unique memento. None of the cars feature a number other than the date, nor do any have a name other than the IETCA and its logo, which has been altered several times. The series ended after 1988 due to the increasing cost of Lionel cars. We appreciate the data supplied by club member John Link.

	GD	VG	EXC	MT

1979 **1979 IETCA:** Boxcar; first in an annual anniversary series produced by the Inland Empire Train Collectors Association; white body with cluster of oranges decal; green door; green lettering; IETCA logo featuring black locomotive and red arrowhead design; standard Lionel 9414 Cotton Belt boxcar redecorated by PVP (designator "505-1136"); other details same as regular issue 9414 boxcar (see Volume I); the oranges signify Redlands, California, one of the nation's major orange-producing centers; about 50 made. J. Link Collection.
— — — 15

1980 **1980 IETCA:** SP-type caboose; second in an annual anniversary series produced by the IETCA; yellow body; black lettering "2nd Anniversary/IETCA/1980"; red tri-city logo under cupola; tri-city refers to Redlands/Riverside/San Bernardino, California; standard Lionel 9187 Gulf, Mobile & Ohio caboose redecorated by PVP (designator "205-1150"); about 50 made. J. Link Collection.
— — — 15

1981 **1981 IETCA:** Quad hopper; third in an annual anniversary series produced by the IETCA; medium blue body; dark blue lettering; orange cluster decal and IETCA arrowhead logo; "3rd Anniversary/IETCA/1981"; standard Lionel quad hopper redecorated by PVP (designator "305-1186"); about 50 made. J. Link Collection.
— — — 15

1982 **1982 IETCA:** Three-dome tank car; fourth in an annual anniversary series produced by the IETCA; silver body; black and red lettering; orange cluster decal; "4th Anniversary/

GD   VG   EXC   MT

IETCA/1982"; standard Lionel 9327 Bakelite tank car redecorated by NTW ("4-82"); about 50 made. J. Link Collection.

             —　　—　　—　　15

1983 **1983 IETCA:** 9800-style refrigerator car; fifth in an annual anniversary series produced by the IETCA; orange body; green roof and ends; black lettering "5th Anniversary/IETCA/1983"; club logo altered to appear as a locomotive on tracks; green mountain valley scene; standard Lionel 9885 Lipton refrigerator car redecorated by NTW ("4-83"); about 50 made. J. Link Collection.

             —　　—　　—　　15

1984 **7518 CARSON CITY:** Bullion car; sixth in an annual anniversary series produced by the IETCA; standard 7518 bullion car with added lettering on the clear windows "6th Anniversary IETCA 1984" and gold locomotive and tender IETCA logo; decorated by Guy Liggan; the only IETCA car in which the original Lionel identity of the car remains visible; about 50 made. J. Link Collection.

             —　　—　　—　　40

1985 **No production:** The club had plans to apply an IETCA decal to a tender as an engine, offering to complete the set, but this never materialized.

1986 **1986 IETCA:** bunk car; eighth in an annual anniversary series produced by the IETCA; gray body; maroon lettering; gold locomotive and tender logo; decal featuring arrowhead with Statue of Liberty inset; "8th Anniversary/IETCA/1986"; standard Lionel 5727 United States Marines bunk car repainted by John Link; about 50 made. J. Link Collection.

             —　　—　　—　　15

1987 **IETCA:** The club offered a K-Line hopper as its anniversary car.

1988 and 1989 **IETCA:** The club produced several K-Line accessories as its anniversary offering. The series ended after that.

THE LIONEL COLLECTORS ASSOCIATION OF CANADA

This small but active organization of Lionel collectors has gained attention in recent years due to its unique offerings of annual commemorative special cars. All the LCAC cars reflect Canadian railway themes and are highly prototypical of the railroads represented. Many collectors in Canada and the northern United States find these pieces attractive and desirable. The set includes several Canadian road names not made by Lionel. None of the cars described in this section were made entirely by Lionel, because the LCAC is too small to place orders large enough for the Mt. Clemens factory to accept. Therefore, all the cars are original Lionel pieces which have been overstamped or redecorated. We are grateful for the assistance of LCAC member Geoff Swan and LCAC General Manager Tom Gascoigne, who compiled the data in this section. Mr. Gascoigne is the principal designer and driving force for this commemorative car series.

The LCAC was founded in 1978 and began its annual issues in 1979. All of its special cars can be identified by the LCAC's circular logo, which shows the words "Lionel Collectors Association of Canada" in a circle around a central Lionel "L". The most common of these cars (if any can be called that)

GD   VG   EXC   M

are the annual releases available by mail order to all LCAC members. But the group has also made a very small number (usually 36) of overstamped or otherwise redecorated cars as souvenirs for several of their conventions, available only to convention attendees. For a while during the 1980s, the LCAC held national conventions like the other national train organizations. But the association has so far preferred to stay small, and found the cost of national conventions, particularly in a country the size of Canada, prohibitive. After losing money on several, the association has not held national conventions recently, choosing to concentrate its energies on the annual car. The LCAC does publish a twice-yearly *Switchlist* of items to buy and sell.

The LCAC uses its own special numbering system: the first two digits designate the year, and the last several digits designate the sequence number of the car in the series (except in cases where the original Lionel number is still on the car). For example, the first car to have its own number was the 1981 boxcar, which was the third in the series, so its number was "8103". LCAC also fills in zeroes as appropriate (e.g. "840006" to achieve the correct number of digits appearing on the prototype car.

All the LCAC cars described in this section were made in extremely limited quantities and are consequently very difficult to find.

────────────

1979 **9718 CANADIAN NATIONAL:** Boxcar; first annual special commemorative by the LCAC; standard Lionel 9718 CN classic-type tuscan boxcar with doors painted green rather than yellow as on standard-issue 9718 car; LCAC logo included as large red, white and blue decal; sticker in blue with LCAC serial number affixed to underside; designated "7901" by LCAC, but that number is not on car; see 9718 entry in Volume I for further construction details of the car; only 46 cars made. These cars came from the factory with green doors, not yellow, before the decals were applied. It is possible Lionel used leftover doors from other boxcars on these four cases of cars. T. Gascoigne comment. As the first and least-produced of the LCAC cars, this one is also the hardest to find.
             NRS

1980 **9413 NAPIERVILLE JUNCTION:** Boxcar; second annual LCAC commemorative car; standard Lionel 9413 NJ yellow boxcar with red roof and ends; doors repainted to red from original yellow; silver and black heat-stamped "80" to right of doors; small LCAC circle logo placed inside the "0"; sticker in blue with LCAC serial number affixed to underside; designated by LCAC as "8002" but that number is not on car; see 9413 entry in Volume I for further construction details; 97 made. G. Swan Collection.
             NRS

1981 **8103 TORONTO, HAMILTON & BUFFALO:** Boxcar; third annual LCAC commemorative car; Lionel classic-type boxcar redecorated by the Pleasant Valley Processing Co./Newbraugh Brothers Toys (PVP/NBT); this was done on a variety of underlying 9700-series Lionel cars — Conrail, Lehigh Valley and others; yellow sides; black roof and ends; black doors; black lettering; number under- and over-scored; black LCAC logo to left of doors; PVP designator "505-1153"; Symington-Wayne trucks; "BUILT LCAC"; 200 made. G. Swan Collection. There were also 36 American Flyer cars (No. 8103-S) available in 1981 as convention souvenirs.
             NRS

A selection of rarely seen Lionel train club cars, all made by PVP.

B. Greenberg photograph

Top shelf: LCAC 8103 Toronto Hamilton & Buffalo boxcar from 1981; LCAC 8204 Algoma Central boxcar from 1982.
Second shelf: LCAC 830005 Canadian National boxcar from 1983; Virginia Train Collectors 7685 VTC boxcar from 1985.
Third shelf: TCA 5727 Southern Division 20th Anniversary bunk car from 1986; TCA Sacramento-Sierra Chapter 9452 Western Pacific boxcar from 1983.
Bottom shelf: TCA Sacramento-Sierra Chapter 6401 Virginian bay window caboose from 1984; an unusual "window" car (created by cutting the sides from a hi-cube boxcar) made by PVP for TCA's Toy Train Museum in 1983.

	GD	VG	EXC	MT

1982 **8204 ALGOMA CENTRAL:** Boxcar; fourth annual LCAC commemorative car; Lionel classic-type boxcar redecorated by PVP/NBT; again these were a variety of underlying Lionel boxcar types; dark red body and doors; white lettering; black and white Algoma Central bear logo; LCAC logo at far left; PVP designator "505-1212"; Symington-Wayne trucks; "BUILT LCAC"; 120 made. G. Swan Collection. **NRS**

1982 **6100 ONTARIO NORTHLAND:** Covered quad hopper; special overstamped car produced by the LCAC for its convention in Niagara-On-The-Lake; standard Lionel 6100 quad hopper with LCAC logo at center and convention notation overstamped in red, white and blue by PVP; PVP designator "305-1187"; see Volume I for further details on 6100; only 36 cars made. **NRS**

1983 **830005 CANADIAN NATIONAL:** Boxcar; fifth annual LCAC commemorative car; Lionel classic-type boxcar decorated by PVP/NBT; Lionel supplied blank boxcar bodies to PVP for this production — the first time LCAC or any train organization had arranged this (Note: PVP is an authorized Lionel decorator, among several other firms); tuscan body and doors; white lettering; green Maple Leaf with white "CNR" to right of car; "Serves All Canada"; white LCAC circle logo to left of doors; PVP designator "505-1282"; "BUILT LCAC"; 138 made. G. Swan Collection. **NRS**

1983 **5710 CANADIAN PACIFIC:** Wood-side refrigerator car; special overstamped car produced by LCAC for its 1983 convention in Montreal; standard Lionel 5710 refrigerator car (see Volume I for details) with powder blue LCAC logo and "See You In Montreal" lettering; overstamped by PVP (designator "606-1245"); 36 made. **NRS**

1984 **840006 CANADIAN WHEAT BOARD:** Covered quad hopper; sixth annual LCAC commemorative car; Lionel 6424 D & H quad hopper repainted by PVP/NBT; chocolate brown body and roof; yellow stripe on lower sides; yellow lettering in English and

	GD	VG	EXC	MT

French; LCAC circle logo at top left; "BUILT LCAC 7-84"; PVP designator "305-1364". Apparently the red plastic of the original Lionel hopper caused a problem for PVP in the repainting process. G. Swan Collection. — — — 160

1985 8507/8508 CANADIAN NATIONAL: F-3 AA diesel shells only; seventh annual special commemorative from LCAC; green body; gold nose; gold stripe with black highlights along lower edge of sides; gold, black and white lettering; CNR maple leaf logo on nose; LCAC circle logo on sides; "BUILT BY LCAC". These were unpainted blank Lionel F-3 shells decorated by PVP/NBT; PVP designators "105-1416" and "105-1417" respectively, though these numbers are not on the body because the shells were not originally decorated by Lionel; 125 sets made; very hard to find. Note: LCAC used two sequence numbers on these shells, so the sequence numbers on later cars are one ahead of the number of years the series has been in operation! NRS

1985 5714 MICHIGAN CENTRAL: Wood-side refrigerator car; special overstamped car produced by LCAC for its 1985 convention in London and Port Stanley; standard 5714 refrigerator car (see Volume I for details) overstamped by PVP with convention logo; PVP designator "606-1392"; 36 cars made, most were given away as convention prizes or raffle prizes. This is the last convention special made (or envisioned) by LCAC — the association no longer holds national conventions. NRS

1986 86009 CANADIAN NATIONAL GREAT LAKES REGION: Bunk car; eighth annual LCAC commemorative car; red sides, white lettering; LCAC circle logo; not illuminated; this is a 5727 Marines bunk car (see Volume I for other details) stripped and redecorated by PVP/NBT; PVP designator "706-1420"; "BUILT LCAC"; 160 made. G. Swan comment. — — — 130

1987 87010 CANADIAN NATIONAL EXPRESS: Wood-side refrigerator car; ninth annual LCAC commemorative car; green sides; black roof and ends; green doors; yellow lettering; yellow LCAC logo to right of doors; blank Lionel wood-side refrigerator car were supplied to and decorated by PVP; PVP designator "605-1464"; Standard O sprung trucks; "BUILT LCAC"; 190 made. G. Swan Collection. NRS

1988 88011 CANADIAN NATIONAL: Wood-side caboose; 10th annual LCAC commemorative car; orange body; white lettering; high cupola; green CNR maple leaf logo with "Serves All Canada"; LCAC circle logo is on the rear of the body; illuminated; this is a blank 17600-series Lionel caboose decorated by PVP; die-cast leaf-spring trucks; "BUILT 11-88 LCAC"; reportedly 200 produced. G. Swan comment. NRS

1989 8912 CANADA SOUTHERN: Operating short hopper; 11th annual LCAC commemorative car; black body; white lettering, numbers and logos; LCAC circle logo at top left; Standard O sprung trucks; this is a blank 19800-series Lionel O27 operating hopper decorated by PVP; PVP designator "305-1486"; "BUILT 11-89 LCAC"; 265 made. G. Swan Collection. — — — 125

1990 900013 CANADIAN NATIONAL: TOFC flatcar; 12th annual LCAC commemorative car; black body; white lettering on flatcar; two vans, one of each type (rounded ends and squared ends); square-end double-axle van is in CN orange with a black roof, lettered in gold and red "Express Services" with CN wafer logo; round-end single-axle van is CN green with white roof, lettered "Cartage Services" in gold and red with CN logo; LCAC circle logo is on flatcar and ends of vans; Standard O sprung

trucks; "BUILT 11-90 LCAC"; 375 made. Lionel blank flatcar body and vans decorated by PVP. T. Gascoigne comments. NRS

1991 914 THE BRITISH AMERICAN OIL COMPANY LIMITED*: Single-dome tank car; 13th annual LCAC commemorative car; black plastic tank body painted black; white lettering; white, green and red British American "oil drop" logo to right side; numbered "BAOC914"; frame is stamped "LCAC"; black metal dome platform and ladder; wire handrails; Standard O trucks; 450 to be made; Lionel blank tank car decorated by PVP; the BAOC, Ltd. is the Canadian subsidiary of Gulf Oil. T. Gascoigne comments. NRS

THE LIONEL COLLECTORS CLUB OF AMERICA

The Lionel Collectors Club of America (LCCA) is the largest train organization devoted exclusively to Lionel in the United States. Its newsletter, *The Lion Roars*, is a principal source of any and all information relating to Lionel collecting. The LCCA's separately published buy-sell-trade magazine, *The Interchange Track*, may well be the premier source for mail-order Lionel purchases anywhere.

Founded in 1970, the LCCA held its first national convention in Little Rock, Arkansas in 1971. At that time no special cars were made, but at the second convention in Kansas City in 1972, 265 individually stamped and decaled 9701 B & O boxcars were distributed. Since then LCCA has issued one special edition convention car each year. The 1972 car, produced at a time when Lionel itself was in the throes of serious retrenchment, has some fascinating stories behind it. From 1973 onward, Lionel has produced exclusive cars for LCCA, and all are eagerly awaited each year. Some of the most unusual modern era pieces can be found in this series. Of late, the LCCA has been moving into the scale-size Standard O realm, and cars from the last decade have featured more prototypical decorating schemes than the earlier pieces from the 1970s.

In addition, LCCA produced an interesting series of meet cars between 1975 and 1982, as well as two anniversary (10th and 20th) engines to pull the cars. The meet cars were intended to entice members to hold local meets and to encourage members to attend, since the cars would only be available at the meets. That was true for a while, until the cars started showing up in mail-order ads in *The Interchange Track*! The LCCA holds many local meets around the country in addition to its national convention.

As with other train clubs, the LCCA's convention cars are initially available only through the club itself — announcements are placed in the club publications. Of course, all the cars are still available today on the open market, but usually at a considerable premium over the initial ordering price.

Almost all the LCCA cars are desirable and a few are quite scarce. An exception would be the 9728 UP stock car, which seems to be available everywhere. Only those pieces

	GD	VG	EXC	MT

from the late 1970s, which were made in quantities far too great for the membership to support, can be considered plentiful.

On the other hand, since many are relatively common, these cars represent a good special collecting area for a beginning hobbyist. The LCCA cars have many desirable collectable features: made exclusively by Lionel (not redecorated outside the factory), bright graphics, great diversity of rolling stock, and, in many cases, affordable prices — although this last is not true for all pieces. Still, a good collection of LCCA cars can be obtained at a modest price.

The meet car collection, despite their somewhat garish graphics, may also represent a "sleeper" area of collecting. These pieces, all O27, are very inexpensive even today.

We are grateful to LCCA President Bill Schmeelk for his assistance with the details and our photography of the LCCA cars, and to LCCA Secretary Bill Button, whose excellent series on the cars in *The Lion Roars* proved an invaluable reference source for our data. Our readers who are interested in more details are also referred to this fine series (June 1989 to August 1991).

1972 **9701 BALTIMORE & OHIO:** Double-door automobile boxcar; first annual convention car special from the LCCA (issued for second annual LCCA convention); glossy black-painted black body; flat black-painted black doors; white lettering; white decaled "L.C.C. of A./K.C. Mo. 1972" appears over "Baltimore and Ohio" and word "Convention" is decaled in smaller letters vertically to side; underside rubber-stamped with LCCA membership numbers and "2nd Annual/L.C.C.A./Convention/Kansas City, Mo."; came in a Type II box. 124 of these cars were lettered and stamped before LCCA ran out of decals, leading to much confusion and disappointment. Further decals were not sent to members. These cars were not obtained directly from Lionel, but obtained through the TCA, which had used them for its 1971 convention. The LCCA convention hosts spent the days before the 1972 Kansas City convention stamping the cars. J. R. Hunt Collection and comments. Many of the non-decaled cars were faked later by rubber-stamping. R. Vagner comment.

(A) As described above; decaled version; 124 made.

		125	175

(B) Same as (A), but without decaling; rubber-stamped convention data and member number on bottom; about 140 of this type exist. Beware of faked versions; authentic Type II original boxes should have a hand-lettered member's name and address in green ink.

		110	140

(C) Flat black-painted black body and doors; Symington-Wayne trucks; no stamping on frame or separate decals. These unstamped cars may have been leftovers from LCCA's lot or leftovers from the TCA's Detroit-Toledo chapter. Reader comments requested. Type II box has paper sticker with "B AND O/9701-B" in black ink on one end only. R. LaVoie Collection.

		100	125

1973 **9727 T. A. G.:** Boxcar; annual LCCA convention car; Type IX maroon classic-style boxcar body, white-lettered "TENNESSEE ALABAMA & GEORGIA" and "1973 LCC of A"; white tag logo at right center; white Huntsville convention notation; Symington-Wayne trucks; Type II frame; "BLT 1-73"; 1,176 made. Cars are serially numbered by rubber stamp on the bottom frame; buyers should double-check correctness of the number and pre-

vious owners before completing purchase — faked cars have surfaced. This is by far the hardest of the LCCA convention cars to find, probably because it was the first LCCA car produced entirely by Lionel. W. Schmeelk Collection.

		200	250

1974 **9118 CORNING:** Covered quad hopper; annual LCCA convention car; white and mist green body; mist green roof; large "CORNING" in blue on broad white stripe on upper half of body; other lettering in black; convention note "1974 L.C.C. of A./Corning, N.Y."; spreader bar hole and builder's plate; Symington-Wayne trucks; metal plate holding trucks; "BLT 1-74"; 1,500 made; came in Type II box. Car is serially stamped on the bottom. M. Solly Collection.

		75	90

1975 **9155 MONSANTO:** Single-dome tank car; annual LCCA convention car; white tank body; black lettering; red "M" logo on left of tank; 1975 St. Louis convention note to right; metal platform and ladder; wire handrails; Symington-Wayne trucks; "BLT 1-75"; 2,200 made; came in a Type II box. This was the last of the LCCA cars to be serially stamped (in this case on the ends). M. Solly Collection.

	50	65	75

1976 **9212 SEABOARD COAST LINE (SCL):** TOFC flatcar; annual LCCA convention car; highly unusual long flatcar body painted tuscan; the body is not a standard flatcar, but the bottom deck of an auto carrier car; two extra-long trailer vans which were not standard for Lionel at the time — these were made by a "CM Corp." as stamped on the van bodies; white vans with large orange "GHE" ("Georgia Highway Express") and "IHI" logos; white flatcar lettering with Atlanta convention note; Symington-Wayne trucks; "BLT 1-76"; 3,500 made; came in a plain white box. Originally the flatcars were stamped only on one side. LCCA offered to restamp them for members and many were restamped. Operators note: like the auto carriers, this car has trouble negotiating switches and sharper curves. It did not meet with

---

A Note on the LCCA's 1977 and 1978 Special Convention Cars: *In 1977 and 1978, the LCCA sponsored two national conventions in which the hosts decided it would be good if the officers and workers received a "special" commemorative for their efforts. These were regular production cars overstamped with "LCCA" and convention data. In 1977, 48 N & W boxcars (9771) were so stamped and given out or raffled. In 1978, about 60 of the yellow 9739 Rio Grande boxcars were also overstamped. This is a handsome car, even unstamped, and the overstamping simply created an instant collector's item. At the 1978 convention in Denver, several Rio Grande cars were auctioned, bringing in more than $200 apiece. Nearly all are now in the hands of LCCA officials. Needless to say, the general membership raised a ruckus over this, claiming that the cars were not equally available to all, as per previous club policy. As a result, this unusual circumstance of a "second convention car" was ended and has not been repeated. This may also explain why the regular 1978 convention car, a Union Pacific stock car, is more abundant than other LCCA cars — the special boxcar was considered better looking.*

R. Kaptur and W. Schmeelk Collections; B. Greenberg photo.

These photographs document the complete collection of convention cars from the LCCA through 1990:
Top shelf: **Two rare cars — 9701 B & O auto boxcar from 1972; 9727 TAG boxcar from 1973.**
Second shelf: **9118 Corning hopper from 1974; 9155 Monsanto tank car from 1975.**
Third shelf: **9212 Seaboard Coast Line TOFC flatcar from 1976; 9728 Union Pacific stock car from 1978.**
Bottom shelf: **9733 Airco boxcar (contains tank 97330) from 1979; X9259 Southern bay window caboose from 1977.**

	GD	VG	EXC	MT

much favor at the time of the 1976 LCCA convention, but has since gained some notoriety in collecting circles due to its many unusual features.

	GD	VG	EXC	MT
(A) One flatcar side stamped.	—	—	35	40
(B) Two flatcar sides stamped.	—	—	40	70

1977 **X9259 SOUTHERN:** Bay window caboose; annual LCCA convention car; red body; white lettering; Cincinnati city shield to right; "L.C.C.A." imprinted under bay window; Symington-Wayne trucks; illuminated; no "BLT" date, but convention date "JULY 23, 1977" printed at right; 4,500 made; came in a Type III box. It is not clear why the number of this car is preceded by an "X".
(A) White lettering. C. Kruelle Collection.

			35	40

(B) Gold lettering. C. Lang Collection. — — 35 40

1977 **9771 NORFOLK & WESTERN:** Boxcar; special overstamped car commemorating the 1977 LCCA convention in Cincinnati; standard-issue 9771 boxcar (see Volume I for details) except with overstamped convention data; 48 made; most dis-

tributed to LCCA members and officers involved in the convention; quite hard to find. **NRS**

1978 **9728 UNION PACIFIC:** Stock car; annual LCCA convention car; yellow-painted yellow body; silver-painted roof and ends; unpainted yellow doors; red lettering; red LCCA convention data and red, white and blue UP shield logo stamped on yellow rectangular plate which is glued to slats to the right of door; Type III box ends read "LCCA CONVENTION CAR"; Symington-Wayne trucks; "BLT 1-78"; 5,500 made. The plate bearing "LCCA" and the UP shield is sometimes missing from the car. R. Garrott comment. This is the most abundant of the LCCA convention cars. An interesting footnote: These cars originally came with black doors by mistake. So far as is known, all the doors were eventually changed to yellow, but a few black-door versions may still exist. M. Solly and R. LaVoie Collections. — — 35 45

1978 **9739 RIO GRANDE:** boxcar; special commemorative made for 1978 LCCA convention; standard-issue 9739 car (see Volume I for details) with special LCCA markings overstamped; long stripe; "L.C.C.A./THE LION ROARS" and heat-stamped lion

R. Kaptur and W. Schmeelk Collections; B. Greenberg photograph

middle years of LCCA's convention car series:
shelf: 97330 Airco tank (found inside 9733 boxcar); 9358 Sands of Iowa hopper from 1980.
nd shelf: 9435 Central of Georgia boxcar from 1981; 9460 Detroit & Toledo Shore Line auto boxcar from 1982.
d shelf: 6112 Commonwealth Edison hopper from 1983; 7403 LNAC boxcar from 1984.
ɔm shelf: 6567 Illinois Central Gulf crane car from 1985.

	GD	VG	EXC	MT

logo in black to right of door; about 60 were made and distributed to LCCA officers and related parties, and a few were auctioned off by LCCA at various times. Very hard to find. H. Argue, J. Breslin, and L. Bohn comments; J. Breslin Collection. **NRS**

1979 **9733/97330 AIRCO:** Box/tank car; annual LCCA convention car; a unique Lionel car in that inside the Type IX classic-style boxcar there is a full-sized white molded unpainted tank with an orange-painted base; blue tank lettering cannot be seen unless boxcar shell is removed from frame, leaving only the tank; the tank is secured to the boxcar frame by a screw through a crudely punched hole; essentially two cars in one. Tank car is numbered "97330"; white boxcar and tank car bodies; light blue lettering; orange and blue striping; Wheeling, West Virginia convention notation to right of door; boxcar originally came with Symington-Wayne trucks; "BLT 1-79"; 6,000 made; tank car cap is packed separately in the Type III box. Reportedly, many collectors have fitted the tank car body with a frame, trucks and trim pieces to make up a second Airco car. Price is for original

configuration; add $10 if tank car has been fitted with trim, but be aware that these cars should not be purchased separately, even though they are sometimes seen apart. C. Lang and R. LaVoie comments. — — 40 55

1980 **9358 SANDS OF IOWA:** Covered quad hopper; annual LCCA convention car; bright powder blue body; powder blue cover; black lettering; yellow and black SOI circle logo at top left; no builder's plate; black frame and ends; Symington-Wayne trucks; plastic truck-holding plate; no "BLT" date, but Des Moines convention date "AUG. 1, 1980" shown at upper right; 4,500 made; Type III box. R. LaVoie and M. Solly Collections.
— — 30 40

1980 **8068 THE ROCK:** Powered GP-20 diesel; 10th anniversary commemorative issue for the LCCA; light blue Type V GP-series body (see Volume I for diesel motor and body type descriptions); white nose front; white lettering and convention data; black and white "R" logo; nose decal; "1980" on locomotive cab; the number "8068" is found only on the box; Type IIb motor;

The most recent LCCA convention cars:

W. Schmeelk Collection; B. Greenberg photograph

Top shelf: **6323 Virginia Chemicals** tank car and matching truck given to convention attendees from 1986.
Second shelf: **17870 East Camden & Highland** Standard O boxcar from 1987; **17873 Ashland Oil** tank car from 1988.
Third shelf: **17876 Columbus Newberry and Laurens** Standard O boxcar; **17880 DR & G** Standard O wood-sided caboose from 1990.
Bottom shelf: **18090 Denver & Rio Grande Western** LCCA 20th anniversary steam engine from 1990.

	GD	VG	EXC	MT

Type IV railings; white-painted stamped-metal frame; three-position E-unit; two operating couplers; 2,700 made. Essentially the same as the regular-issue 8750 Rock GP-7 engine from 1977 except for the nose design. — — **100 150**

1981 **9435 CENTRAL OF GEORGIA:** Boxcar, annual LCCA convention car (the 10th in the convention car series, even though it commemorates the 11th annual LCCA convention); black Type IX classic-style body with large silver-painted oval on sides; silver-painted gray doors; black and white lettering; yellow and black "CENTRAL/of/GEORGIA" rectangle to right of doors; number under- and over-scored; Chattanooga convention notation in black; Type III frame; Symington-Wayne trucks; "BLT 1-81"; 3,500 made; came in Type III box. J. Vega Collection, C. Lang and C. Rohlfing comments. — — **40 50**

1982 **9460 DETROIT & TOLEDO SHORE LINE:** Double-door automobile boxcar; annual LCCA convention car; blue body and doors; white lettering; metal door guides; bright red and white D & TSL logo to right of door; "EXPRESSWAY FOR INDUSTRY" under-scored in white to left of door; Dearborn convention notation to left; number under- and over-scored; Symington-Wayne trucks; "BLT 7-82", an unusual built date which corresponds to the convention date; 3,000 made; came in Type III box. The D & TSL is part of the Grand Trunk Railroad system. C. Rohlfing comment, J. Vega and C. Lang Collections. — — **35 60**

1983 **6112 COMMONWEALTH EDISON:** Quad hopper with coal load; annual LCCA convention car; tuscan body; one-third of car side painted black with "Little Bill" logo (used by Comm Edison between 1955 and 1970) in white; white lettering and Rockford, Illinois convention notation; spreader bar holes; no builder's plate; Symington-Wayne trucks; plastic truck-holding plate; "BLT 7-83"; 2,500 made; came in a Type III box. Somewhat hard to find. M. Kruse comment. This is reportedly the first hopper to use a coal load, and may have influenced Lionel to use it on many later hoppers. — — **75 95**

GD VG EXC MT

1984 **7403 LNAC:** (Louisville, New Albany & Corydon) boxcar; annual LCCA convention car; dark blue-green classic boxcar body and doors, red and white LNAC logo to left; white lettering; Louisville convention notation at upper right; Symington-Wayne trucks; "BLT 1-84"; 2,650 made; came in Type III box. This car's color is quite unusual. D. Daugherty Collection.

— — 35 45

1985 **6567 ILLINOIS CENTRAL GULF:** Crane car; annual LCCA convention car; gray cab; black base; black boom; orange trim; orange and white lettering on cab; the number on the car body is not "6567" but a prototypical "100408"; "6567" is on the box; New Orleans convention notation at rear of cab; white lettering on base; die-cast six-wheel passenger trucks; "BLT 1-85"; "Made in Mexico"; 2,500 made; came in a Type V Collector box, an acknowledgment by Lionel that train club cars were now considered collector-level pieces. M. Solly Collection.

— — 60 75

1986 **6323 VIRGINIA CHEMICALS:** Single-dome tank car; annual LCCA convention car; black body; white lettering; 1986 Norfolk convention notation to left side; large red, white and black Virginia Chemicals logo to right; white end lettering; "6323" stamped on frame — an unusual practice; black metal dome platform and ladder; wire handrails; Standard O sprung trucks (a first for an LCCA car); "BLT 1- 86"; 2,500 made; came in Type V box.

— — 40 55

1987 **17870 EAST CAMDEN & HIGHLAND:** Standard O boxcar; annual LCCA convention car; orange body; cream stripe across sides and door; silver-painted roof and catwalk; black lettering and logo; black Arkansas map at right center; Little Rock convention notation at upper right; Standard O trucks; "BLT 1-87"; 2,500 made; came in Type V box. The first Standard O car commissioned by the LCCA. There was some discussion in the club about how the car would look with the earlier smaller cars in the series. M. Solly comment. J. Bratspis Collection.

— — 60 75

1988 **17873 ASHLAND OIL:** Three-dome tank car; annual LCCA convention car; black body; white lettering; red, white, blue and black Ashland Oil decal; white Lexington, Kentucky convention notation; Symington-Wayne trucks; "BLT 1-88"; number and built date stamped on frame; came in a Type V box. Somewhat hard to find. Came with special token only available at convention. Two variations exist. The initial run was dull black. Later cars were oversprayed to help the Ashland decal stick to the paint. Add $30 to value for presence of token. M. Solly Collection.
(A) Shiny black; 2396 made. H. Overtoom comment.

— — 40 50

(B) Dull black; 924 made. H. Overtoom comment.

— — 75 90

1989 **17876 COLUMBIA NEWBERRY AND LAURENS:** Standard O boxcar; annual LCCA convention car; tuscan body; white lettering; Columbia, South Carolina convention notation in white; number under- and over-scored; Standard O trucks; 2,650 made; came in Type V box. The CNL is a subsidiary of the Atlantic Coast Line. M. Solly Collection.

— — 60 75

1990 **17880 DENVER & RIO GRANDE WESTERN:** Standard O wood-sided caboose; annual LCCA convention car; black body; white lettering; white Ft. Collins, Colorado convention notation at lower front; white "Royal Gorge Route Scenic Line" logo under cupola; high cupola; illuminated; die-cast arch bar trucks; 2,785 made; came in Type V box. Intended as a match to

GD VG EXC MT

the 18090 LCCA special Rio Grande 4-6-2 steam engine. M. Solly Collection.

— — 65 85

1990 **18090 DENVER & RIO GRANDE WESTERN:** 4-6-2 Pacific steam locomotive; 20th anniversary commemorative engine for the LCCA; black Baldwin-style die-cast boiler; white "1990" lettering on cab with small "LCCA" underneath; white running board stripe and wheel rims; silver-painted boiler front and "1990" number plate under headlight; 2224-type die-cast tender in black with white "DENVER & RIO GRANDE WESTERN" lettering; first use of this type tender with a Pacific or Baldwin locomotive; tender includes steam RailSounds; pad-printed logo on tender rear reading "D & RGWRR/Scenic Line/Royal Gorge Route"; smoke; headlight; Magnetraction; Type III AC six-wheel motor; three-position E-unit; comes in a Type V collector box. This attractive engine was issued to mark LCCA's 20th anniversary, intended to match the 17880 wood-sided caboose released the same year; 1,866 made. M. Solly Collection.

— — — 400

1991 **17887/17888 CONRAIL:** Dual Standard O TOFC flatcars; annual special edition for the LCCA (this is the 20th car(s) in the convention series, though it commemorates LCCA's 21st convention); first time any train club has commissioned a two-car convention car set; tuscan Standard O flatcars; white flatcar lettering; two long-style trailers with multicolor logos; one for Ford New Holland and the other for Armstrong floors, two well-known companies in the area of the Lancaster, Pennsylvania convention; 17887 is the Armstrong van, white with blue stripe along lower edge and blue and red lettering; 17888 is the Ford van, white with red and blue stripes along lower edge, Ford logo at one end; both vans have silver underframes; both cars have Standard O trucks; both cars are "BLT 1-91"; both cars originally came together in a mailer, but each is also individually packed in a Type V collector box. The convention souvenir was an LCCA tractor which can be used to pull these vans. Due to an oversight by Lionel, no LCCA convention data was printed on the van ends, as intended. These are the only LCCA cars lacking this information. M. Solly Collection.
(A) Individual cars.

— — — 70

(B) Two-car set. Note: Lionel uses a stock control number of "17892" to designate the paired set.

— — — 120

THE LCCA'S MEET SPECIALS

Between 1975 and 1982, the LCCA created several special overstamped Lionel cars designated as "Meet Specials." These short O27-style cars were intended as fundraisers for the club, designed to encourage members to hold local train meets around the country. They could be used as door prizes and raffles at the meets. This was important to the club for recruiting new members and establishing fellowship among the members in the area. Anyone, of course, can hold a train meet at any time, but these cars were offered as an incentive so that LCCA folks could have something unique and different to offer, over and above the run-of-the-mill old trains for sale.

The idea worked well for a while. LCCA's roster of meets expanded each year. Over time, however, the special cars reached the open market and therefore no longer provided sufficient incentive for either meet hosts or members. The program was terminated in 1982, after six cars (really, 5-1/2) were made. The pièce de résistance was the last car — an otherwise nondescript SP caboose from 1982. The surprise is that it was made *specially* for the meet car program, not an

	GD	VG	EXC	MT

overstamped regular-issue like the others were. As such, this car is somewhat in demand.

The pieces are all regular-issue O27 cars overstamped with LCCA data. With the exception of the last caboose, it is not currently known who did the work, though Curt Fischbach, at the time LCCA treasurer and responsible for the meet cars, was certainly a principal player.

The cars have not gained any further collector interest of which to speak, and they can still be found on the market at very low prices. In fact, the plentiful overstamped 9142 Republic Steel gondola can be found almost anywhere. As such, this set constitutes an interesting possibility for a "sleeper" set, particularly for hobbyists who can accept not having large O Scale trains, and who do not mind a splash of oddly color graphics. Some of the cars even have interesting stories behind them. The April 1980 issue of *The Lion Roars* carries excellent photo coverage of these cars:

1975-1976 **6014-900 FRISCO:** O27-style short boxcar; first car in the LCCA Meet Special series; these were postwar-leftover 6014 Frisco boxcars overstamped with "LCCA" listed vertically to right of doors in red; blue "Meet Special" to right and "1975-1976" to left; otherwise white body and black lettering as with the postwar car; like the postwar models they have AAR trucks; came in a Type I Fundimensions box labeled "6014-900/LCCA 75-76" on its side. This car was previously reported as version 6014(I) in the postwar volume by C. Rohlfing. The previous editions of the modern era guide suggested that postwar Lionel had stamped them for LCCA. This is not possible since LCCA was formed in 1970 and was not in the car business until 1971. The fact that these are meet specials helps to clear up the mystery about them — they are leftover postwar stock which Fundimensions (or someone else) overstamped for the LCCA. D. Doyle Collection.
        —   —   **50**   **75**

1976-1977 **NO NUMBER:** Long streamlined 2046-type steam engine tender only; made for 1976-1977 LCCA Meet Specials; like the 6014 car listed above, these were leftover postwar production tenders acquired by LCCA at some point and overstamped with a Meet Special logo; "LCCA Meet Special '76 '77" heat-stamped in gold below "LIONEL LINES"; came with either AAR or plastic arch bar trucks. Best available data is that the tenders were made sometime around 1968. The odd part about this offering is that LCCA never issued a "Meet Special" engine with which to pull this and the other cars! We do not know how many shells were produced. Further reader comments invited.
        —   —   **25**   **30**

1977-1978 **9142 REPUBLIC STEEL:** Long gondola; medium green body; standard-issue 9142 (see Volume I for details) overstamped "LCCA /MEET SPECIAL 1977 1978" in red; originally issued in 1971; 1200 made. This car is the most plentiful of the LCCA meet special cars. C. Rohlfing Collection.
        —   —   **15**   **20**

1978-1979 **9036 MOBILGAS:** Short single-dome tank car; white tank; red lettering; standard-issue 9036 tank car (see Volume I for details) overstamped for 1978-79 LCCA Meet Specials; 800 made.
        —   —   **25**   **35**

1979-1980 **9016 CHESSIE:** Short hopper; yellow body; blue lettering; standard-issue 9016 (see Volume I for details) with "LCCA MEET SPECIAL 1979 1980" overstamp in green. C. Rohlfing and C. O'Dell comments.
        —   —   —   **25**

1982 **6483 NEW JERSEY CENTRAL:** SP-type caboose; heat-stamped for LCCA meets in 1981-82; unpainted red Type VII plastic body; Type II ends; white lettering; "1982 LCCA MEET SPECIAL"; one operating and one dummy coupler attached by metal rivets; Symington-Wayne trucks; "BLT. 9-82". This car is the only one of the six in the series made specially by Lionel itself for the meet car program — the others were overstamped regular-issue cars. Reportedly only 503 examples made. Last issue of the LCCA Meet Car program; sold on a subscription basis only. Hard to find. J. R. Hunt and C. Lang comments; C. Darasko and C. Rohlfing Collections.
        —   —   —   **40**

1986 **6523 SPOKANE, PORTLAND & SEATTLE:** Double-door boxcar; yellow body; black roof and ends; black doors; black lettering; Symington-Wayne trucks.
        —   —   **50**   **65**

THE LIONEL CENTRAL OPERATING LINES

In 1976, a small group of Lionel collectors and operators from Long Island, New York formed the Lionel Central Operating Lines (LCOL). The club was intended to provide a social outlet for its membership and to create a large layout which the members would maintain. The group, now numbering 33, has had four layouts in four separate buildings, and has endeavored to conduct open houses at least twice a year. The organization is currently without a home, but has survived by means of get-togethers, meets, picnics, a newsletter, and the issuance of an annual special car, which brings the club to our attention.

Ernie Knudsen, founder of the Lionel Central Operating Lines, decided the club needed a special commemorative unique to it, to act as a fundraiser and to advertise the club as the trains traveled around the layouts during the public open houses. The car series started in 1981 and continues today. Like several other groups, the club changed its most recent cars to KMT and K-Line due to the cost of Lionels. All the cars display an oval steam engine logo lettered "Lionel Central Operating Lines" somewhere on the body, either as a decal or screened lettering. PVP decorated the first several cars, and later cars were created by Frank Rash. Most recently, the club has simply provided decal sheets for members to install on regular-issue cars on an individual basis. In all cases, less than 50 of each car exists — the club is small. We thank Ernie Knudsen for providing this data.

1981 **1981 LIONEL CENTRAL OPERATING LINES:** Boxcar; first in an annual series by the LCOL based in Long Island, New York; orange body; blue lettering and oval LCOL steam engine logo; standard Lionel 9700-series boxcar (underlying car type unknown) redecorated by PVP (designator "504-1158"); only 30 made. E. Knudsen Collection. —   —   **25**

1982 **9184 ERIE:** Bay window caboose; second in an annual series by the LCOL; standard 9184 caboose with the word "ERIE"

GD   VG   EXC   MT

removed and the LCOL oval logo included in white; redecorated by PVP (designator "205-1177"); about 50 made. E. Knudsen Collection. — — — **25**

1983 **6508 CANADIAN PACIFIC:** Crane car; third in an annual series by the LCOL; standard 6508 crane car with the beaver decal removed and an LCOL oval logo printed in maroon to match the car colors; on the rear of the cab are the letters "1983 — New Home," because at the time the club had just moved its layout to a new building; redecorated by PVP (designator "706-1229"); about 50 made. E. Knudsen Collection. — — — **45**

1984 **5724 PENNSYLVANIA:** Bunk car; fourth in an annual series by the LCOL; standard 5724 PRR bunk car with the oval LCOL decal added, as well as an interesting electronic chugging sound effects board placed inside; created by Frank Rash; about 50 were made. E. Knudsen Collection. — — — **40**

1985 **9475 I LOVE NY:** Boxcar; fifth in an annual series by the LCOL; standard 9475 boxcar with the LCOL decal added; about 50 were made. E. Knudsen Collection.
— — — **30**

1986 **1986 LCOL:** Work caboose shells only; sixth in an annual series by the LCOL; blank Lionel work caboose cabs obtained by PVP and painted gray with the LCOL oval logo added in white (designator "206-1449"); cabs only, with no frame or trucks, although of course many members have added these; about 50 made. Price for cab only. E. Knudsen Collection.
— — — **18**

1987 **No Production:** For the first time, the club did not purchase Lionel pieces due to costs. A Central of New Jersey stock car in green from KMT was used as the annual commemorative. A sticker with the LCOL logo was provided. About 50 cars exist.

1988 **LCOL:** About 50 2046-style reproduction tenders (not original Lionel) were obtained by the club for its 1988 annual car (eighth in the series); black with bold "LIONEL CENTRAL OPERATING LINES" in white along the sides; created by Frank Rash.

1989 and 1990 **LCOL:** About 50 K-Line cars were purchased as the club commemoratives each year. In 1989, a Pennsylvania three-dome tank car was sold and supplied with the LCOL oval decal. In 1990, the club made a K-Line flatcar in tuscan with a trailer decaled for LCOL.

THE LIONEL
OPERATING TRAIN SOCIETY

Formed in 1980, LOTS represents the newest and smallest of the national train societies. A dynamic group in the train hobby, it devotes its energies to the operation and enjoyment of Lionel's trains and accessories. LOTS sponsors local meets and national train conventions every year. Each year, the club creates a special car for the convention, available only to the membership. This practice began in the first year of its existence.

Because the society was small during its first eight years, it was unable to persuade Lionel to make the convention cars. The club therefore turned to John Newbraugh and Seymour Knight of the Pleasant Valley Process Co., who overstamped or redecorated LOTS's cars from 1981 through 1987. At last,

GD   VG   EXC   MT

in 1988, LOTS was able to generate enough orders for its convention car to enable Lionel to make them entirely at Mt. Clemens. This first Lionel-produced car, the 17874 Milwaukee Road log dump car, is quite difficult to find today. Since then, membership in LOTS has been growing rapidly.

The LOTS convention cars differ in many ways from the convention or meet specials of other clubs. First, the club set a policy that the LOTS and convention notations on the cars would be very small and inconspicuous. It is, in fact, often difficult to spot the differences in LOTS overstamped cars vs. the Lionel originals, except for the PVP/NBT notations. LOTS's convention notations are often worked into the body of the technical information on the car. For example, one will find "TESTED 7-13-85 St. Louis, Mo." on the 1985 car to indicate the date and site of the 1985 convention. This is in contrast to the sometimes garish graphics found on convention cars from other clubs. Second, LOTS's policy has been to create highly prototypical cars, with markings and numbering systems representative of the actual cars, not of Lionel's system. While the practice is confusing to number-series collectors, this policy (prototypical cars with prototypical numbers) has since become the norm for nearly all the other Lionel-related train clubs. For example, "17874" will not be found on the Milwaukee Road log carrier mentioned earlier. The number stamped on the frame of that car is "59629". Third, being a Lionel train society, LOTS sticks strictly with O Gauge Lionel equipment for its special production pieces. In contrast, TCA and TTOS have issued convention souvenirs produced by many toy train manufacturers, in many scales. Finally, LOTS restricts its sales to a maximum of two per member, and produces only the number ordered, guaranteeing limited production and collector's item status as soon as the car is released.

LOTS concentrates on convention cars typical for the cities in which it holds its conventions. It also made one meet car for a Seattle meet in 1986, and several special accessories for convention-goers in 1984 and 1988. For its 10th anniversary in 1989, LOTS also commissioned a variation of the Union Pacific RS-3 with a small anniversary notation.

All LOTS cars have proven desirable and scarce. Some, such as the 1982 Michigan Central boxcar, were produced in such limited quantities that they are nearly impossible to find today. Recent production has been in greater numbers, so these items may show up at more meets. Another interesting note about LOTS cars: the actual quantity produced is printed somewhere on the car.

We are grateful to LOTS's members Dick Johnson and Kit Walshock for compiling the data in this section. Readers interested in more details are referred to Johnson's comprehensive article on the cars in the June 1989 issue of LOTS's magazine, the *SWITCHER*.

1980 **9414 COTTON BELT:** Boxcar; first annual convention car made for LOTS; standard Lionel tuscan 9414 Cotton Belt boxcar (see Volume I for further details) with additional white overstamped car and convention data applied by the Good Decal Co; 360 made; came in a Type III box. This is the most plentiful of LOTS's early convention cars — many more were made than there were club members at the time. — — — **40**

Convention cars from LOTS, with inconspicuous convention notations. All the cars in this photo, except the engine, were decorated by PVP:
Top shelf: 18805 Union Pacific RS-3 from 1989, same as regular-issue except for red block.
Second shelf: 9414 Cotton Belt boxcar from 1980; 3764 Kahn's reefer with red roof from 1981.
Third shelf: 3764 Kahn's reefer with brown roof from 1981; 80948 Michigan Central boxcar from 1982.
Bottom shelf: 6111 Louisville & Nashville hopper from 1983; 121315 Pennsylvania hi-cube boxcar from 1984.

	GD	VG	EXC	MT

1981 **3764 E. KAHN'S SONS CO.:** Wood-side boxcar; second annual LOTS convention car; Lionel 7700-series Tobacco Road boxcar redecorated by PVP/NBT; yellow sides; black "Brine Tank Refrigerator"; red "Kahn's" logo; number on car is "3764"; PVP designator "605-1160"; Symington-Wayne trucks; came in Type II box.
(A) Red roof and ends; 124 made. C. Lang, M. Solly and "Triple T" Collections. — — — 60
(B) Brown roof and ends; 176 made. M. Solly and "Triple T" Collections. — — — 55

1982 **80948 MICHIGAN CENTRAL:** Boxcar; third annual LOTS convention car; Lionel 9620-series sports boxcar redecorated by PVP/NBT; Type IX body with green sides; black roof and ends; white lettering; number on car is "80948"; PVP designator "505-1204"; Type III frame; Symington-Wayne trucks; 150 made; came in Type III box. Due to its very limited production, this is by far the most difficult LOTS convention car to obtain. M. Solly Collection. — — — 175

1983 **6111 LOUISVILLE & NASHVILLE:** Covered quad hopper; fourth annual LOTS convention car; standard-issue gray 6111 quad hopper (see Volume I for further details) including an additional coal load insert; red overstamped car data and convention markings by PVP/NBT; PVP designator "306-1268"; 200 made; came in Type III box. M. Solly Collection. — — — 50

1984 **121315 PENNSYLVANIA:** Hi-cube boxcar; fifth annual LOTS convention car; Lionel 9600-series hi-cube boxcar redecorated by PVP/NBT; tuscan body; white lettering and yellow "Cushioned Car"; white "excess height" end panels with black lettering; number on car is "121315"; PVP designator "705-1333"; Symington-Wayne trucks; "BLT 3-63"; 225 made; came in Type III box. One of the more difficult of the LOTS cars to find. M. Solly Collection. — — — 90
Note: LOTS also made special versions of the 2320 flag pole kit for its 1984 convention souvenir at Pittsburgh.

1985 **303 STAUFFER CHEMICAL:** 1985, single-dome tank car; sixth annual LOTS convention car; Lionel 9329 Tootsie Roll

Recent LOTS convention cars:

M. Solly and F. Stem Collections; B. Greenberg photograph

Top shelf: 38356 Dow Chemical Company tank car from 1987; 6211 Chesapeake & Ohio gondola from 1986.
Middle shelf: 303 Stauffer Chemical tank car from 1985; 17874 Milwaukee Road log dump from 1988 — first car made entirely by Lionel for LOTS.
Bottom shelf: 17875 Port Huron & Detroit boxcar from 1989.

	GD	VG	EXC	MT

tank car redecorated by PVP/NBT; gray body; black dome, center band and lower third of tank; design similar to postwar 6315 Gulf tanker; black lettering; orange Stauffer logo; black number and capacity data on tank ends; black metal dome walkway and ladders; black-painted wire handrails; number on car is "303"; PVP designator "705-1391"; Symington-Wayne trucks; "BUILT 7-47"; 300 made; came in Type III box.
(A) As described. M. Solly Collection. — — — **70**
(B) With "LOT 6-300" and "St. Louis, Mo. LOTS" data lines removed. Five cars were made this way and given to Stauffer Chemical, in appreciation for its assistance in the decoration of the car. **NRS**

1986 **6211 CHESAPEAKE & OHIO:** Long gondola; seventh annual LOTS convention car; Lionel black 6211 C & O gondola (see Volume I for details), except this car is a variation to the regular run in that the number is over-and-under-scored (regular run had no scoring lines); additional data and convention markings in yellow applied by PVP/NBT; car came with two dark blue canisters and bag of coal; PVP designator "306-1437"; Symington-Wayne trucks; one dummy coupler; 454 made; came in Type III box.
(A) As described. M. Solly Collection. — — — **35**
(B) No overstamped car data; 23 exist. — — — **50**

1986 **1223 SEATTLE & NORTH COAST:** Hi-cube boxcar; special souvenir car for a LOTS April 1986 Seattle, Washington train meet; Lionel 9600-series hi-cube boxcar redecorated by PVP/NBT; forest green body; yellow and white lettering and "S & NC" logo; yellow-painted doors with large green "V" and black door lettering; white "excess height" end panels with

black lettering; number on car is "1223"; PVP designator "705-1431"; Symington-Wayne trucks; only 47 made. This is LOTS's only meet car to date, and difficulties in obtaining the cars led LOTS to forswear using meet cars in the future. Very hard to find.
(A) As described. G. Swan Collection. — — — **150**
(B) Tuscan body, and without "V" on doors. Prototype. **NRS**

1987 **38356 DOW CHEMICAL COMPANY:** Three-dome tank car; eighth annual LOTS convention car; Lionel 6314 B & O three-dome tank car redecorated by PVP/NBT; sky blue tank body; dark blue lettering; yellow "DOW" logo; dark blue lettering and capacity data on sides and tank ends; yellow-painted wire handrails; "38356" is the number on the car; number under-scored; PVP designator "705-1454"; Symington-Wayne trucks; 450 made; came in Type III box. M. Solly Collection. — — — **60**

1988 **17874 MILWAUKEE ROAD:** Log dump car; ninth annual LOTS convention car; first car for LOTS produced by Lionel; tuscan body and log cradle; white lettering; three 9"-long barked logs with chains and spring, similar to postwar 6361 log carrier; number on car is "59629"; 17874 is Lionel's catalogue number but this does not appear on the car or the box; Standard O trucks (first LOTS car with them); "BLT 1-88"; "INSP 7-16-88"; 519 made; came in Type V box. Somewhat difficult to find. M. Solly Collection. — — — **125**

Note: 100 specially-produced 12707 billboards with small LOTS notations were distributed to attendees at the 1988 LOTS convention in Seattle.

1989 **17875 PORT HURON & DETROIT (PH & D):** Boxcar; 10th annual LOTS convention car; dark blue classic boxcar-type body; silver roof; white lettering and number; white "PH-D"

GD   VG   EXC   MT

logo with red bar between "PH" and "D"; number on car is "1289"; "17875" appears only on box; Standard O trucks; "BLT 7-15-89"; 808 made; came in Type V box. M. Solly Collection.

— — — 100

1989 **18805 UNION PACIFIC:** RS-3 diesel; 10th anniversary LOTS special; same as regular-issue yellow 18805 RS-3 diesel (see Volume I for details) except for added red warning signs on cab; lettering reads "10th Anniv./LOTS — 1989"; 400 made. M. Solly Collection.

— — — 150

1990 **17882 BALTIMORE & OHIO:** Double-door automobile boxcar with End-of-Train Device; 11th annual LOTS convention car; tuscan body; white lettering and B & O dome logo; number on car is "298011"; number under- and over-scored; "17882" appears only on box; first train club car to sport an End-of-Train device; intended as a reissue of the scarce 6468 postwar tuscan B & O automobile boxcar; ASF strong-arm trucks; "NEW 2-47" — the same notation as on original 6468; 1216 made; came in Type V box. M. Solly Collection.

— — — 90

1991 **17890 CSX:** Two-tier enclosed-style auto carrier; 12th annual LOTS convention car; yellow flatcar body; silver-painted side slats and roof; white ends on roof; yellow side posts; sliding double doors at each end; black lettering on frame; "CSX Transportation" in black on plate insert; white "TRAILER TRAIN" and "TTGX 151161"; separate door and ladder pieces included in envelope; small LOTS convention notation to upper right side; "17890" is on the box only, not on the car; Standard O trucks; "BLT 7-91"; 1350 made; came in Type VI box. M. Solly Collection.

— — — 80

THE LIONEL RAILROADER CLUB: "THE INSIDE TRACK"

Introduction by John Kouba

In 1982, when General Mills was the parent company of Lionel, the corporate heads decided to develop their own train special interest group. This was the genesis of the Lionel Railroader Club (LRRC) — a club designed to cater to both novice and seasoned railroaders. To entice veteran collectors, the LRRC offered a special uncatalogued car, with special markings and graphics, on a yearly basis.

Certain parameters have regulated this series to date: 1) car types (ie., boxcar, tank car, hopper, etc.) would not be repeated (despite Lionel's diversity, it will be interesting to see if this rule holds as the set continues); 2) each car would be uncatalogued; 3) each would carry the "Inside Track" logo, year of issue, and the notation "Special Edition", as well as an LRRC club logo; and, 4) all the cars would be higher end O27-style cars. As of 1991, none have been issued with die-cast or sprung trucks, nor have any had 1/48-scale dimensions.

The club's newsletter, *The Inside Track,* is published quarterly by Lionel itself at the plant in Mt. Clemens. The magazine mostly prints announcements about new releases or upcoming Lionel products. But it also occasionally prints some interesting operating tips and railroad historical notes,

and it is the only publication in which the LRRC club cars are announced.

The series began in 1982 with the 0780 boxcar, followed by the 0781 TOFC flatcar in 1983, the 0784 covered quad hopper in 1984, and the 0782 single-dome tank car in 1985. It is not clear why Lionel chose such unusual numbers for the cars, except that it wanted the numbers to be as separate from the catalogue production as possible.

The change in ownership in 1986 brought about a change to five-digit identifiers for the LRRC cars. The next car was the 16800 ore car in 1986 (which also happens to be one of the first cars of any kind issued with a five-digit number). No car was released in 1987, nor was any reason given by Lionel. Production resumed in 1988 with a 16801 bunk car, followed by the 16802 tool car in 1989, a 16803 searchlight car in 1990 and the 16804 bay window caboose in 1991.

Thus, Lionel has released a total of nine cars in this series so far. With the searchlight car, Lionel brought operating cars into the collection. It can now pick from log or coal dump cars, crane or derrick cars, track maintenance cars, or an animated gondola. In fact, many options for non-operating cars also remain: including standard gondolas, auto carriers, flatcars with loads, refrigerator cars and stock cars.

When it released the caboose in 1991, Lionel hinted the next item in the series would be a matching 10th anniversary engine. It even encouraged subscribers of *The Inside Track* to write in with suggestions. Most likely, in order to keep the purchase price manageable, the engine choice will be from the diesel series, such as an RS-3, an Alco, or a GP.

Although the cars have not received much collector interest (because of the non-prototypical graphics and non-scale size), *The Inside Track* series from the LRRC is a logical choice for a beginning collector interested in obtaining a complete series of cars. There are no variations of which to speak, all are readily available (although the earlier cars are becoming difficult to find), and the small number released so far makes the set manageable and affordable. The real incentive to collecting the LRRC club cars is the small number made — the run is directly tied to the number of orders LRRC receives, assuring a limited-production run.

There is one unusual and collectable quirk about the Lionel Railroader Club cars — many sport accurate "BLT" dates. The great majority of Lionel modern era production is printed with BLT dates reading "1-XX", where "XX" stands for the year. Lionel cannot accurately predict the month in which most pieces will be made, so it prints January on nearly everything. The LRRC cars, however, are an exception. Apparently, Lionel does know when it can make the cars (it controls distribution), so one will find dates such as "9-82" and "10-86" on these cars, reflecting the actual month of production.

For the modest fee of $5 a year, young Lionel enthusiasts receive the newsletter and an opportunity to order the special cars direct from Lionel. It may surprise our veteran collectors out there to find that the LRRC now boasts more active members than any other national train club, including the TCA!

For now, the LRRC's *The Inside Track* series provides the hobbyist with the best of all worlds: low cost, diversity, reasonable quality and limited production.

The full set of LRRC cars through 1990:
Top shelf: 0780 boxcar from 1982; 0781 TOFC flatcar from 1983.
Second shelf: 0784 hopper from 1984; 0782 tank car from 1985.
Third shelf: 16800 ore car from 1986; 16801 bunk car from 1988.
Bottom shelf: 16802 tool car from 1989; 16803 searchlight car from 1990.

M. Solly Collection; B. Greenberg photograph

	GD	VG	EXC	MT

1982 **0780 LIONEL RAILROADER CLUB:** Boxcar; first annual special car from the LRRC; classic-style boxcar; white-painted white body; red-painted white doors; red roof and ends; black steam locomotive electrocal to right of door; red and black "INSIDE TRACK" logo to left; red and black lettering; Symington-Wayne trucks; "BLT 9-82"; Type III box. First car in a special series only available to members of the Lionel Railroader Club, a Fundimensions-sponsored organization continued by Lionel Trains, Inc. M. Solly and F. Stem Collections.

	—	—	50	65

1983 **0781 LIONEL RAILROADER CLUB:** TOFC flatcar; second annual special car from the LRRC; black body; white lettering; silver-painted vans with red and black lettering; "LIONEL/RAILROADER CLUB" and black train logo on one van and "SPECIAL EDITION/THE INSIDE TRACK" on the other; long Type I (mold 6424-11) flatcar body; Symington-Wayne trucks; "BLT 11-83"; Type III box. M. Solly and D. Spoto Collections.

	—	—	45	50

1984 **0784 LIONEL RAILROADER CLUB:** Covered quad hopper; third annual special issue from the LRRC; white body; black and red lettering; red cover; black engine logo to right; black "INSIDE TRACK" logo at lower center; Symington-Wayne trucks; "BLT 12-84"; Type III box. It is not clear why the numbers on this car and the 0782 tank car are out of sequence. M. Solly and T. Ladny Collections.

	—	—	50	60

1985 **0782 LIONEL RAILROADER CLUB:** Single-dome tank car; fourth annual special issue from LRRC; maroon tank car body; white lettering; LRRC logo and steam engine to right; "INSIDE TRACK" logo to left; black dome; metal dome platform and ladder; wire handrails; Symington-Wayne trucks with one dummy coupler; "BLT 12-85". Unlike the rest of the series, which used Traditional-type boxes, this car came in a Type V collector box. M. Solly, F. Stem and T. Ladny Collections.

	—	—	40	45

1986 **16800 LIONEL RAILROADER CLUB:** Ore car; fifth annual special issue from LRRC; yellow body; black lettering; steam engine logo at lower center; "SPECIAL EDITION/THE

	GD	VG	EXC	MT

INSIDE TRACK" at lower left; Symington-Wayne trucks; "BLT 10-86"; Type VI box. This may have been one of the first Lionel cars numbered with five digits, and one of the first issued in a Type VI box. Somewhat harder to find than other LRRC cars. C. O'Dell comment; M. Solly Collection. — — **50 60**

1986 **0785 LIONEL RAILROADER CLUB:** ACF two-bay center flow hopper; dark blue body; yellow lettering; Standard O trucks. — — **75 100**

1987 **No Production**

1988 **16801 LIONEL RAILROADER CLUB:** Bunk car; sixth annual special issue from LRRC; dark blue-green body; yellow lettering; LRRC steam engine logo to right side; "INSIDE TRACK" logo to left; illuminated; Symington-Wayne trucks; "BLT 2-88"; Type VI box. M. Solly Collection. — — **50 60**

1989 **16802 LIONEL RAILROADER CLUB:** Tool car; seventh annual special issue from LRRC; dark blue-green body; yellow lettering; LRRC steam engine logo at right center; illuminated; Type V plastic arch bar trucks — a variation from earlier cars which had Symington-Wayne trucks; "BLT 1-89"; Type VI box. Intended as a match for the 1988 car. M. Solly Collection. — — — **50**

1990 **16803 LIONEL RAILROADER CLUB:** Searchlight car; eighth annual special issue from LRRC; red Type II flatcar body (6511-2 mold); white lettering; gray superstructure with red "SPECIAL EDITION" and "INSIDE TRACK" logo; black searchlight hood; white flatcar lettering; ASF strong-arm trucks; "BLT 5-90"; Type VI box. M. Solly and J. Kouba Collections. — — — **45**

1991 **16804 LIONEL RAILROADER CLUB:** Bay window caboose; ninth annual special issue from LRRC; red body; gold-painted bay window; dark gray roof; white lettering; red LRRC steam engine logo on bay window; "INSIDE TRACK" logo to left; illuminated; ASF strong-arm trucks. Lionel has hinted its 1992 LRRC release will be an engine. M. Solly Collection. — — — **45**

THE NASSAU LIONEL OPERATING ENGINEERS

The Nassau Lionel Operating Engineers Club is a small group of dedicated Lionel railroaders located in Levittown, New York. It has been in existence since 1983, and recently fulfilled its goal of creating a large permanent operating Lionel layout, which is opened for public viewing during holiday open houses. Since 1989, the group has commissioned PVP to create some handsome, special Lionel-based cars, which brings them to our attention (despite the fact that the club is not a national organization).

The Nassau Engineers' principal goal was (and is) to create a large permanent Lionel layout which can exercise the skill and creativity of its members, provide them with an enjoyable means to operate their trains, and publicize Lionel and the hobby through public exhibitions. The club, whose membership is naturally local, holds monthly meetings in the

	GD	VG	EXC	MT

layout room and requires each member to contribute some activity in relation to maintaining or operating the layout.

The club has been quite successful in this endeavor, after some early fits and starts in finding a suitable location for its huge layout.

Once the setup was ready to go in 1988, the group dedicated itself to modifications and enhancements, as well as the fun of running its trains privately and publicly. Beginning in 1989, it sponsored a small number of special cars, available only to the members, decorated for the Long Island Railroad, a road which Lionel itself has only rarely used on its pieces. The idea and the designs for the series came from club member Rich Williams. Our thanks to club officials Al Schwartz and Rich Williams for providing this data:

1989 **8389 LONG ISLAND RAILROAD:** Boxcar; first in a series of special cars produced for the Nassau Lionel Operating Engineers club in Levittown, New York; tuscan body and doors; white lettering; black and white LIRR keystone; Symington-Wayne trucks; "BUILT 9-7-89"; 51 made. This is a standard Lionel classic-style boxcar redecorated by PVP. It was created using redecorated 9620-series sports boxcars. Discerning readers will find a good picture of this car on the Nassau Club's huge layout in the June 1991 issue of *O-Gauge Railroading*. **NRS**

1990 **8390 LONG ISLAND RAILROAD:** Covered quad hopper; second in a series of special cars made for the Nassau Lionel Operating Engineers club in Levittown, New York; gray body; orange end panels and ends; orange lettering; LI logo in orange circle to upper right; Symington-Wayne trucks; "BLT 2-90"; 48 made. This is a standard Lionel quad hopper body (a 19309 Seaboard) redecorated by PVP. **NRS**

1991 **8391A/8391B LONG ISLAND RAILROAD*:** Bunk tool car set; third in a series of special cars made for the Nassau Lionel Operating Engineers club in Levittown, New York; orange body; gray roof and ends; gray LIRR lettering and "Route of the Dashing Commuter" logo; both cars are illuminated; "BLT 6-91"; 51 sets made. These matching cars are based on standard Lionel bunk and tool car bodies (using the 19654 and 19655 Amtrak cars or the 19652-3 Jersey Central cars) redecorated by PVP. **NRS**

THE TRAIN COLLECTORS ASSOCIATION

The TCA is the largest and oldest organization of train hobbyists in the United States. It is broken into 20 regional divisions and 23 local chapters around the nation, and dates back to a small meeting of veteran Lionel train enthusiasts in a barn in Yardley, Pennsylvania in 1954. The intervening 37 years have seen the group's active membership grow to nearly 20,000, all collectors and operators of a variety of train scales and manufacturers. Approximately half the membership are Lionel collectors of prewar, postwar and modern era.

The TCA conducts many regional train meets around the country each year, including the prominent York, Pennsylvania meet held each April and October. This incredible

R. Kaptur and F. Stem Collections; B. Greenberg photograph

...ection of TCA national convention cars.
...shelf: 9123 auto carrier from 1973.
...nd shelf: 9774 Southern Belle boxcar from 1975; 9779 Bicentennial boxcar from 1976.
...d shelf: 9319 bullion car from 1979; 6926 extended vision caboose from 1986.
...m shelf: 19879 short Madison diner car from 1989; 17883 General-style passenger car from 1990.

...vent, considered by most to be the Mecca of traindom, encom-
...asses over six buildings. At York, one can really shop for
...rains, including many rare and hard-to-find pieces, although
...; can be difficult to see all the tables and items for sale even
...hen walking at a brisk pace!

The club has a national headquarters and museum in
...trasburg, Pennsylvania. It publishes *Quarterly*, which fea-
...ures articles of interest on all types of trains, and a quarterly
...leadquarters News which contains buy and sell ads. TCA also
...onducts a national convention each year, sponsored by a
...ivision or chapter, and for these it commissions annual con-
...ention cars (often several a year in a variety of scales).

With its conventions, divisions and museums as inspira-
...ion, the TCA has produced far more special train cars (Lionel
...nd otherwise) than any other club. The total is astonishing
...– more than 100 Lionel-derivative cars alone at last count,
...nd there are probably many more unaccounted for. Many
...ivision or meet cars are obscure and hard-to-find, but since
...hey are often inexpensive and brightly-decorated, some may
...nd them attractive collecting possibilities.

This Guide restricts its detailed discussion to
Lionel-made and Lionel-derivative cars, and mentions other
gauges and items made by other manufacturers to provide a
complete picture. The national convention car series are listed
first, followed by the special series or individual cars made for
various TCA chapters and divisions.

TCA NATIONAL CONVENTION CARS

The TCA began its convention car series in 1965 with a
variation of the classic 6464 boxcar series (6464-1965). Made
for the group's 11th annual convention in Pittsburgh, Pennsylvania, it was the first train club convention car made for
anyone, and essentially established the concept. A 6517 Erie
bay window caboose followed in 1966, and another intriguing
group of 6464 boxcars were commissioned in 1967. In this
case, Lionel was unable to make the cars itself (postwar
collectors will remember that Lionel catalogued *nothing* in
1967), so TCA had a unique set of brass boxcar doors made up
which it substituted onto otherwise standard variations of the
6464 cars. The cars from this period (1965 to 1967) are quite

GD   VG   EXC   MT

scarce and expensive today. In 1968, a steam engine tender shell (2671-type) was offered at the Cleveland, Ohio convention, and 1969 saw a 6436-1969 quad hopper in red to mark the association's convention in Clearwater, Florida. This brings us to the beginning of the modern era cars.

In addition to the convention car, which was announced in the club's national magazines, TCA would occasionally create a special convention souvenir car available only to attendees. These were generally overstamped or redecorated regular-production cars, not specials made entirely for TCA by Lionel, as the main cars were.

During most of the modern era, TCA was also producing convention cars from a variety of other manufacturers, and in gauges other than O. So it is not unusual to find a group of TCA cars, in HO, S, O and Large Scales, decorated similarly and offered together in one year.

1970 **6464-1970 TCA SPECIAL:** Classic-type boxcar including postwar number; TCA Chicago national convention car; Type V yellow-painted lighter yellow body; red door; no decals; white heat-stamped lettering; about 1,100 made. This may have been one of the very first cars produced by MPC/Lionel. E. Davis comment.
(A) Unpainted red door.   —   —   125   160
(B) Red-painted red door.   —   —   125   160

1971 **6464-1971 TCA SPECIAL:** Classic-type boxcar including postwar number; TCA Disneyland national convention car; Type VI white-painted white body, roof and ends; dark orange-yellow-painted yellow doors; metal door guides; red, white and blue heat-stamped Disneyland logos; postwar bar-end trucks; 1500 made. Designed by Ward Kimball.
                                  —   —   200   250
See also Factory Errors and Prototypes chapter.

1971 **9701 BALTIMORE & OHIO:** Double-door automobile boxcar; this variation of the 9701 was made as a special souvenir for attendees at the 1971 TCA national convention; shiny black-painted black body; flat-black painted black doors; white lettering; Type I frame; Symington-Wayne trucks; reportedly 900 were made. The cars were serially stamped with silver rubber-stamped lettering on the bottom of the frame. Beware of fake stamping.
                                  —   —   100   125

1972 **6315 TCA PITTSBURGH:** Single-dome tank car; made for TCA national convention at Pittsburgh; orange tank body; black dome; black "7-11"; postwar bar-end trucks; 2000 made.   —   —   75   95
Note: A special 671-type boiler front was also made by TCA in 1972. See description under the TCA Other Production, Ft. Pitt division subsection of this chapter.

1973 **9123 TCA:** Automobile carrier; made for TCA national convention in Dearborn; black body; TCA logo in gold on one letterboard; "NATIONAL CONVENTION/DEARBORN, MICH./1973" in gold on second letterboard, same side; all lettering deep heat-stamped; gold "TRAILER TRAIN" reporting marks on flatcar side; came in 9123 Lionel Type II automobile carrier box, but 9123 does not appear on car side; Symington-Wayne trucks. C. Lang Collection.   —   —   45   55

1974 **9864 TCA SEATTLE:** 9800-series refrigerator car; TCA national convention car; Type II body with metal door guides and channel; white body with medium royal blue roof, ends and

---

THE 1973 TCA CONVENTION SPECIALS
Norman Fuhrmann was the chairman and host of the 1973 TCA National Convention in Dearborn, Michigan. In that capacity, he asked Lionel for special donations of cars to be used as door prizes and special awards. Richard Branstner, Lionel's Vice President of Engineering at the time, suggested 60 or so cars that had been shown at the 1973 Toy Fair. These turned out to be unique pieces, and Fuhrmann and convention co-host Ed Barbret received them enthusiastically. The following is a complete list of the cars supplied by Fundimensions for the 1973 TCA National Convention. Since they are all considered prototype pieces, these items are listed also in the Factory Errors and Prototypes chapter. One complete set of these cars, including the unique gray 9820 Wabash gondola, is in the collection of Edward Barbret.

Qty.	Car Number	Road Name	Body Color	Letter Color	Door Color	Type
10	9123	C & O	yellow	blue	—	3-tier auto car
6	9123	—	blue	white	—	2-tier auto car
12	9701	B & O	blue	yellow	black	boxcar
5	9703	CP Rail	green	black	green	boxcar
10	9705	D & RGW	silver	orange	silver	boxcar
11	9705	D & RGW	silver	red	red	boxcar
4	9706	C & O	black	yellow	black	boxcar
5	9802	Miller	gray	red	—	reefer
2	9820	Wabash	gray	white	—	gondola
3	9821	SP	black	white	—	gondola

GD   VG   EXC   M'

doors; black, red and blue Seattle World's Fair Space Needl Tower logo at left of door; "1954-1974" in red and TCA logo in blac above large blue "20" at right of door; Symington-Wayne trucks reportedly 3,000 made.   —   —   35   4

1975 **9774 THE SOUTHERN BELLE:** Boxcar; TCA na tional convention car; Type IX body; orange sides and silver roc and ends painted on orange body; green-painted white door green and black lettering; Southern Belle and TCA logo to left c door; Type II frame; Symington-Wayne trucks.
                                  —   —   30   5

1976 **9779 TCA BICENTENNIAL:** Boxcar; TCA nationa convention car; unpainted white body; unpainted blue door red-painted roof and ends; brown, black, white and gold eagl electrocal and TCA logo to left of door; TCA Philadelphia conven tion data to right of door; "9700-1976"; "9779" is not on the car Symington-Wayne trucks; "BLT 1-76". The word Philadelphia i misspelled "Philadephia" on all examples. C. Lang comment.
                                  —   25   35   5

A truly special TCA train set!
Top shelf: **5484** Hudson steam engine and tender from 1985.
Second shelf: **0511** St. Louis baggage car from 1981; **5734-85** Railway Express wood-sided reefer from 1985.
Third shelf: **7206** Louisville passenger coach from 1983; **7205** Denver combine from 1982.
Bottom shelf: **9544** Chicago observation car from 1980; **7212** Pittsburgh passenger coach from 1984.

	GD	VG	EXC	MT

1977 7812 TCA HOUSTON: Stock car; TCA national convention car; brown body; brown-yellow plastic plaque inserted in place of double doors; center metal door guide removed; yellow lettering on car body, "23rd NATIONAL CONVENTION/HOUSTON TEXAS / JUNE 1977"; brown lettering and logos on plaque; Symington-Wayne trucks; "BLT 1-77". — — 35 45

1978 9611 THE FLYING YANKEE: Hi-cube boxcar; TCA Boston national convention car; light blue sides; black roof and ends; white doors; black lettering, "TWENTY FOURTH NATIONAL CONVENTION BOSTON MA", "Home of the Flying Yankee"; white clearance boards on car ends; Symington-Wayne trucks; disc couplers with tabs. Some of these cars were repainted into the 1018-1979 Mortgage Burning Ceremony Car. See entry 1018-1979 in the TCA Other Production section of this chapter for details of this interesting story.
(A) As described. — — 35 45
(B) With silver overstamped lettering "New England Division" and "CAPY 152000" with other data. Car was purchased and overstamped by the division for its local members. F. Wilkins Collection. — — 40 50

1979 9319 TCA SILVER JUBILEE: Bullion car; for TCA's 25th anniversary national convention in Disneyland; gloss dark blue body; silver bullion; white lettering on clear sides; special coin

available only at the convention, coin sits in car slot but does not fall into car; coin lettered "TCA 25 Years", and about size of half-dollar; Symington-Wayne trucks; "BLT 1-79"; 6,000 made. The other regularly catalogued bullion cars had Standard O sprung trucks, this is the only bullion car without them.
(A) Car only. — — 250 325
(B) Car with coin. — — 300 375

> **THE TCA PASSENGER SPECIAL**
> *From 1980 through 1985 the TCA released a handsome set of "Brunswick" green passenger cars as its National Convention commemoratives, each lettered for the city in which the convention was held. This set, and particularly the Hudson designed to pull them (released in 1985), have become quite desirable today. An add-on car was made in 1989 (the 17879 Valley Forge diner car).*

1980 9544 TCA CHICAGO: 9500-series short Madison-style observation car; TCA national convention car; Brunswick green body; black roof; gold "LAND OF LINCOLN/CHICAGO"; gold stripes above and below windows; white TCA logo; illuminated with passenger silhouettes in windows; "9544" on box only; num-

	GD	VG	EXC	MT

ber on car is "1980"; six-wheel die-cast passenger trucks. First in a series of convention passenger cars. It is interesting TCA would start the train with the observation car.

| | — | — | — | 75 |

1981 **0511 TCA ST. LOUIS:** 9500-type short Madison baggage car; TCA national convention car; "THE GATEWAY TO THE WEST/ST. LOUIS" in rubber-stamped gold lettering; REA logo in red; otherwise matches 9544; "0511" on box only; "1981" at both ends of car. J. Bratspis Collection.

| | — | — | — | 75 |

Note: There were also several "banquet" cars made from Lionel 5700 Oppenheimer Turn-of-the-Century refrigerator cars, produced for the 1981 convention. See the Gateway division heading in the TCA Other Production section of this chapter for more details.

1982 **7205 TCA DENVER:** 9500-type short Madison combine car; TCA national convention car; gold-lettered "THE ROCKY MOUNTAIN ROUTE/UNITED STATES MAIL/RAILWAY POST OFFICE/DENVER"; otherwise matches 9544; "7205" on box only; "1982" on car at both ends. J. Bratspis Collection.

| | — | — | — | 75 |

1983 **7206 TCA LOUISVILLE:** 9500-type short Madison Pullman car; TCA national convention car; gold "GREAT LAKES LIMITED/LOUISVILLE"; otherwise matches 9544; "7206" on box only.

| | — | — | — | 75 |

Note: There were also several "banquet" cars, made on Lionel bodies, produced for the 1983 convention. See the Great Lakes division heading in the TCA Other Production subsection of this chapter for more details.

1984 **7212 TCA PITTSBURGH:** 9500-type short Madison Pullman car; TCA national convention car; gold "FORT PITT LIMITED" above windows and "CITY OF PITTSBURGH" below; otherwise matches 9544. F. Stem and J. Bratspis Collections.

| | — | — | — | 75 |

Note: In addition to the official convention car, no less than three different versions of "banquet" cars were made by various members of the Ft. Pitt division for this convention. See the TCA Other Production subsection of this chapter.

1985 **5734-85 REA:** Wood-sided refrigerator car; TCA Seattle convention car; dark green body; black roof and ends; gold lettering; red REA diamond with white lettering; Seattle convention logo; "TRAIN COLLECTORS ASSOCIATION" above and below diamond logo; Standard O trucks; car actually numbered "5734/1985". Available to match previously issued locomotive and passenger cars. C. Rohlfing, W. Berresford, C. Wallace and E. F. Monck comments.

| | — | — | — | 150 |

1985 **5484 TCA HUDSON:** 4-6-4 small Hudson; dark green, die-cast Alco-style boiler; white trim and number; smoke; Magnetraction; Sound of Steam; 224W die-cast tender; six-wheel die-cast passenger trucks; large circular white TCA emblem on tender side. Released as a match to the series of TCA passenger cars produced from 1980 to 1985, and is quite hard to find now.

| | — | — | 400 | 450 |

1986 **6926 TCA NEW ORLEANS:** Extended vision caboose; TCA national convention car; white body; dark blue-painted main and cupola roofs; black "32nd National Convention/JUNE 1986/Lone Star Div."; large red heart with picture of Superdome centered under cupola with black lettering "You'll Love New Orleans/And New Orleans/Will Love You Back!"; TCA logo in dark blue at lower right side corner; Symington-Wayne trucks; "BLT 6-86". H. Lotstein Collection.

| | — | — | — | 80 |

	GD	VG	EXC	M

Note: In addition to the official convention car, a small number of overpainted 7522 New Orleans bullion cars were produced and given only to attendees of the 1986 TCA convention banquet. See the details in the TCA Other Production subsection of this chapter.

1987 and 1988 **Non-Lionel production:** For the first time in its history, the TCA did not offer Lionel-produced convention cars. Actually, as was mentioned earlier, TCA had been producing a variety of convention cars in many sizes. But 1987 marked the first time Lionel did not participate. In 1987, the O Gauge convention car was a 6406 K-Line boxcar labeled for Carolina RT to mark the 33rd TCA convention in Raleigh. In 1988, K-Line made a 6705 "Gold Rush" ore car to celebrate what turned out to be a tumultuous TCA convention in Oakland.

1989 **19879 TCA VALLEY FORGE:** 9500-series short Madison diner car; TCA national convention car; gold "PENNSYLVANIA LIMITED" above windows, "DINER" to upper right, "VALLEY FORGE, BY GEORGE" in gold at lower right; TCA logo to left side; otherwise matches 9544 from 1980; "19879" is not on the car, only on box; "1989" is on car. Intended as a matching add-on for the TCA Passenger Special set released from 1980 to 1985.

| | — | — | — | 8 |

Note: There were several banquet souvenir cars from other manufacturers also produced for this convention.

1990 **17883 NEW GEORGIA RAILROAD:** General-style passenger car; TCA national convention car; gray body; light blue roof; red stripes highlighting windows; Confederate flag at lower center; black "ATLANTA 1990" and "DIXIE DIVISION"; illuminated; TCA logo to left in red and white; Type IX die-cast arch bar trucks; "BLT 1-90"; "17883" is not on the car; "1990" is the only number on the car. In fact, many, if not all, boxes are mislabeled with the number reading "17873" rather than "17883". 17873 is the number of an LCCA tank car from 1988. J. Greytak Collection

| | — | — | — | 8 |

TCA OTHER PRODUCTION

The Train Collectors Association, in addition to its regular annual convention cars, has produced an enormous quantity and variety of other cars marking all sorts of club-related occasions, from the opening of its national museum to a train meet in Sacramento. By far the largest percentage of these are special cars made by and for the myriad divisions and chapters of the TCA, which are semi-independent local assemblies of neighboring members. The great majority of the division and chapter cars were not made completely by Lionel but rather are Lionel pieces overstamped and/or redecorated by some outside agency, such as PVP, NTW or other individuals such as E. C. Kraemer or Owen Upp.

This represents a growing area of interest to collectors, as well as an interesting addendum to our knowledge of what has happened to some of Lionel's production. That is, many pieces simply disappear, having been redecorated as something else. We have assembled the cars here in logical combinations based on division, chapter, or museum categories and within each group the cars are listed by year.

The TCA has issued several sets of cars commemorating its national Toy Train Museum in Strasburg, Pennsylvania and continues to release special cars today marking museum

Toy Train Museum Collection; B. Greenberg photograph

ecial museum and division boxcars from TCA. The cars on the top three shelves are part of a Toy Train Museum Special set made by Pleasant Valley rocess Co.

shelf: **7780 Toy Train Museum from 1980; 7782 Carlisle Finch from 1982.**
ond shelf: **7783 Ives from 1983; 7784 Voltamp from 1984.**
rd shelf: **7785 Hoge from 1985.**
tom shelf: **Regular 9740 Chessie with Great Lakes Division overstamp from 1976; regular 9754 Pacemaker car from 1976 with METCA (New York TCA)** verstamp.

events, such as its recent expansion. Several divisions of the TCA also supported the National museum with their own sets of cars used as fundraisers for the museum.

The club released a "Bicentennial Special" in the early 1970s, headed by a red, white and blue U36B diesel. This set was announced through a flyer to the general membership and sold nationally, not related to any particular division or chapter.

Many of the divisions and chapters have an ongoing annual car series (primarily intended as a fundraiser) which has produced an astonishing total of cars and engines. Most notable among these are the long series from the New England division, the Midwest division, the North Texas chapter, the Atlantic division, the Southern division, the Detroit/Toledo chapter, and the Sacramento-Sierra chapter. These are listed

below, grouped under the division which sponsored them. Many chapters or divisions have produced no special cars at all, while others have made one or more per year for 20 years.

Other cars have been produced as *convention banquet* souvenirs, available only to those who actually attend the convention. This practice began in 1981 and continues sporadically. In some cases, these are sponsored by the club, or by the division hosting the convention, but in other instances they are the initiative of individual members.

Finally, there is a group of miscellaneous cars which represent isolated events or division releases — again usually intended as fundraisers. We have assembled as much information as we could research, and we apologize beforehand to any division or chapters whose cars are not shown here. We

	GD	VG	EXC	MT

strongly encourage our readers to write and add to our information base for future editions.

TCA Museum-Related Cars

The Midwest Division's "Museum Express": These are regular-issue Lionel cars overstamped with a TCA "Museum Express" logo. They were released between 1977 and 1980 as fundraisers for the National Museum and were sold mainly at the Midwest division's big annual meets.

1977 **9785 CONRAIL:** Boxcar; medium blue-painted body and doors; overprinted "TCA MUSEUM EXPRESS"; dated "August 20, 1977", the date of the Midwest division's meet. First of four cars in Midwest division's "Museum Express" set. Only 108 examples made. Pinta and C. Rohlfing observations. **NRS**

1978 **9264 ILLINOIS CENTRAL:** Quad hopper; metal plate holding trucks; no builder's plate; stamped "TCA MUSEUM EXPRESS"; dated "March 18, 1978". Second of four cars in Midwest division's "Museum Express" set. 108 made. C. Rohlfing and W. Schimke Collections. — — — **100**

1979 **9786 CHICAGO & NORTH WESTERN:** Boxcar; tuscan-painted tuscan body; stamped "TCA MUSEUM EXPRESS"; dated "March 17, 1979". Third of four cars in Midwest division's "Museum Express" set. Only 144 examples made. C. Rohlfing comment. **NRS**

1980 **9289 CHICAGO & NORTH WESTERN:** N5C caboose; two operating couplers; overstamped "TCA MUSEUM EXPRESS, MARCH 8, 1980", which is date of the annual Midwest division meet. Last of four cars in Midwest division's "Museum Express" set. Only 144 examples made. C. Rohlfing comment. — — — **85**

The "Toy Train Museum Special" Series: This outstanding set of classic-style boxcars was commissioned by the museum itself, as fundraisers for maintaining the building and its exhibits. All the cars were produced by PVP and feature some of the best graphics ever put on O Scale boxcars, by Lionel or otherwise. The lettering is crisp and detailed, the colors are very bright, and all the painting is precisely done. Part of the reason may be that these were accomplished on blank Lionel bodies, so that there were no previous heat-stamp depressions or paint residue to mar the surface of the car. The cars were made from 1980 through 1986, and were used to honor the many toy train manufacturers in United States history, though for some reason Marx was not included. Ironically all, except the last one, were made on Lionel boxcars! Each features the Toy Train Museum logo, which is a rectangular design showing a General-style steam engine and the phrase "ONLY A WHISTLE STOP AWAY" somewhere on the body.

1980 **7780 TOY TRAIN MUSEUM:** Boxcar; red body; white doors; Toy Train Museum logo in white to right side; large outline of museum at left in white; Symington-Wayne trucks; "BLT 4-80". This is a Lionel blank classic-style boxcar decorated by PVP (designator "504-1135"). Part of the Toy Train Museum Special Series. — — — **30**

1981 **7781 HAFNER:** Boxcar; silver body; black doors; black Toy Train Museum logo to right side; multicolor Hafner trains logo to left of door; "Hafner's Golden Years 1914-1951"; Symington-Wayne trucks; "BLT 3-81". This is a Lionel blank classic-style

boxcar decorated by PVP (designator "504-1156"). Part of the Toy Train Museum Special Series. — — — **30**

1982 **7782 CARLISLE FINCH:** Boxcar; straw yellow body; brown doors; brown lettering; detailed Carlisle-Finch script design to left with a multicolored train; Symington-Wayne trucks "BLT 3-82". This is a Lionel blank classic-style boxcar decorated by PVP (designator "504-1195"). Part of the Toy Train Museum Special Series. — — — **30**

1983 **7783 IVES:** Boxcar; pale green body; gold doors; white and black lettering; "IVES TOYS MAKE HAPPY BOYS"; red, black and white train design to left side; Symington-Wayne trucks; "BLT 3-83". This is a Lionel blank classic-style boxcar decorated by PVP (designator "504-1249"). Part of the Toy Train Museum Special Series. — — — **30**

1984 **7784 VOLTAMP:** Boxcar; pale yellow body; blue doors; black lettering; black "VOLTAMP" trademark and multicolor train to left side; Symington-Wayne trucks; "BLT 9-83". This is a Lionel blank classic-style boxcar decorated by PVP (designator "504-1309"). Part of the Toy Train Museum Special Series. — — — **30**

1985 **7785 HOGE:** Boxcar; gray sides; black roof and ends; black doors; blue lettering; very detailed blue, black and gray streamlined train scene on left side; Symington-Wayne trucks; "BLT 9-84". The graphics on this car may be the best of the series. It is a Lionel blank classic-style boxcar decorated by PVP (designator "504-1379"). Part of the Toy Train Museum Special Series. — — — **30**

1986 **7786 DORFAN:** KMT boxcar; this was the last car in the Toy Train Museum Special series produced by PVP for the TCA (designator "527-1426"). It is not a Lionel boxcar, but is part of the series. **NRS**

Other Museum-Related Cars: Obviously, since the TCA and its museum are not constrained to one gauge or manufacturer, many other makes and sizes of cars and accessories (other than Lionel O) have been made for the Museum. One set of note (in O Gauge) was made beginning in 1986 by K-Line. It consists of five cars available in 1986 (5116 boxcar, 5414 tank car, 6115 red caboose, 5314 hopper and 5714 auto boxcar). The series continued in 1987 with a 6412 car marked for the Museum's 10th anniversary. In 1988 three more cars appeared: a 6615 orange flatcar with load, a 6516 green gondola, and a 6222 brown hopper. K-Line completed the train in 1989 with a 2017 powered and dummy Alco combination, as well as a yellow version of the 6115 caboose. We mention these cars to round out the story for Museum car collectors.

1018-1979 TCA MORTGAGE BURNING CEREMONY CAR: 1979, hi-cube boxcar; light tan-painted gray plastic body; light yellow-painted white door; orange, black and red rectangular mortgage burning logo at left; orange Toy Train Museum logo and black lettering at right. There is an intriguing story behind the making of this car: In 1978 the TCA held its convention in Boston. The 9611 "Flying Yankee" hi-cube boxcar was produced for this convention in official Boston and Maine sky blue and black. Large anticipated sales of the Flying Yankee car never materialized, and at convention's end the TCA found itself in possession of a considerable backlog of unsold cars. In the next year, the organization was to finish paying the mortgage on its museum in Strasburg, Pennsylvania. Rather than order a special car, the TCA shipped its entire backlog of 9611 Flying Yankee cars to the Pleasant

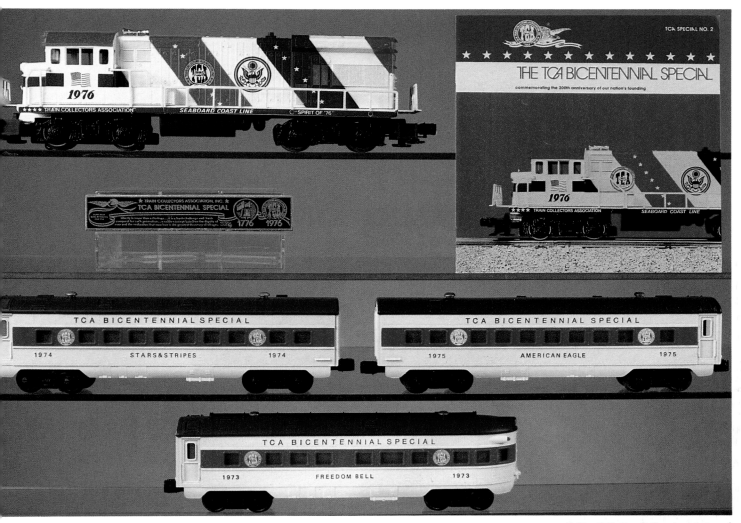

F. Stem Collection; B. Greenberg photograph

's Bicentennial Special from 1973-1976, with its special booklet and commemorative plaque
helf: 1976 Seaboard Coast Line U36B; compare to standard-issue 1776 SCL version.
le shelf: Two O27 passenger cars: 1974 Pullman; 1975 Pullman.
m shelf: 1973 observation.

	GD	VG	EXC	MT

Valley Process Company. There, the Flying Yankee cars were repainted into the Mortgage Burning Ceremony car. Faint traces of the original black paint show through the light tan paint on the ends and roof. J. Bratspis observation. — — — **95**

5731 MUSEUM EXPANSION CAR: 1990, refrigerator car; tuscan roof, sides and doors; this is a standard-production 5731 Lionel L & N refrigerator car (see Volume I for details) imprinted with TCA museum expansion data; TCA gazebo logo in white to left of door; "TCA/Toy Train Museum/ Expansion Dedication/April 19,1990 in white to right of door. Exactly 100 made. These were given out to the first 100 visitors to the museum's expansion party of April 19, 1990. It was part of a group of cars which included S Gauge, HO Gauge and Standard Gauge pieces. It is not known who decorated them. R. Artelli Collection.

— — — **300**

9771 NORFOLK AND WESTERN: 1977, boxcar; this is a standard Lionel 9771 N & W boxcar overstamped "TCA Museum & National Headquarters" in silver at upper right of doors; "Dedication, April 14, 1977" in blue lettering under and to right

of silver lettering. Issued as a fundraiser and commemorative at the opening of the TCA museum in Strasburg, Pennsylvania in April 1977. C. Weber Collection. — — **30 40**

The Bicentennial Special

This TCA special set commemorates the United States Bicentennial in 1976. It was available equally to all TCA members and, unlike most of the other cars in this section, was made entirely by Lionel. It consisted of a red, white and blue Seaboard U36B engine and three O27 streamlined passenger cars, and was announced in a flyer mailed to all TCA members in 1973. The cars were made one at a time in 1973, 1974 and 1975, with the engine following in 1976. Each of the cars has white sides, a blue roof and red window stripes with two white TCA logos somewhere on the red stripe. Each also has blue "TCA BICENTENNIAL SPECIAL" lettering above the windows and the year printed in blue toward the front and rear below the windows. And each has the Type VI die-cast pas-

GD   VG   EXC   MT

senger trucks, which is the only time they were used on this type of passenger car until very recently. The entire set came with a special silver plaque.

Note: There are, of course, other special sets like this, in O Gauge and other sizes, produced by other manufacturers for the TCA. These are properly the province of other publications. For the benefit of O Gauge collectors, we must mention a fine TCA 25th anniversary set produced for the club in 1979 by Williams. This consisted of a silver GG-1 electric locomotive and six Madison-style silver-painted passenger cars, numbered 2501 through 2506. The cars are named for towns in which the first TCA conventions were held. This set was called the "Twenty-Fifth Anniversary Limited" and proceeds from its sale were used to retire the mortgage on the TCA Museum.

1973 TCA BICENTENNIAL SPECIAL: O27 streamlined observation car; red, white and blue; "FREEDOM BELL"; no numbers on car other than "1973". See set description above.
(A) Price for car.   —   —   40   50
(B) Price for three-car set.   —   —   125   150

1974 TCA BICENTENNIAL SPECIAL: O27 streamlined Pullman; "STARS & STRIPES"; otherwise matches 1973.
                                     —   —   40   50

1975 TCA BICENTENNIAL SPECIAL: O27 streamlined Pullman; "AMERICAN EAGLE"; otherwise matches 1973.
                                     —   —   40   50

1976 SEABOARD COAST LINE U36B: 1976, diesel; special for TCA; TCA logo and three TCA passenger cars; stamped metal railings; red, white and blue body; blue numbers and underframe; lighted; nose decal; Type II motor; four white stars and white "TRAIN COLLECTORS ASSOCIATION SEABOARD COAST LINE SPIRIT OF 76" on edge of frame. Price for locomotive only. C. Rohlfing Collection.   —   —   100   150

The Midwest Division

In 1974, the Midwest division of TCA began a series of cars made as fundraisers for the division. It consisted of regular Lionel cars (except the first one in 1974) either redecorated or overstamped with Midwest division data. The set continued through 1979. Each car is numbered sequentially 1 through 6, worked into the car data in one way or another. We are grateful to Chris Rohlfing of the Midwest division for his fine summary of this data:

1974 **XMWTCA 00001:** KMT-based boxcar; the first in the Midwest division's fundraising series. C. Rohlfing Collection.
                                                          NRS

1975 **9725 (00002) MKT:** Stock car; yellow-painted yellow body; black doors; green and silver Midwestern division TCA plate added, reading "XMWTCA 00002"; this is a standard-production Lionel M stock car with Midwest TCA data added. 200 made. Second car in a division fundraiser series begun in 1974. C. Rohlfing Collection.   **NRS**

1976 **7600 (00003) FRISCO:** N5C caboose; Type II; red, white and blue sides; stamped "MIDWEST DIVISION, TCA". This is a standard Lionel 7600 Frisco caboose with added Midwest

GD   VG   EXC   MT

division data. Plate reads "XMWTCA 00003". Third in a division fundraiser series begun in 1974. H. Azzinaro Collection.
                                     —   —   —   50

1977 **MWDX4 CHICAGO & NORTH WESTERN:** F-3 diesel cab shell only; no frame; blank Lionel F-3 cabs decorated in C & NW green and yellow; stamped "MIDWEST DIVISION TCA". 600 made. Fourth in a division fundraiser series begun in 1974. The division decided on this design because Lionel has never made C & NW F-3 diesels.   **NRS**

1978 **XMWTCA 00005 MIDWEST DIVISION:** Quad hopper; dark blue body; yellow "MWD". This is a repainted Lionel 9114 Morton Salt hopper; it is not known who repainted it. 350 made. Fifth in a division fundraiser series begun in 1974. C. Rohlfing Collection.   **NRS**

1979 **9872 (00006) PACIFIC FRUIT EXPRESS:** Refrigerator car; Type III body; silver roof and ends; orange body and doors; Standard Lionel 9872 refrigerator car overstamped "MIDWEST DIV. TCA 1979" and "XMWTCA 00006" in silver; only 300 examples made. Last in a series of cars created by the Midwest division as a fundraising series. C. Rohlfing comment.
                                                          NRS

The Midwest division created two other cars to mark its 25th anniversary in 1983 and its 30th in 1988. These are not related to the above series:

1983 **1287 CHICAGO & NORTH WESTERN:** Refrigerator car; green and yellow body and lettering; TCA logo to left of doors over "TCA MID WEST DIVISION/TRAIN COLLECTORS ASSOCIATION" lettering; right side has lettering "25th ANNIVERSARY/1959-1984/OF THE/MWD" with "MWD" inside the division logo. These were repainted Lionel billboard refrigerator cars decorated by Ken Hein. Only 12 were made. They were awarded as door prizes at the division's December 1983 Christmas and Anniversary meet. C. Rohlfing comment. **NRS**

1988 **MWD1988 ILLINOIS CENTRAL:** Boxcar; brown body; white lettering; "Main Line of/ MID-AMERICA" to right side; "ILLINOIS CENTRAL/IC/MWD1988" to left side. Only five cars made. These were Lionel 9400-series classic-type boxcars redecorated by Rich Sherry for the 30th anniversary of the Midwest division of the TCA. They were awarded to attendees of the division's Christmas and Anniversary meet in December 1988. C. Rohlfing comment.   **NRS**

Finally, the division sponsored a one-of-a-kind repainted Lionel set to mark its 25th Anniversary, and auctioned it at the December 1983 division meet. The locomotive was a repainted 8206 Hudson decorated in silver, black and brown, and numbered "5984" (the years of the founding and 25th anniversary of the division). It pulled five 9500-series short Madison cars decorated in yellow and green C & NW colors (underlying Lionel car type unknown). The cars were lettered for "KANKAKEE, HINSDALE, NORTHLAKE, ADDISON and SOUTH HOLLAND", towns important to the division. This unique train was decorated by Rich Sherry.

The New England Division (NETCA)

The TCA's New England division (NETCA) has produced perhaps the most extensive collection of cars of any of the TCA

	GD	VG	EXC	MT

divisions. It has an annual car series which started in 1972 with an NW-2 switcher engine and continues today, with only a few missing years. The intent of the series is to provide exclusive issues for division members and to act as fundraisers for the division. Most of the pieces have been Lionel items redecorated by E. C. Kraemer, and fortunately most were overstamped rather than redecorated, so the original Lionel identity is visible. The division always chooses roadnames that serve New England, such as the Boston & Maine, Vermont Northern, New York, New Haven & Hartford, etc. Trains from KMT and K-Line were used in a few of the years. We are grateful to NETCA member Ted Brahm for the outstanding work he accomplished in collecting and recording this data.

1972 **1203 BOSTON & MAINE:** NW-2 switcher; cab only, no chassis, made for NETCA as the first item in a projected annual car series; light blue cab; white lettering and NETCA circular steam engine logo; running lights, headlight lenses, and antenna supplied separately; "BUILT 1972"; 600 made. These are Lionel shells painted and silk-screened by E. C. Kraemer. T. Brahm comments. — — — **70**

1973 and 1974 **No production:** During these years, NETCA did not produce Lionel pieces. In 1973, about 300 KMT boxcars were decorated for the VTRR and were painted green with white lettering and numbered "12273". The 1974 car was a maroon KMT boxcar numbered "12174" and lettered in white for the NY, NH and Hartford. About 300 of these were produced. Each car featured the circular NETCA "steam engine" logo.

1975 **9753 MAINE CENTRAL:** Boxcar; fourth in an annual series of NETCA cars; yellow-painted yellow body; green lettering; this is a standard Lionel 9753 Maine Central boxcar with a NETCA imprint; 300 made; Type II box. Silk-screened by E. C. Kraemer — — **25 30**

1976 **9768 BOSTON & MAINE:** Boxcar; fifth in an annual series of NETCA cars; standard Lionel 9768 B & M boxcar with NETCA circle logo added by E. C. Kraemer; 300 made; Type II box. — — **25 30**

1977 **9181 BOSTON & MAINE:** N5C caboose; sixth in an annual series of NETCA cars; standard Lionel 9181 B & M caboose with NETCA circle logo added by E. C. Kraemer; 400 made; Type III box. — — **25 30**

1978 **9400 CONRAIL:** Boxcar; seventh in an annual series of NETCA cars; standard Lionel 9400 Conrail tuscan boxcar with NETCA overprint in silver, done by E. C. Kraemer; 192 made; Type III box. — — **25 30**
This is one of two cars made in 1978.

1978 **9785 CONRAIL:** boxcar; seventh in an annual series of NETCA cars; standard Lionel 9785 blue boxcar with NETCA "Flying Yankee" logo in silver added by E. C. Kraemer; logo is on left side under "CONRAIL" lettering; 192 made; Type III box. Note the NETCA Flying Yankee logo was new this year, and was used again on several of the later cars in this series, as well as the 1978 TCA National Convention car. — — **25 30**

1979 **9415 PROVIDENCE & WORCESTER:** Boxcar; eighth in an annual series of NETCA cars; red-painted body; white and black lettering; this is a standard Lionel 9415 boxcar with NETCA logo overprint in silver added by E. C. Kraemer. This year the division logo was changed to a depiction of a Pilgrim's hat. 216 made; Type III box. C. Lang Collection. — — **25 30**

1980 **9423 NEW YORK, NEW HAVEN & HARTFORD:** Boxcar; ninth in an annual series of NETCA cars; tuscan-painted tuscan sides and doors; black roof and ends; this is a standard Lionel 9423 NY, NH & H boxcar overprinted with NETCA Pilgrim hat logo in white, added by E. C. Kraemer; 228 made; Type III box. C. Lang Collection. — — **25 30**

1981 **9445 VERMONT NORTHERN:** Boxcar; 10th in an annual series of NETCA cars; yellow body; silver roof; black lettering; this is a standard Lionel 9445 VN boxcar with added NETCA Pilgrim hat logo and data in silver heatstamped by E. C. Kraemer; 192 made; Type III box. — — **25 30**

1982 **5710 CANADIAN PACIFIC:** refrigerator car; 11th in an annual series of NETCA cars; brown body; white lettering; this is a standard Lionel 5710 CP refrigerator car with added NETCA Pilgrim hat logo and data in silver heat-stamped by E. C. Kraemer; 144 made; Type III box. — — **25 30**

1983 **5716 CENTRAL VERMONT:** Refrigerator car; 12th in an annual series of NETCA cars; silver sides; green roof, ends and doors; green lettering; this is a standard Lionel 5716 CV refrigerator car with added NETCA Pilgrim hat logo and data in red, heat stamped by E. C. Kraemer; 144 made; Type III box. — — **25 30**

1984 **6124 DELAWARE & HUDSON:** Quad hopper; 13th in an annual series of NETCA cars; red body; yellow lettering; this is a standard Lionel 6124 D & H hopper with NETCA Pilgrim hat logo and data added in silver, heat stamped by E. C. Kraemer; 144 made; Type III box. — — **25 30**

1985 **No production.**

1986 **GARE8051 HOOD'S GRADE A MILK:** Wood-side boxcar; 14th in an annual series of NETCA cars; green body; maroon ends and roof; yellow and red lettering; silver NETCA Flying Yankee logo to right of door, red "H.P. HOOD & SONS MILK" logo to far right; Symington-Wayne trucks; no "BLT" date; 156 made; Type III box. This is a Lionel 7700-series Tobacco Road wood-side boxcar stripped and redecorated by PVP (designator "605-1440"). It is one of the more popular cars in the NETCA series and prompted the division to produce more prototypical cars in the following years. — — **45 55**

1987 through 1989 **Non-Lionel production:** Because of the popularity of the Hood's car, NETCA decided it would make greater quantities of cars in the following years, but it could not acquire Lionel cars in such large numbers at a reasonable price, so cars from other manufacturers were used:

1987 **12687 GUILFORD INDUSTRIES/BOSTON & MAINE:** KMT boxcar; gray body; orange doors; white lettering; silver NETCA Flying Yankee logo; 144 made; came in plain white box. This is a KMT boxcar decorated by PVP. Designed by A. C. Moore. **NRS**

1988 **6315 BAKER'S CHOCOLATE:** Single-dome tank car; K-Line; cream body; brown ends and dome; brown lettering; silver NETCA data on tank end; fragile plastic and metal platform. Designed by A. C. Moore. This is a highly prototypical car, reminiscent of Kusan construction of some years ago. 400 made. T. Brahm comments. **NRS**

1989 **622901 REVERE SUGAR:** Covered quad hopper; K-Line; black body with large white stripe at top; black and white

GD   VG   EXC   MT

lettering; NETCA logo in white. Designed by A. C. Moore. 300 made; came in plain white box. Fifteen cars exist with gold lettering, rather than white, and one has a green body (rather than black) with yellow lettering. T. Brahm comments. **NRS**

The Atlantic Division — County Series

Like several other TCA divisions, the Atlantic division has an annual car series it advertises exclusively to its own members. This series has an interesting twist, however — each car is made to honor one of the Pennsylvania and New Jersey counties which comprise the division. The division attempts to use cars at least somewhat related to the county involved, although sometimes the connection is stretched — such as the Burlington hopper intended to honor Burlington County, New Jersey — despite the fact that the Burlington serves the Midwest and West!

The series began in 1978 and continues today. The intent was to have an annual car, but member Ray Connolly says the division did not meet this goal. For a variety of reasons (including inability to acquire desired cars or decorating schemes, and sometimes inability to acquire people to do it), the division skipped certain years. The members have talked of going back and filling in the missing ones over time, but this may or may not happen. By the mid-1980s, the division was a year or two behind, releasing the 1988 car, for example, in 1991! To date, including the next planned car, the division has cars honoring 10 of the 14 counties within it.

The early cars were redecorated or overstamped Lionels, while as with other TCA division series, the later cars reverted to the less expensive K-Line production. The cars display the division's circular "Liberty Bell" logo on them and have a sequential numbering system on the bottom and on the boxes. We are grateful to Raymond Connolly and Dr. Charles Weber of the Atlantic division for their assistance in supplying data on these cars.

1978 **9788 LEHIGH VALLEY:** Boxcar; first in an annual series of TCA Atlantic division county cars. This is a standard-issue Lionel 9788 LV classic-style boxcar overstamped with red Atlantic division Liberty Bell logo in red to the lower left. It is also labeled for Atlantic County, New Jersey. It is not known who accomplished the overstamping. 195 made.
    —   —   20   25

1979 **9186 CONRAIL:** N5C caboose; second in an annual series of TCA Atlantic division county cars. This is a standard Lionel 9186 Conrail caboose with gold Atlantic division Liberty Bell sticker affixed over the Conrail logo. Also labeled for "Bucks County/1979" at left in black. It is not known who accomplished the overstamping. 300 made, which was more than the division could support, so the car is the most common of the series. The division reduced the number made in following years.
    —   —   15   20

1980 and 1981 **No production:** No county series cars were made, although a 10th anniversary TOFC car was made in 1981 (see below). It is possible the division will issue cars for these years in the future.

1982 **6101 BURLINGTON:** Covered quad hopper; third in an annual series of TCA Atlantic division county cars. This is a standard Lionel 6101 Burlington hopper with Atlantic division circle logo and "Burlington County, Atlantic division, TCA" rubber-stamped in yellow. This was done by a small Philadelphia printing firm. 217 made.
    —   —   20   25

1983 **9466 WANAMAKER:** Boxcar; fourth in an annual series of TCA Atlantic division county cars. This is a standard Lionel 9466 boxcar with the division's Liberty Bell logo and "Philadelphia County/1983" stamped in white. 215 made. The same firm which decorated the 1982 car stamped this one **NRS**

1984 **9193 BUDWEISER:** Vat carrier; fifth in an annual series of TCA Atlantic division county cars. This is a standard Lionel 9193 vat carrier with vats modified with added stickers as follows: one has "ATLANTIC DIVISION/TCA" lettered in red; a second has "CAMDEN COUNTY/1984" in green letters; the third vat has a picture of a tomato and the fourth has a picture of a pickle. Camden County is the home of the Campbell Soup Company. The stickers were added by Charles Weber and the Atlantic division board. 157 made.
    —   —   20   25

1985 **PENNSYLVANIA-READING SEASHORE LINES:** Bunk car; sixth in an annual series of TCA Atlantic division county cars. This is a Lionel 5727 Marines bunk car stripped and redecorated by PVP (designator "705-1436"). Tuscan/maroon body; yellow lettering and Liberty Bell logo; lettered for Cape May County; 156 made. One of the most popular cars of the series, it was actually released in 1986. The sequential numbering system used by the Atlantic division was terminated for this and later cars.
    —   —   65   80

1986-1989 **Non-Lionel production:** The Atlantic division reverted to K-Line pieces. Actually, it plans on releasing the "1989" car in 1992. For 1986, a black short hopper with white lettering and "Mushroom Capital Of The World" logo was commissioned from K-Line in honor of Chester County, Pennsylvania. 192 of these were made. For 1987 (made in 1990), a Silica Sand ore car based on the K-Line ore car body was released. It was blue with orange lettering and included the Liberty Bell logo as well as a Jersey Central notation. 204 were made, and were dedicated to Cumberland County, New Jersey. The 1988 car was a K-Line tank car decorated for the Sun Oil Co., and dedicated to Delaware County, Pennsylvania. It was black with yellow lettering and the famous yellow and red Sunoco emblem. 252 were ordered. The club has current plans for the 1989 car, to be released in 1992, to be a Reading Lines refrigerator car from K-Line. It will be lettered for Gloucester County, New Jersey.

The Atlantic division created one other car, not related to its county series, for its 10th anniversary:

1980 **1981 ATLANTIC DIVISION 10TH ANNIVERSARY:** TOFC flatcar; bright green body; one van is medium orange with "ATLANTIC DIVISION/TCA" lettered in black and a black steam engine logo; other van is light yellow-orange with "10th ANNIVERSARY" in black with an electric engine logo; no numbers on the car. This is a 9133 Southern Pacific TOFC car repainted by PVP (designator "705-1151"). Made in early 1981 though the anniversary year was 1980. 192 were made.
    —   —   25   30

Finally, the division has plans to have a car to (somewhat belatedly) mark its 20th anniversary in 1990. Tentatively, it will be a green boxcar from K-Line.

GD   VG   EXC   MT

The Southern Division

The Southern division of TCA has also had an annual series of cars sold exclusively to its own members (at least at first). The series began in 1975 and continues today, although in 1989 and 1990 only special billboards were made, not cars. The first car in the series was a KMT boxcar; the remainder have been Lionel. Fortunately, most were not painted over — only a circular Southern division logo (which is similar to the Southern Railroad's) was stamped on a blank area of the Lionel car. It is not known, except in one case, who accomplished the overstamping — reader comments are requested. Less than 125 were made of each car. As with several of the other TCA division sets, the Southern division group endeavored to use Lionel cars featuring prototype roads that actually served the South. We are indebted to Southern division member Ron Artelli for assisting us in gathering this data.

1975 **Non-Lionel production:** The first car in 1975 was a KMT boxcar in blue.

1976 **1976 FLORIDA EAST COAST:** F-3 diesel ABA cab shells only; Lionel F-3 shells painted in the red and yellow scheme of the Florida East Coast; no numbers on the shells except 1976. It is not known who decorated them. Lionel has never regularly catalogued a set of FEC F-3s.   **NRS**

Since the decorating scheme with the SD logo is the same for most of the remaining cars, we refer the reader to the details of the base Lionel car in Volume I and describe the series in tabular form; the value for **New** condition for each piece is $30:

Year	Number	Road Name	Car Type
1977	9287	Southern	N5C caboose
1978	9403	Seaboard Coast Line	boxcar
1979	9405	CIRR	boxcar
1980	9352	Circus Car	TOFC flatcar w/vans
		(Above repainted C & NW TOFC flatcar)	
1981	9443	Florida East Coast	boxcar
1982	No Production		
1983	6111	L & N	quad hopper
1984	9471	Atlantic Coast Line	boxcar
1985	9482	Norfolk & Southern	boxcar
1986	5727	Marines	bunk car
		(Above repainted yellow and marked for 20th Anniversary of Southern Division)	
1987	No Production		
1988	16606	Southern	searchlight car
		(Above overstamped by PVP, Code #705-1469)	

1989 and 1990 **BILLBOARDS:** The Southern division made several billboards with inserts bearing division logos and the slogan "Fellowship, Trading, and Open Houses!"

Great Lakes Division — Detroit-Toledo Chapter

The Detroit-Toledo chapter, which is a part of the TCA's Great Lakes division, produced a set of cars intended as a "Season's Greetings" train in the late 1970s. Four cars and an engine were made from 1976 through 1980, all overstamped on Lionel original pieces. The last release was a Burlington Northern GP-20 to head the train, which was one of the few times any TCA division or chapter has produced a complete engine. According to Richard Mertes, President of the Great Lakes division, proceeds from the sale of the cars were used to construct the flagpole and surrounding landscaping at the TCA Museum in Strasburg, Pennsylvania. The market for the cars dried up after the engine came out and the series ended, though more cars had been planned.

The Great Lakes division itself produced a 10th anniversary car in 1976 and another chapter, the Western Michigan chapter, had a boxcar overstamped for its fifth anniversary in 1974. Also, the division sponsored an interesting banquet car at the 1983 convention in Louisville, Kentucky. This information was graciously supplied by Richard Mertes.

1974 **9730 CP RAIL:** Boxcar. This appears to be a standard Lionel 9730 with overstamping commemorating the 5th anniversary of the Western Michigan chapter of the Great Lakes division. We do not know any other details. Reader comments invited.   **NRS**

1976 **9730 CP RAIL:** Boxcar; first in the Detroit-Toledo chapter "Season's Greetings" train series; standard-issue Lionel 9730 CP Rail boxcar (white-lettered version) overstamped with "Season's/Greetings/1976" in red lettering and "Detroit-Toledo/Chapter/Great Lakes TCA" in green; red and green holly wreath design surrounds Pacman "C" at the end of the car. Decorated by Curt Fischbach. About 400 made. L. Dellapenna Collection; R. Mertes comments.   — — — 40

1976 **9740 CHESSIE:** Boxcar; standard-issue Lionel 9740 yellow boxcar with overstamping for Great Lakes division 10th anniversary; "Great Lakes division TCA" stamped in large red letters to right of door; "10th/Anniversary/1966-1976" to left of door in blue letters; red stars around the blue lettering. The stamping on this car is rather blurred and somewhat clumsy.   — — — 25

1977 **9119 DETROIT & MACKINAC:** Quad hopper; second in the Detroit-Toledo chapter "Season's Greetings" train series; standard-issue Lionel 9119 D & M hopper stamped "SEASON'S GREETINGS" and a green and silver Christmas ornament with gold lettering overstamped in middle of car side; "1977" overstamped in green to left; "Detroit-Toledo Chapter" overstamped in silver at right; 400 made. Decorated by Curt Fishbach. H. Azzinaro Collection.
(A) As described.   — — 35 45
(B) Ornament is white rather than green; "1977" overstamp is white; Detroit-Toledo chapter lettering in gold instead of silver; 12 exist. Distributed to chapter members.   **NRS**

GD   VG   EXC   MT

1978 **9401 GREAT NORTHERN:** Boxcar; third in the Detroit-Toledo chapter "Season's Greetings" train series; standard-issue 9401 GN boxcar on which stamping was added showing the Great Northern ram holding a bar lettered "Detroit-Toledo Chapter" with three bells reading "T", "C" and "A"; "1978" stamped under the car number; all stamping is in red; 300 made.
(A) As described.   —   —   —   30
(B) Same as (A), except stamping is in gold; 12 exist; distributed to chapter members.   **NRS**

1979 **9272 NEW HAVEN:** Bay window caboose; fourth in the Detroit-Toledo chapter "Season's Greetings" train series; standard-issue Lionel 9272 NH caboose with silver overstamping to the left side; outline map of Michigan to far left with Detroit and Toledo named and located; "Seasons Greetings/1979" in script; 300 made.
(A) As described.   —   —   —   35
(B) Same as (A) but with stamping in gold; 12 exist; distributed to chapter members.   **NRS**

1980 **8957 BURLINGTON NORTHERN:** GP-20 diesel; fifth and final offering in the Detroit-Toledo chapter "Season's Greetings" train series; standard-issue Lionel 8957 BN locomotive with "Seasons Greetings/Detroit Toledo Chapter" stamped in red; white Christmas tree outline and "TCA 1980"; 104 made. **NRS**

1980 **8958 BURLINGTON NORTHERN:** GP-20 diesel dummy unit. Same as 8957 described above (made as a companion for it), except overstamped lettering is in gold and Christmas tree outline is in silver; 14 exist; distributed to chapter members.   **NRS**

1983 **1983 CHURCHILL DOWNS:** Classic-style boxcar; created by the Great Lakes division as a banquet table prize for the 1983 TCA National Convention in Louisville, Kentucky; beige body; red doors; blue logo of Churchill Downs to left of door and blue paddle-wheel river boat depicted to right; red lettering "29th ANNUAL TCA CONVENTION — 1983"; this is a redecorated 9443 Florida East Coast boxcar made by PVP (designator "505-1256"); no number on the car other than "1983". 132 made, according to a certified letter distributed with them by convention chairman William Manne. R. Mertes comments.
(A) As described.   **NRS**
(B) Same decorating scheme as (A), except produced on a 9800-series refrigerator car body; underlying Lionel car unknown. This was also made by PVP (same code number). 19 exist. **NRS**

1991 **Non-Lionel production:** A 25th anniversary boxcar was produced by K-Line for the Great Lakes division. It is a silver car with black roof and ends, red doors and red lettering. It is marked "1966-1991", the years the division has been in existence, and lists the six chapters which make up the division.

The Sacramento-Sierra Chapter

The series for this Western chapter of the TCA began in 1973 as a fundraising project for the chapter. The series was terminated in 1984 due to lagging sales.

These cars have several common features. All of them are Lionel cars to which the Sacramento-Sierra chapter logo, in the form of a roughly 1-inch diameter circular decal, has been added. The decals are lettered with the chapter name and an old-style engine. Each car also has a "May, 'XX" decal on the doors (the cars were mostly boxcars), where "XX" is the year. The cars were all released at the annual May train

meets which the chapter held. About 100 were made each year, except the first one, used as a seeding project to finance the start of the series. The earliest cars were decaled by Tom Gibson and other members of the chapter. Later cars were decorated by Owen Upp and eventually by PVP during the last years.

Oddly, the chapter did not seem to make an attempt to use cars prototypical to the Northern California area. Its apparent concern was to find cars with open areas large enough for the decal. The chapter used many types of boxcars, including the 9730 CP Rail and the 9414 Cotton Belt, which were used in the many thousands by TCA and other clubs for special issues. The first and last releases in this series warrant individual mention, but given the common features of the others, we will list them in tabular form.

We are grateful to chapter member and TTOS President Tom Gibson for this data.

1973 **9723 WESTERN PACIFIC:** Boxcar; standard-issue Lionel 9723 car with Sacramento-Sierra chapter circle logo added; only 12 exist. These were made up in payment to members who donated seed money to start the chapter's annual car series in 1975. All the later cars in this series featured this same circular logo depicting an old-style engine. T. Gibson comment. **NRS**

The remaining cars in the series are listed in the following table; the value for New condition for each piece is $45:

Year	Number	Road Name	Car Type
1975	9705	Denver & Rio Grande	boxcar
1976	9301	U.S. Mail	operating boxcar
1977	9730	CP Rail (white lettering)	boxcar
1978	9785	Conrail	boxcar
1979	9726	Erie-Lackawanna	boxcar
1980	9414	Cotton Belt	boxcar
1981	9427	Bay Line	boxcar
1982	9444	Louisiana Midland	boxcar
1983	9452	Western Pacific	boxcar
1984	6401	Virginian	bay window caboose
The three cars listed for 1982-84 were done by PVP and include a designator code to that effect on the box.			

1984 **LIONEL LINES:** 1130-type short streamlined tender shell only; final offering in Sacramento-Sierra chapter annual series, even though a steam engine was never part of the series; chapter's circle logo added below "LIONEL LINES"; about 100 made. This piece was produced by PVP (designator "105T-1390"). T. Gibson comment. **NRS**

GD   VG   EXC   MT

The Lone Star Division — North Texas Chapter

The North Texas chapter (one of the four in the Lone Star division) joined the specialty car craze in the late 1970s. Its cars were sold as fundraisers and commemoratives for the chapter's annual meet in Dallas. The first car was not sponsored by the Lone Star division, but the division and chapter worked together on the last two. The cars are basic standard-issue Lionel cars with chapter and meet data overstamped on them, but they were made in larger quantities than most of the other divisions typically made. The set runs from 1976 to 1978. Three cars were released, although it is possible others were made. Reader comments are requested regarding other Texas division or chapter cars not listed here.

We are indebted to members J. P. Neil and Newton Derby for this data:

_____

1976 **9739 DENVER RIO GRANDE:** Boxcar; first in a series of three cars marking the annual Dallas meet of the TCA's North Texas chapter; standard Lionel 9739 boxcar with chapter and meet data overstamped in black; "DALLAS, TEXAS, OCT 30/31, 1976"; TCA logo added. The TCA national officers complained that its logo should not have been used on the car, only the chapter's, so the following two cars in the series do not display the TCA's national emblem. 250 made by Curt Fischbach. Distributed as a fundraiser for the chapter.
—   —   —   25

1977 **9184 ERIE:** Bay window caboose; second in a series of three cars marking the annual Dallas meet of the TCA's North Texas chapter; standard Lionel 9184 caboose with North Texas chapter insignia heat-stamped in gold; "Dallas Meet, October, 1977"; no TCA logo. 350 made by Curt Fischbach. Distributed as a fundraiser for the chapter.
—   —   —   25

1978 **9119 DETROIT & MACKINAC:** Quad hopper; last in a series of three cars marking the annual Dallas meet of the TCA's North Texas chapter; standard Lionel 9119 hopper with North Texas chapter logo and lettering overstamped in black; "DALLAS, TEXAS/OCTOBER 28, 29, 1978" at upper right. 300 made. Decorated by Tom Petr. The sluggish sales of this car prompted the chapter to end the series.
—   —   —   25

The Lone Star division also had several other projects of interest outside the Dallas meet series. The most impressive of these were a banquet car produced for the 1986 convention and a series of F-3 shells made in the early 1980s:

_____

1981 **TEXAS SPECIAL:** F-3 A shells only; blank cabs specially decorated for the TCA's Lone Star division by PVP; they are painted similar to the famous postwar Texas Special F-3 engines with "Lone Star division" lettering. 100 shells were produced as fundraisers for the division. In 1982, 50 matching B-unit shells were made. Authentic shells were marked with serial numbers and accompanied by a letter of authenticity to the original owners. Owners have, of course, added F-3 frames, trucks and motors to create operating diesels. **NRS**

1983 The division produced 25 sets of red metallic name stripes for application to Lionel's long extruded aluminum passenger cars. There were eight stripes in each set, enough for four cars. The wider top stripes are lettered "Lone Star Division", while the

7522 New Orleans bullion car from 1986; note name and likeness of TCA president Dom C. Schwab on brass-plated coin.

GD   VG   EXC   MT

lower stripes are lettered with the names of the four cities where chapters are located. An aluminum "Limited" edition plate was included, made to attach to a baggage car. Four gold-colored sets of stripes also exist, created by the manufacturer without the authorization of the division officers. **NRS**

1986 **7522 NEW ORLEANS:** Bullion car; standard-production 7522 car with white lettering added to the windows; lettering on left window reads "32nd Annual Convention Banquet June 28, 1986"; TCA seal also on left window; right window has the same "You'll Love New Orleans/and New Orleans Will Love You Back" heart logo as found on the national convention caboose also issued this year; car comes with brass-plated coin with Dom C. Schwab's name and likeness on it; other construction details as found on regular issue 7522 car. This is a banquet souvenir car created by the Lone Star division and distributed only to attendees of the TCA 1986 convention banquet which honored past president William Tunstall and president Dom C. Schwab. 109 cars were made. The car was made by Newton Derby. This is the second of two TCA mint cars, the first being the 9319 National Convention car of 1979, which was made entirely by Lionel. J. Kouba Collection.
—   —   —   275

The New York Metropolitan TCA Division

Despite the potential membership concentration in this division, METCA has only produced three division pieces (as far as we know). The first one has a very interesting story with it:

_____

1971 **10 JERSEY CENTRAL:** F-3 A-unit diesel shells only; blue plastic molds painted in yellow/orange Jersey Central striping; "BUILT 1971 BY METCA"; made as a special for members of the METCA division of TCA; commissioned to commemorate the 10th Anniversary of the division, thus the number; lettered "TCA 10/1971" on nose; shells made at the Lionel Hillside, New Jersey plant before the firm moved to Michigan; because the mold was in blue, colors are reversed from prototypical Jersey Central practice. Note: postwar and modern Lionel have never made Jersey Central F-3s. About 600 sets made. No B-units were included in the initial release, but some were apparently made up later by E. C. Kraemer. A trim kit, including ornamental horn, railings and headlights, was also available separately. Obviously, many hobbyists have made operating F-3

	GD	VG	EXC	MT

engines from these shells. It is not known who accomplished the decorating, but the original shells were made by Lionel. J. Francis and G. Feyh comments. **NRS**

1976 **9754 NEW YORK CENTRAL:** Boxcar; Pacemaker Freight color scheme; standard Lionel 9754 boxcar with an added "METCA DIVISION/1976" imprint in yellow lettering; black TCA stylized logo.
(A) As described. — — 25 35
(B) Same as (A) except lettering stamped in silver. A very few of these were made and given to division officers. **NRS**

1979 **9272 NEW HAVEN:** Bay window caboose; standard Lionel 9272 caboose overstamped by METCA to mark the TCA's 25th anniversary in 1979; the METCA wheel logo is stamped in gold above the car number; approximately 400-500 made. The color of the stamping was a mistake; it was intended to be silver (25 years) but came in gold instead. A few were made in silver and given to the TCA Museum and division officers. It is not known who overstamped the car. G. Feyh comments.
— — — 35

Ozark Division — Gateway Chapter

The Gateway chapter of the TCA's Ozark division produced a set of Lionel-based Christmas cars in the late 1970s. Don Lorance, Jan Ostberg and Jon Lundvall were responsible for the series. We are grateful to Mr. Lundvall for sharing this information with us.

The chapter attached a round medallion reading "Merry Christmas" to standard Lionel car bodies. They were used as fundraisers for the chapter, and the series stopped in 1978 due to an apparent lack of interest.

The chapter also made a special convention banquet car in 1981 when it hosted the National TCA convention in St. Louis. This car featured a similar medallion affixed to the door of the car.

1976 **9068 READING:** Bobber caboose; first in a series of three Christmas cars made as fundraisers for the St. Louis Gateway chapter of TCA; standard Lionel bobber caboose to which a 1"-diameter round medallion is affixed at the center of the body; medallion is white and reads "Merry Christmas/St. Louis Gateway Chapter 1976"; green body; about 120 made. J. Lundvall comments. — — — 25

1977 **9601 ILLINOIS CENTRAL:** Hi-cube boxcar; second in a series of three cars made as fundraisers for the St. Louis Gateway chapter of TCA; standard Lionel 9601 hi-cube car with a 1"-diameter white medallion affixed to the doors; medallion reads "Merry Christmas/St. Louis Gateway Chapter 1977"; about 120 made. J. Lundvall comment. — — — 25

1978 **9767 RAILBOX:** Boxcar; last in a series of three cars made as fundraisers for the St. Louis Gateway chapter of TCA; standard Lionel 9767 boxcar with a 1"-diameter white medallion affixed to the doors; medallion reads "Merry Christmas/St. Louis Gateway Chapter 1978"; about 120 made. J. Lundvall comment. — — — 25

1981 **5700 OPPENHEIMER:** Turn-of-the-Century refrigerator car; standard Lionel 5700 refrigerator car with a yellow disk affixed to the doors, commemorating the 1981 National TCA

	GD	VG	EXC	MT

convention in St. Louis and lettered in black for the St. Louis Gateway division; created as a convention banquet souvenir; about 75 of these cars exist. This is one of the first TCA "banquet" cars. J. Lundvall Collection. — — — 50

Eastern Division — Washington, Baltimore and Annapolis Chapter

This chapter produced a set of four boxcars in the late 1970s intended as a fundraiser to build the O Gauge layout at the TCA Museum in Strasburg, Pennsylvania. Available only to the chapter membership, each boxcar represented a prototype railroad which served the Washington-Baltimore area. Andy Kriswalus created the pieces, using standard Lionel cars with a WB & A chapter logo either decaled or overstamped. The WB & A logo is a depiction of an old-style trolley similar to the ones which used to run in Washington and Baltimore. The first two cars were overstamped and the last two were decaled. About 100-150 of each car were made. We appreciate WB & A chapter member Dan Danielson's assistance in acquiring the facts on these cars.

1976 **9740 C & O:** Boxcar; first in a series of four boxcars produced by the TCA's WB & A chapter as a fundraiser for the layout at the TCA national Museum; standard Lionel 9740 car with a black WB & A trolley logo overstamped; about 100-150 made by Andy Kriswalus. D. Danielson Collection.
— — — 30

1977 **9783 B & O TIMESAVER:** Boxcar; second in a series of four boxcars produced by the TCA's WB & A chapter as a fundraiser for the layout at the TCA national Museum; standard Lionel 9783 car with a WB & A trolley logo over-stamped; about 100-150 made by Andy Kriswalus. D. Danielson Collection.
— — — 30

1978 **9771 NORFOLK & WESTERN:** Boxcar; third in a series of four boxcars produced by the TCA's WB & A chapter as a fundraiser for the layout at the TCA national Museum; standard Lionel 9771 boxcar with a white WB & A chapter trolley logo decal added; about 100-150 made by Andy Kriswalus. D. Danielson Collection. — — — 30

1979 **9412 RICHMOND, FREDRICKSBURG, AND POTOMAC:** Boxcar; last in a series of four boxcars produced by the TCA's WB & A chapter as a fundraiser for the layout at the TCA national Museum; standard Lionel 9412 boxcar with a WB & A chapter trolley logo decal added; about 100-150 made by Andy Kriswalus. D. Danielson Collection. — — — 30

Ft. Pitt Division

The Ft. Pitt division has not had an annual series of cars like other divisions, but it certainly made the most of its opportunities when it hosted the 1972 and 1984 TCA annual conventions in Pittsburgh, Pennsylvania. This Western Pennsylvania division produced no less than three banquet cars for the 1984 get-together!

The division had also hosted the 1972 TCA convention, where it sponsored the nationally available orange tank car. Members also produced a 671 boiler front at that convention, as a souvenir. Thanks to member Gordon Hinkle for sharing this information with us:

	GD	VG	EXC	MT

972 **671 BOILER FRONT:** This item, produced by the Ft. Pitt division as a special convention souvenir, had a white-painted boiler front door with TCA stickers and 1972 dating. It was intended to allow members to replace boiler fronts on the common postwar 671 locomotives (and other similar types), to create a sort of "TCA special" engine without the expense of buying a complete engine. Since the TCA had a convention caboose from 1966, as well as other freight cars from 1965 to 1971 and even a steam engine tender shell from the 1968 Cleveland convention, the idea here was to complete the first "TCA Train". In fact, there was serious talk of terminating the convention car program at that time; but the issue became moot when another car was made the very next year. Devised by Bill Nelson and Jim Crone. G. Hinkle comments. **NRS**

984 **1984-30X HEINZ KETCHUP:** Boxcar; white sides; red roof, ends and doors; red Heinz ketchup bottle to left; TCA logo and 30th anniversary convention data to right; produced as a banquet souvenir at the TCA National Convention in Pittsburgh, Pennsylvania; also marked the 30th anniversary of the TCA hence the "30X"); Lionel boxcar redecorated by PVP (designator 505-1334"); the "official" banquet car sanctioned by the convention committee; 220 made. M. Gural Collection.

— — — **200**

984 **1984 IRON CITY BEER:** Boxcar/refrigerator car; produced as an alternative convention souvenir for the 1984 TCA convention by several Ft. Pitt division members. Gordon Hinkle produced them for fun when he could not understand why the Heinz car had been selected by the convention committee. He had also intended it as a salute to the Pittsburgh Brewing Co., makers of Iron City, at its 50th anniversary. Although it started as a joke, this car has become a collector item. 108 cars were made, split evenly between Lionel boxcars and refrigerator cars. They are white, with red ends and roofs; red, white, black and gold Iron City Beer decal to the left; "You've Got a Friend In Pittsburgh" in black with a Pittsburgh Brewing Co. notation to the right side; each car serially stamped on the bottom from "1" to "108"; four cars also made with gold roofs and doors, and given to officials of the brewing company. Naturally, beer car collectors have created demand for this car and it is now quite hard to find.

— — — **170**

984 **HEINZ PICKLES:** Boxcar; another 1984 TCA convention souvenir car, this time produced by Tom Shepard. We have no other data on the car and presume it is Lionel-based. We know Walthers decals were used and that Heinz was not thrilled by the use of its logos on the car. Further reader comments requested. **NRS**

Miscellaneous TCA Division Production

Several other TCA divisions and chapters have produced one-time specials not since repeated:

974 **1974 PACIFIC NORTHWEST DIVISION:** F-3 diesel AA cab shells only; silver bodies; black lettering; TCA 1974 Seattle convention notations; produced by the Pacific Northwest division of the TCA as a souvenir for the 1974 National Convention; cabs include the division logo. T. Carney comments; R. Meerly Collection. — — — **75**

	GD	VG	EXC	MT

1976 **1971-1976 ROCKY MOUNTAIN DIVISION:** 9800-series refrigerator car; white Type I body; blue roof; red doors; red and blue lettering; map of Rocky Mountain division states to right side; Rocky Mountain division logo to the left; lettered "5th Anniversary, 1971-1976"; Symington-Wayne trucks; no "BLT" date. This is a Lionel-based car, but it is not known who redecorated it. The Rocky Mountain division has produced no other cars besides this and the car for the 1982 National Convention, while it lasted. J. Bratspis Collection. **NRS**

1976 **9113 NORFOLK & WESTERN:** Quad hopper; standard Lionel 9113 hopper with an overstamp for the TCA's Three Rivers chapter, a branch of the Great Lakes division; gold overstamping "Three Rivers Chapter/Great Lakes Division — TCA/Oct. 3, 1976" to left, which was the date of a chapter-sponsored train meet; TCA circle logo in green to right; 290 made; decorated by Curt Fischbach. A small number of hoppers were made with the TCA logo in red and lettering in blue. L. Rinehart comments and Collection. — — — **45**

THE TOY TRAIN OPERATING SOCIETY

The Toy Train Operating Society (TTOS) is the second-oldest model train organization in the United States. Founded in 1966 to promote the operating as well as the collecting enjoyment of trains, the TTOS remains principally based on the West Coast, although it has divisions all over the country including an active contingent in Canada. It publishes the bimonthly *TTOS Bulletin* and the *Order Board*, a buy-sell trade journal.

More than any other train club described in this book, the TTOS has expanded its horizons beyond Lionel. Substantial portions of the TTOS membership are involved with HO, N Scale and Large Scale trains, as well as Lionel O Gauge. The TTOS, like most of the other societies, sponsors an annual convention with an annual convention car to commemorate it. But unlike most of the others, TTOS has used convention cars in many scales and from many manufacturers, not just Lionel. As a result, there are several years in which no Lionel cars were issued.

In its first year, the club only issued an HO Scale convention refrigerator car made by Athearn. A Lionel convention car first appeared in 1967 — 460 of Lionel's 6167 plain Army hoppers were purchased and overstamped in gold. Louis Hertz devised the decorating scheme. In 1968, both HO (Athearn) and O (Lionel) cars were made. In this case, the Lionel 6017 SP-style Boston & Maine caboose (quantity 350) was the selected item, with convention notations applied in white. In 1969, TTOS divided the convention car selection between a 6476 short hopper (493 made), a 6057 SP-type caboose (250 made), and a 6257 SP-type caboose (also 250 made). TTOS President and founder Bill Harris designed each of these cars. All the above-mentioned Lionel cars can be referenced in *Greenberg's Guide to Lionel Trains 1945-1969*, and in the 1991 TTOS Directory.

6582 Portland flatcar with lumber load for TTOS 1986 convention; 17871 New York Central TOFC flatcar with Kodak/Xerox trailers for 1987 TT convention in Rochester, New York (home of these firms).

	GD	VG	EXC	MT

During the 1970-1973 period, Lionel was apparently not geared up to do special production cars for the train clubs. Many clubs used either overstamped regular production or cars from other manufacturers during this time. In this case, KMT made cars for the TTOS. By the mid-1970s, Lionel had become more cooperative and offered to make the TTOS cars again.

A series of Madison cars began in 1974. By 1980, Lionel was making TTOS cars by the thousands — more than the membership could support. As a result, many of them are quite easy to find. In the early 1980s, for some reason, TTOS's relationship with Lionel changed, and the quantities of convention cars made dropped dramatically. Lionel did not make the cars during these years: In 1981, TTOS offered a KMT boxcar again, with the decoration accomplished by PVP; and in 1982 through 1985, Lionel-based pieces were redecorated by PVP and NTW. By 1986, Lionel once again supplied the TTOS annual convention cars. The cars from the late 1980s are quite scarce. Since 1990, the TTOS has been offering Standard O cars.

We are grateful to the TTOS National Business Office and the Board of Directors for their assistance in generating the following list of TTOS special production cars.

1970 **6076 SANTA FE:** Short O27 hopper; first modern era convention car made for the TTOS; fifth car in the sequence of TTOS annual convention cars which began in 1966; gray body; TTOS circle logo hot-stamped to right side; postwar carry-over car and number; Type I AAR trucks; 496 made. **NRS**

1971-1973 **Non- Lionel production:** Lionel made no TTOS cars. KMT cars were supplied for conventions in these years. In **1971**, 225 KMT orange and green boxcars were made; **1972**, 200 blue-green KMT stock cars with yellow doors and lettering were produced; **1973**, 1,000 white KMT boxcars with multicolor graphics were commissioned and decorated by Ward Kimball for the TTOS convention in Disneyland.

1974 **9512 SUMMERDALE JUNCTION:** Short Madison-style passenger coach; special commemorative for TTOS national convention in Harrisburg, Pennsylvania; canary yellow body with tuscan roof; black lettering; TTOS circle logo near one end; "TOY TRAIN OPERATING SOCIETY" lettered above windows; "Summerdale Junction" banner and number centered below windows; illuminated; window inserts with no silhouettes; Type IV woodbeam passenger trucks; two dummy couplers; 2050 made.

	—	—	40	50

1975 **9520 PHOENIX TTOS:** Short Madison-style passenger combine; special commemorative for TTOS national convention in Phoenix, Arizona; matches 9512; illuminated; Type IV woodbeam passenger trucks; two dummy couplers; 2100 made.

(A) No decal.   — — 40 5
(B) With Phoenix decal for convention attendees.
    — — 55 7

1976 **9526 SNOWBIRD:** Short Madison-style observation car special commemorative for TTOS national convention in Utah matches 9512; illuminated; Type IV woodbeam passenger trucks two dummy couplers; 2200 made.

(A) No Utah decal.   — — 40 5
(B) With Utah decal for convention attendees.
    — — 55 7

1977 **9535 COLUMBUS:** Short Madison-style baggage car special commemorative for TTOS national convention in Columbus, Ohio; matches 9512; illuminated; Type IV passenger trucks; two dummy couplers; 2400 made.

(A) No Ohio decal.   — — 40 5
(B) With Ohio decal for convention attendees.
    — — 55 7

9512, 9520, 9526, and 9535: Approximate set price for all four above cars.   — — — 16

1978 **9678 HOLLYWOOD:** Hi-cube boxcar; special commemorative for TTOS national convention in Los Angeles, California; white plastic body painted white; red ends and roof; red doors blue, red, yellow and black lettering "Hooray for Hollywood" an very large "TOY TRAIN OPERATING SOCIETY"; Symington Wayne trucks; two operating couplers; cars come with TTOS decal convention attendees received a special decal showing Chaplin with "78" on his derby; "BLT 1-78"; 2500 made. The garish decoration and the relatively large quantity made may explain why this car can be found for sale almost anywhere.

(A) Regular car.   — — 25 3
(B) With Chaplin decal.   — — 35 4

1979 **9347 NIAGARA FALLS:** Three-dome tank car; special commemorative for TTOS national convention in Niagara Falls New York; powder blue tank; black lettering; black frame, end and dome caps; wire handrails; metal ladder; "NIAGARA FALL FOR TTOS/NEW YORK 1979/NORTHEASTERN DIVISION" Standard O trucks; "BLT 1-79"; 2000 made.
    — — 40 5

1980 **9868 OKLAHOMA CITY:** 9800-style refrigerator car special commemorative for TTOS national convention in Oklahoma City, Oklahoma; yellow body; dark blue roof and ends dark blue lettering; lettered "SOONER DIVISION"; covered

F. Stem Collection; B. Greenberg photograph

... of TTOS convention cars. TTOS has also made cars from other manufacturers.
... shelf: 9512 Summerdale Junction passenger car from 1974, one of a set of four; 9678 Hollywood hi-cube from 1978.
...dle shelf: 1984 Sacramento Northern boxcar, made by NTW; 17877 M-K-T tank car from 1989.
...om shelf: The start of a handsome series of TTOS ore cars by its Gadsden-Pacific Division — 17872 Anaconda from 1988; 17878 Magma from 1989; 17881 ...elps-Dodge from 1990.

	GD	VG	EXC	MT

...wagon with sign reading "1980" on left side; lettered "TTOS ...980/National Convention/OKLAHOMA CITY, OK." on right side ...long with two oil derricks; Symington-Wayne trucks; "BLT 1-80"; ...000 made. A. Passman and C. Rohlfing comments.

— — 40 50

...981 **Non-Lionel production:** No Lionel cars were made this ...ear. 893 KMT boxcars were decorated in blue and yellow with ...white doors for the national convention in San Diego. PVP ...decorated the cars.

> **1982:** *For its National Convention this year in Hartford, Connecticut, the TTOS commissioned a series of Lionel-based bay window cabooses as the convention cars. Lionel could not over-stamp them for the Society, so the group contracted with PVP and NTW to do the job. The modifications essentially consisted of added decals. We know that the 9355, 9361, 9382 and 9326 cabooses were involved, and we know there were one or two others. A total of 480 were made of all the types. We would be interested in hearing from readers on the relative quantities made of all the 1982 bay window cabooses, and to clarify who made what.*

...1982 **9326 BURLINGTON NORTHERN:** Bay window ...caboose; special commemorative made for TTOS national conven-...tion in Hartford, Connecticut; regular-production 9326 caboose ...(see Volume I for details) with blue decals added; produced by ...NTW. **NRS**

1982 **9355 DELAWARE & HUDSON:** Bay window caboose; special commemorative made for TTOS national convention in Hartford, Connecticut; dark blue and gray body; yellow stripe; TTOS decal added; regular-production 9355 caboose (see Volume I for details) with silver and red TTOS decals added; produced by PVP/NBT (designator "252-1214"); probably less than 200 made.

— — — 40

1982 **9361 CHICAGO & NORTH WESTERN:** Bay window caboose; special commemorative made for TTOS national convention in Hartford, Connecticut; regular-production 9361 caboose (see Volume I for details) with silver and red decals added; produced by PVP (designator "252-1214"); probably less than 200 made.

— — — 60

1982 **9382 FLORIDA EAST COAST:** Bay window caboose; special commemorative made for TTOS national convention in Hartford, Connecticut; regular-production 9382 caboose (see Volume I for details) with blue decals added; produced by NTW.

— — — 40

1983 **P9883 PHOENIX:** Refrigerator car; special commemorative made for TTOS national convention in Phoenix, Arizona; 9800-series Lionel refrigerator car (underlying car type unknown) redecorated by NTW; gold sides; black roof, ends and doors; black lettering; "T.T.O.S. 1983/A.T. & N.M. DIVISION"; yellow TTOS logo to left; yellow and red Arizona map to right; Standard O trucks; 350 made. **NRS**

1983 **PHOENIX:** Three-dome tank car; special commemorative made for TTOS national convention in Phoenix, Arizona; Lionel three-dome tanker redecorated by NTW; gold body; apparently matches design of P9883 refrigerator car above; 350 made. Further details requested from readers. **NRS**

	GD	VG	EXC	MT

1984 **1984 SACRAMENTO NORTHERN:** boxcar; special commemorative made for TTOS national convention in Sacramento, California; 9700-series classic Lionel boxcar redecorated by NTW; brown body; white and gold lettering; 19th National Convention logo; Sacramento Valley division and California Capitol logos in gold and light blue; no number on the car other than "1984"; Symington-Wayne trucks; 475 made; "Restoration by NTW" notation on bottom. — — **80 100**

1985 **1985 SNOWBIRD:** Quad hopper; special commemorative made for TTOS national convention in Utah; standard Lionel 6111 L & N quad hopper redecorated by NTW; light blue body; green and white mountain scene on sides; black lettering "T.T.O.S. COMES ALIVE IN 1985"; yellow TTOS circle logo to upper right; Idaho, Colorado, Utah division logo to upper left; Symington-Wayne trucks; 425 made. — — — **40**

1986 **6582 PORTLAND:** Flatcar with lumber load; special commemorative made for TTOS national convention in Portland, Oregon; brown body; yellow flatcar lettering; black lettering on load "PACIFIC NW/DIVISION" and "CANADIAN DIVISION"; Standard O trucks; "BLT 1-86"; 624 made. First TTOS car since 1981 to be made entirely by Lionel. Somewhat hard to find. — — — **100**

1987 **17871 NEW YORK CENTRAL:** TOFC flatcar; special commemorative for TTOS National Convention in Rochester, New York; flatcar with white Kodak and Xerox trailers; red, yellow and black Kodak insignia on one van; black "XEROX" in block letters on the other; black flatcar body with white lettering; car is numbered "81487"; Standard O trucks; "BLT 8-87"; 876 made. The previous edition of this Guide erroneously listed this car as "19417". Exceptionally hard to find now. — — — **200**

1988 **17872 ANACONDA:** Ore car; special commemorative for TTOS national convention in Tucson, Arizona; reddish-brown body; no ore load; white lettering; frame reads "TTOS 88/CONV. CAR"; number on the car is "81988"; Symington-Wayne trucks; "BLT 1-88"; 1824 made. This convention car is also the first in TTOS's series of ore cars sold to raise funds for a TTOS museum in Tucson, sponsored by the Gadsden-Pacific division. D. Mareck Collection. — — — **75**
See also Factory Errors and Prototypes chapter.

1989 **17877 M-K-T:** Single-dome tank car; special commemorative for TTOS national convention in Dallas, Texas; red body; gray frame; black metal platform and ladders; wire handrails; yellow lettering "M-K-T/Missouri-Kansas- Texas" to right side; "Katy" in script to left; Standard O trucks; "17877" is not on the car, only on the box; "3739469" is the number on the car; "BLT 1- 89"; 1425 made. This car replaced the planned Ewing Oil car as the 1989 convention car when Lorimar Productions, owner of the television show *Dallas*, would not grant permission for the Ewing tank car to be manufactured. This car looks very similar to the 6319 MKT tank car produced by K-Line earlier. When the designer of this car sent the initial artwork to Lionel, he scribbled a number on the car, thinking Lionel would insert its own catalogue number. Instead, Lionel obediently decorated the car with the seven-digit number the designer had written, which turned out to be his phone number! J. P. Neil comment and Collection. — — — **70**

1990 **17884 COLUMBUS & DAYTON:** Standard O boxcar; special commemorative for TTOS national convention in Columbus, Ohio; light gray body; maroon lettering "Guaranteed Prompt Delivery"; Standard O trucks; "BLT 1-90"; 1600 made. The decoration scheme on this car is easily the most plain of any of th TTOS convention cars — in fact, the only reference to TTOS at al is the small notation "When Empty Return to TTOS Agen Columbus, Ohio". This car was ordered by TTOS when th originally planned 1990 convention car, a C & O boxcar wit End-Of-Train device, was not ordered in sufficient quantity. — — — **5**

Note: There were also several other TTOS convention cars fror other manufacturers in 1990.

1991 **17889 SOUTHERN PACIFIC:** Standard O flatca with long van; special commemorative for the 25th annual TTO national convention in Long Beach, California; brown flatcar bod with white lettering; cream-colored van with black, yellow, whit and pink Southern Pacific "Golden Pig Service" logo on sides an one end; silver "25TH ANNIVERSARY TOY TRAIN OPERATIN(SOCIETY" on orange strip along lower edge of van; "15791" o car; 178889 appears only on box; Standard O trucks; "BLT 1-91" — — — **6**

TTOS GADSDEN- PACIFIC DIVISION ORE CAR SERIES

In conjunction with its 1988 convention in Tucson, th TTOS, specifically its Gadsden-Pacific division, contracte with Lionel to produce an uncatalogued series of annual or cars, whose sale is intended to raise funds for the construction of a TTOS train museum in Tucson.

Lionel does not usually contract to do more than on specialty car for a train club per year. This sequence of or cars is an exception.

Each of the cars (the Anaconda car was also considere TTOS's annual convention car) is decorated for prominent or and mining companies in Arizona. While the construction i fairly standard, these cars make a fine-looking unit train whe run together. Made in limited quantities (all less than 2000 they are relatively scarce and desirable. It is not known hov long the annual release of ore cars will continue.

An interesting footnote here is that many, if not all, c the Type VI boxes in which these cars were released hav labels with "GADSDEN" misspelled without the first "D".

1988 **17872 ANACONDA:** See listing 17872 above.

1989 **17878 MAGMA:** Ore car; black body; white lettering frame reads "GP 89 MUSEUM CAR"; light gray ore load Symington-Wayne trucks; "BLT 1-89"; 1701 made. M. Solly Co lection. — — **7**

1990 **17881 PHELPS-DODGE:** Ore car; light gray body black lettering; white ore load; frame reads "GP 90 Museum Car" ASF strong-arm trucks; "BLT 1-90"; approximately 1500 made M. Solly Collection. — — — **6**

1991 **17886 CYPRUS:** Ore car; silver body; royal blue an black lettering; frame reads "GP 91 Museum Car"; ore load; AS} strong-arm trucks; "BLT 1-91". M. Solly Collection. — — — **6**

OTHER TTOS PRODUCTION

We have had several unconfirmed reports of other TTO! cars issued to mark special occasions, including the Christma

GD   VG   EXC   MT

olidays or other TTOS division-related events, such as local
rain meets. An Amtrak passenger car with TTOS markings
nay exist, and there may be several Lionel 9400- or 9700-
eries boxcars with TTOS overstamps. We would be inter-
sted in hearing from readers with details on these cars —
egarding who made them, why, when, what the underlying
.ionel car is, and the particulars of the car's appearance — so
hat we may expand our listings in this area for future edi-
ions.

---

984 **NATIONAL HEADQUARTERS:** 2065-style 4-6-4 small
Iudson; redecorated by NTW; black body; Baldwin-style boiler
vith smoke deflectors; red cab roof; yellow running board; yellow
eedwater heater; yellow TTOS circle logo on smoke deflectors; two
ellow stripes run the length of the long 2046-style tender, which
as bar-end trucks. Only 48 of these locomotives were made on
pecial order to individual TTOS members. The member's club
umber is individually stamped below the cab windows, so this
ngine will actually be found with 48 different numbers! This
ssue was used as a fundraiser and commemorative of TTOS
pening its national headquarters in Pasadena, California.

NRS

VIRGINIA TRAIN COLLECTORS

The Virginia Train Collectors (VTC) is a group of about
00 model railroad enthusiasts located mainly in central and
astern Virginia, though it has members in other states. It
egan in 1976 when a group of about 40 Virginia collectors
ttempted to form a Virginia chapter of the TCA but were
nable to secure permission from the national board. They
ormed an independent group with an emphasis on the per-
onal service which is only possible with a local assemblage.
n addition to open meets in Richmond, Hampton Roads and
orthern Virginia, the club sponsors Christmas parties and
icnics. It also publishes a monthly newsletter and an annual
lossy magazine called the *Observation*. The organization
rew quickly in the late 1970s. About 95 percent of the
nembers are residents of Virginia, Maryland or Washington,
).C. The VTC is organized along the lines of the TCA, but its
neets are open to the public.

The annual club car series began in 1979 both as a
undraiser and as a unique commemorative for club member-
hip. Two cars display prototype Virginia names, while the
thers simply say "Virginia Train Collectors". In all cases,
owever, the club's circle logo, featuring a silhouette of the
tate map superimposed on a rising sun, is stamped some-
vhere on the car.

VTC has assigned a four-digit numbering system to its
ars: "76" are the first two digits, the year of the club's
ounding; the last two digits represent the year of production.
The club intends to produce more than one car per year in the
iext few years, so it will add a fifth digit at the end to
lifferentiate them.

These cars may be of interest to Lionel collectors because
he ones through 1986 were O Gauge Lionel bodies
edecorated by PVP. Two trolleys produced originally by

GD   VG   EXC   MT

Bowser in 1988 and 1989 will not be listed here in detail.
Starting in 1991, VTC plans a new passenger set based on O27
streamlined car bodies to be supplied to PVP by Lionel Trains,
Inc. We are grateful to VTC President William Mezger for
providing us with this data.

1979 **7679 VTC:** Boxcar; first in a series of yearly cars
produced by the VTC; silver body; black door; red and black
lettering; large red sideways "V" design across length of car; black
VTC logo; classic-style Lionel boxcar (used the 9414 Cotton Belt
as a base) redecorated by PVP (designator "505-1109"); other
construction details same as 9414 (see Volume I); "BLT 10-79";
200 were made, with 12 later used for the 7685 VTC car, so 188 of
these cars remain. This number was too large for the membership
to support, and unsold cars remained as late as 1986.

— — — 20

1980 **No production.**

1981 **7681 VTC:** N5C caboose; second in an annual series
produced by VTC; red body; white lettering and VTC logo; illuminated; standard Lionel N5C caboose (the 9182 N & W)
redecorated by PVP (designator "205-1173"); other details same
as regular 9182; "BLT 8-81"; 144 made. This second car sold better
than the 7679 car, at a time when club membership was rapidly
increasing.

— — — 25

1982 **7682 VTC:** Covered quad hopper; third in an annual
series produced by VTC; black body; white lettering and VTC logo;
standard Lionel quad hopper (the 6101 Burlington Northern)
redecorated by PVP (designator "305-1227"); other details same
as regular 6101; "BLT 11-82"; 132 made.

— — — 25

1983 **7683 VIRGINIA FRUIT EXPRESS REFRIGERATOR:**
Refrigerator car; fourth in an annual series produced by VTC; light
tan body; red and black lettering; standard Lionel Turn-of-the-
Century wood-sided refrigerator car (using the 5704 Budweiser as
a base) redecorated by PVP (designator "605-1278"); "BLT 9-83";
120 made; like the original Budweiser car, this has the Standard
O sprung trucks, the only VTC car to have them.

— — — 28

1984 **7684 VITRACO OIL:** Three-dome tank car; fifth in an
annual series produced by VTC; dark green body; white lettering
and VTC logo; "SERVING THE MID-ATLANTIC HEARTLAND";
standard Lionel tank car based on the 9279 Magnolia and the 9148
Du Pont; PVP redecorated about 108 of these cars (designator
"705-1362"); "BLT 6-84". — — — 25
Note: In 1984, VTC also produced an S Gauge single-dome tank
car (numbered 8476) in dark green with white lettering, for the
benefit of its S Gauge contingent. It matched the O Gauge car.
Sluggish sales led VTC to forswear any further S Gauge cars in
the near future.

1985 **7685 VTC:** Boxcar; sixth in an annual series produced by
VTC; blue sides; silver roof and ends; yellow door; yellow lettering
and VTC logo; "SERVING THE OLD DOMINION"; standard
Lionel classic-type boxcar redecorated by PVP, using the 9463
Texas and Pacific car as a base (designator "505-1401"); "BLT
5-85". VTC also repainted a dozen of its slow-selling 7679s into
this car. A total of only 84 exist, because by this time Lionel was
in the throes of moving to Mexico, and the club had trouble finding
cars to repaint. About half the 9463S were rubber-stamped, and
the other half heat-stamped. The heat tended to bleed the underlying T & P lettering through, leading to the poorest paint job in

	GD	VG	EXC	MT

the VTC series. Still, this car sold well because of its very low quantity. — — — 30

1986 **7686 VTC:** GP-7 diesel; seventh in an annual series produced by VTC, and the first engine (intended to complete VTC's first train); bright red body; white lettering and VTC logo; black frame; Lionel 8263 Santa Fe GP-7 redecorated by PVP (designator "105-1424"; see construction details under 8263 in Volume I; no "BLT" date; 72 made. This engine also marked VTC's tenth anniversary. — — — 90

1987 **No production.**

1988 and 1989 **Non-Lionel production:** In both these years VTC produced a Brill trolley based on Bowser bodies redecorated by PVP. 166 were made of the 1988 version (numbered "1888-1988"), plus a few were made for two-rail scale operation. About 106 of the 1989 trolley, numbered "7689", exist.

1990 **No production.**

1991 and Future **VTC:** The club has plans to make a Norfolk & Western passenger train in the standard tuscan red with black roofs and gold lettering. It plans to use Lionel O27 streamlined cars, supplied as blanks to PVP for decorating. The sets in 1991 and 1992 will consist of three cars each, so the numbering system will require a fifth digit. Later plans are to produce a matching refrigerator car and engine.

PLEASANT VALLEY PROCESS COMPANY

FILLING IN LIONEL'S GAPS

There is a huge market for customized and specialized trains which, to a great extent, Lionel cannot fill. A specially-decorated train car is a great novelty item. With its production geared to the mass train market, Lionel cannot make runs of specialty cars less than several hundred. Therefore, a gate is opened for small entrepreneurs who can make a living redecorating train cars for special events. They can commemorate literally anything — such as the Rose Bowl, a small-town Spring festival, a grocery store opening, or the election of a President. Lionel could not possibly respond to all the requests it gets for such customized pieces. But others have.

Two of the most successful such entrepreneurs are John Newbraugh and Seymour Knight of Pleasant Valley Process/Newbraugh Brothers Toys (PVP/NBT). Newbraugh is a West Virginia teacher and train collector who started a sideline toy business in 1974 with his two brothers. Now and then he decorated a train car for some special event. He admits he was not very good at it, though, and eventually he encountered Seymour Knight, who is a printer/decorator from southwestern Pennsylvania. This occurred in the mid-1970s and since then Seymour has done the bulk of the professional graphics and overstamping from his Pleasant Valley Process shop.

Together, the two men began producing more professional-looking specialty train cars in the late 1970s.

They used all scales and makes, but a large amount of their work involved O Scale Lionel. Today, many of their trains are quite valuable, and since they have been intimately involved in the Lionel hobby for over a decade, it is appropriate that their work be brought to light in our focus on special Lionel production. PVP/NBT has been closely involved in the production of Lionel-derivative division and Museum cars for TCA, national convention cars for LOTS and TTOS, and annual commemorative cars for the LCAC, all of which have lately received much collector interest.

Lest the Lionel purists raise concerns over fakes or unauthorized reproductions, PVP/NBT clearly marks every piece it makes (either on the side of the piece, stamping on the bottom frame, and/or on the box) with a special seven-digit code that bears no resemblance to the usual Lionel catalogue numbers. To Newbraugh's knowledge, PVP has never made a close reproduction of a valuable Lionel car, although sometimes, as in the case of the Guinness train, it will overstamp existing cars. In this case, the added graphics are usually obvious, and the PVP code is added to the bottom.

Business really expanded for PVP/NBT in 1979 with the company's idea for a radioactive waste train set based on the Three Mile Island incident. The boxcar from that set is now a popular collector's item.

Thereafter, the reputation of PVP/NBT spread in train-collecting circles. Some of the train clubs who were seeking special cars for meets, conventions or fundraisers contracted Newbraugh and Knight to do runs of between 5 and 1000 cars, too few for Lionel to do an "official" production piece, but just right for PVP/NBT. In addition, PVP/NBT has produced countless specialty cars for small and large businesses throughout the country. At last count, trains from 2 different manufacturers have been decorated or redecorated by the firm, including KMT, Lionel, Marx, Williams and K Line in the O Gauge world. Of these, the majority of the work involves Lionel pieces — to date, 268 different Lionel-derivative items have been produced, the total quantity exceeding 10,000. Boxcars are the most popular car requested, followed by refrigerator cars and cabooses.

It is no wonder, then, that many of PVP's cars show up regularly at train meets, nor that the quantity of Lionel cars on the market sometimes seems lower than it should. The 9414 Cotton Belt boxcar — because it has smooth sides, open areas for overstamping and is an attractive tuscan color — has been redecorated by the thousands, as have some of the Tobacco Road cars, which (not being hot sellers) were available inexpensively in great numbers for special production.

This section describes some of the more important production groups from PVP/NBT, the cars which are most likely to show up at train meets, and have become active part of the collector market.

TCA

PVP has had a long relationship with the Train Collector's Association. While not generally involved in the TCA's national convention cars, PVP has produced several interesting sets for the association. Detailed listings on all these pieces are found in the TCA subsection of this chapter. Highlights:

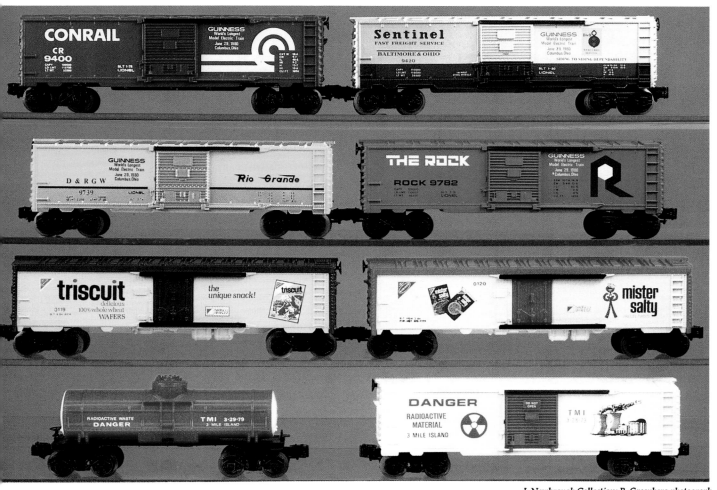

J. Newbraugh Collection; B. Greenberg photograph

A sampling of the artisan's work of Pleasant Valley Process/Newbraugh Bros. Toys. All the cars are based on Lionel bodies.
Top two shelves: Four of the cars used in the Guinness World's largest model train run in 1980. The B & O Sentinel is the most common.
Third shelf: Two of the cars from PVP's unusual Nabisco set.
Bottom shelf: Two of the cars from PVP's popular Three-Mile Island set.

Museum Set

From 1980 through 1986, PVP produced a set of cars honoring the major players in the toy train industry through the years: Hafner, Carlisle-Finch, Ives, Voltamp, Hoge, and Dorfan. Ironically, all these cars, except the Dorfan (made on a KMT-Williams car) were made on Lionel cars. The cars, numbered 7780 through 7786 (in addition to the PVP code), were commissioned by the TCA's Toy Train Museum in Strasburg, Pennsylvania (for which there is a logo on each car) as fundraisers. Several hundred of each car were made. PVP has also produced other Museum-related cars, as have several other manufacturers. The Museum often issues special cars to commemorate various events.

Division and Chapter Cars

PVP produced cars for the many of the TCA divisions through the years, including anniversary cars for the Atlantic division, a redecorated refrigerator car for the New England division, a series for the Sacramento-Sierra chapter, and several convention banquet cars, which are usually sponsored by the division hosting the national convention. In many cases, PVP would also produce cars with matching designs in other scales from other manufacturers.

Mortgage-Burning Ceremony Car

This is possibly PVP's most famous piece, a redecorated Flying Yankee hi-cube car commissioned by the TCA Museum to help retire the mortgage on the building.

LOTS

Through the first eight years of the Lionel Operating Train Society's existence, PVP produced seven of their national convention commemorative cars, and one meet car in 1986. Starting in 1988, LOTS's cars were made directly by Lionel. See the LOTS subsection in this chapter for more details.

TTOS

Though not as closely associated with the Toy Train Operating Society as it is with TCA and LOTS, PVP has produced several cars for the West Coast-based TTOS. Two important ones are the 9355 and 9361 cabooses with added decals for the 1982 convention. Of course, the TTOS does not restrict itself to Lionel production, so many of its convention cars and other production are done on non-Lionel pieces. See the TTOS subsection in this chapter for a more complete list.

LCAC

The Lionel Collectors Association of Canada opened its doors in 1978. In recent years, the association and its annual commemorative cars have experienced an explosion of new interest. PVP has produced nearly all of the LCAC's cars, which are based on Canadian railway lines. Included are two valuable Canadian National F-3 diesel shells produced in 1985. These cars have been gathering much collector interest recently. See the LCAC subsection in this chapter for more details.

VIRGINIA TRAIN COLLECTORS

PVP has produced all of the Virginia Train Collectors special cars beginning in 1979. The series from 1979 to 1986 consisted of Lionel-based O Gauge cars. In 1988 and 1989 PVP redecorated two Bowser trolleys for the club, and in 1991 and future years, there are plans for an O27 streamlined passenger set, using Lionel shells, decorated in Norfolk & Western colors. See the Virginia Train Collectors subsection of this chapter for full details on the club's production.

LIONEL CENTRAL OPERATING LINES

The LCOL is another small group of Lionel enthusiasts in Long Island, New York. PVP was involved with at least four cars for the group in the 1980s. See the Lionel Central Operating Lines subsection of this chapter for more details.

THREE-MILE ISLAND SET

In 1979, PVP/NBT produced a boxed set of cars and an engine, commemorating the Three-Mile Island incident. The set included a boxcar, tank car, searchlight car, engine and work caboose. A hopper and another tank and boxcar were added later. All are fully redecorated Lionel cars, although the original Lionel identity of the cars is unknown. The set was produced in 1979 (the last four digits of the PVP/NBT number codes range from 1112 through 1133), and at least 1,000 boxcars were produced, so that it shows up quite frequently at meets.

PVP'S SEASON'S GREETINGS CARS

Like many organizations, including Lionel itself, P V P/N B T has produced a set of Season's Greetings cars. For some reason these cars, nearly always decorated in some variation of red and green, are popular regardless of who makes them. Newbraugh indicates that the Christmas car market is quite competitive, and for the last few years P V P has done its Christmas cars on K M T and/or HO cars which are somewhat less expensive than Lionel. Here is a table of (some) of the Lionel-based Christmas cars P V P has produced since 1979:

Year	PVP Number	Type	Name	Body Color	Lettering Color
1979	605-1111	Reefer	Jack's Tracks	Green	Red
1979	205-1131	Caboose	New Caboose Dist.	White	Red/green
1980	705-1143	Hopper	New Caboose Dist.	White/red	Green/gold
1980	305-1065	Gondola	R & M Dept. Store	Red	White
1981	505-1176	Boxcar	Merry Xmas - '81	White	Red/green
1981	205-1178*	Work Caboose	Seasons Greetings	Red	White/gold
1981	705-1182*	Searchlight	Christmas	Blue/orange	Multicolor
1981	305-1183*	Hopper	Hopper with Gifts	Yellow	Red/green
1981	705-1184*	Tank Car	Happy New Year	Red/white	White
1981	105-1185*	Switcher	Holiday Joy Lines	Green	White/green
1982	705-1217	Window Car	Christmas 1982	Red	Green/red
1982	505-1224	Boxcar	Christmas 1982	White	Red/green
1982	205-1225	Work Caboose	Holiday Joy Lines	Red	Red/gold
1983	505-1308	Window Car	Christmas 1983	Unknown	Unknown
1985	705-1411	Hi-Cube	Christmas 1985	Unknown	Unknown

* These items were included in a boxed 1981 set from PVP, which was designed by Frank Silvagni.

At about the same time, the firm decorated two Lionel refrigerator cars with "The Sky is Falling" graphics marking the somewhat unexpected return of Skylab from space. It is not known who commissioned these sets.

THE GUINNESS WORLD'S LONGEST ELECTRIC TRAIN

See the complete article at the end of this chapter for the fascinating story of this train, which still holds the Guinness record as the world's longest model electric train. PVP/NBT overstamped over one thousand 9400- and 9700-series Lionel boxcars for this event, which took place in 1980. Fortunately the cars are merely overstamped with the Guinness train logo and not fully redecorated, so their original identity remains intact. The most frequently encountered car is the 9420 B & O Sentinel, of which more than 800 were made, but other cars were also stamped:

9400,	9402,	9405,	9413,	9414,	9415
9416,	9420,	9739,	9754,	9768,	9770
9775,	9782,	9783,	9784		

Only 12 of each of the other boxcars exist with the overstamping. All bear the "506-1139" PVP number on them. Also stamped were about a dozen 8850 Penn Central GG-1 electrics, about 20 8056 C & NW Fairbanks-Morse Trainmasters, plus a few other engines, and eventually several 9289 C & NW cabooses.

NABISCO SET

Over the years quite a few unique cars decorated for the various products made by Nabisco have shown up at train meets and in the Lionel guides. These have caused some confusion because no one has been fully sure of their source, and rumors have persisted of an uncatalogued Lionel Nabisco set. Research and contacts with PVP have finally helped us clear a little of the fog surrounding this set. We are also grateful to reader Patrick Guzzi for an important letter assisting us in this study.

PVP made all the cars in this "set" (which actually includes a boxed set of engine, caboose and three cars, as well as a host of other associated freight cars released later), during a period from 1983 to 1985. It is not clear who at Nabisco commissioned it (possibly someone with the initials "W.E.M.", which appears on some of the cars), but PVP made nearly 20 pieces during this time with various Nabisco logos on them. Production quantities are not known, but there were certainly more than 100, and perhaps as many as 500, of each piece made. The first boxed set made in 1983 was a combination of Lionel and KMT redecorated items.

PVP/NBT also decorated a refrigerator car for the New Jersey division of Nabisco (No. "705-1407") in 1985, as well as two of its popular Christmas cars, for which it had Nabisco notations added (a KMT refrigerator car in 1983, designator "605-1279", and a Lionel hi-cube car in 1984, designator "705-1385"). Finally, PVP also ran a set of O Gauge Bowser trolleys through its decorating presses for Nabisco in 1984.

1983 NABISCO BRANDS: 1983, NW-2 switcher; teal blue painted gray plastic cab; white panel with "1983" in red; "NABISCO/BRANDS/BISCUIT GROUP" in black; Nabisco logo in white

	GD	VG	EXC	MT

and red near front; black frame and handrails; two-position E-unit; metal power truck frame and plastic dummy truck frame; sliding shoe pickup; illuminated; "BLT 6-83". Lionel-based engine which headed a four-car set produced by PVP for Nabisco (PVP designator "105-1268"). S. Lindsey, Jr. and P. Guzzi Collections.   **NRS**

5583 RITZ CRACKERS: 1983, refrigerator car from KMT; red body; yellow roof and doors; "BLT KMT 8-83"; PVP designator "605-1284"; came in a three-car boxed set headed by the 1983 Nabisco switcher (above). P. Guzzi comment.   **NRS**

0583 CHIPS AHOY: 1983, refrigerator car from KMT; blue body; red roof and doors; "BLT KMT 8-83"; PVP designator "605-1285"; came in a three-car boxed set headed by the 1983 Nabisco switcher (above). P. Guzzi comment.   **NRS**

6283 FIG NEWTONS: 1983, refrigerator car from KMT; yellow body; blue roof and doors; "BLT KMT 8-83"; PVP designator "605-1286"; came in a three-car boxed set headed by the 1983 Nabisco switcher above. P. Guzzi comment.   **NRS**

1984 NABISCO: 1983, work caboose; yellow frame; medium red cab and tool bin; "Nabisco" logo on cab side; Symington-Wayne trucks; one operating coupler; "BLT D.S.M. 9-83". Part of boxed Nabisco set with engine and three cars listed above, made by PVP for Nabisco. This is a Lionel work caboose redecorated by PVP (designator "205-1301"). S. Lindsey, Jr. and P. Guzzi Collections.   **NRS**

PVP also produced a series of add-ons to the above set, listed here in rough order of production:

0120 MISTER SALTY: 1984, refrigerator car; white body; red roof and doors; blue lettering; Mister Salty and pretzel packages to right of doors; Symington-Wayne trucks; "BLT WEM 3-84"; Lionel 9800-series refrigerator car redecorated by PVP (designator "605-1339").   **NRS**

0124 OREO DOUBLE STUF: 1984, refrigerator car; white sides; dark gray roof and ends; black doors; two different illustrations of Oreo Double Stuf cookie packages on either side of door; "BLT WEM 3-84"; Lionel 9800-series refrigerator car redecorated by PVP (designator "605-1340"). S. Lindsey, Jr. and P. Guzzi Collection.   **NRS**

0119 TRISCUIT: 1984, refrigerator car; yellow sides; dark blue-green roof, ends and doors; red and black lettering; large "triscuit" to left of door with dots over "i"s in red; Symington-Wayne trucks; Lionel 9800-series refrigerator car redecorated by PVP (designator "605-1367").   **NRS**

0104 WHEAT THINS: 1984, refrigerator car; yellow sides; black roof, ends and doors; black "Whole Wheat Goodness" and "Wheat Thins" to left of door; black "Wheat Thins" lettering to right of door; "BLT 8-84 WEM"; Lionel 9800-series refrigerator car redecorated by PVP (designator "605-1368"). S. Lindsey, Jr. and P. Guzzi Collection.   **NRS**

1984 RITZ CRACKERS: 1984, hi-cube boxcar; red body; yellow doors; yellow lettering "50th ANNIVERSARY/RITZ 1984"; Ritz canister; Symington-Wayne trucks; Lionel 9600-series hi-cube boxcar redecorated by PVP (designator "705-1387"). S. Lindsey, Jr. Collection.   **NRS**

NABISCO GRAHAMS: 1985, covered quad hopper; other data unknown — reader comments requested. This is apparently a standard Lionel quad hopper redecorated by PVP (designator "305-1393").   **NRS**

GD   VG   EXC   MT

9226 PREMIUM SALTINE (D & H): 1985, TOFC flatcar with two vans; standard Lionel 9226 Delaware and Hudson TOFC flatcar on which the van sides have had a decal reading "PREMIUM/SALTINE CRACKERS" added; additional decals by PVP (designator "705-1398"). S. Lindsey, Jr. Collection.   **NRS**

9106 EASY CHEESE (MILLER): 1985, vat car; regular-production Lionel 9106 Miller beer vat car in which vats with special Nabisco product labels have been substituted for the beer vats; all vats say "EASY CHEESE" in red lettering; one has yellow lettering "American" on a blue band; another has "Chive N' Onion" in yellow on a green band; another has "Cheese N' Bacon" in yellow on a reddish-brown band; the last has "Cheddar" in red on a yellow band; substitute vats were created by PVP (designator "705-1399"), and the box includes a PVP sticker over the printed 9106 label. S. Lindsey, Jr. and M. Gural Collections.   **NRS**

WINDOW CARS

One of PVP/NBT's most novel creations is its set of *window* cars, conceived by Frank Silvagni. In this case, one or both sides of a Lionel boxcar are replaced by clear plexiglass (like the bullion cars), and the interior is decorated for various vignettes. There were 12 or 13 cars made in the 1982-1983 period, most made for various seasons or holidays in the year. One car such car was made for the TCA Museum (705-1296).

OTHER PVP PRODUCTION

There are many other specific topics or events for which PVP has produced special Lionel-based cars, generally in quantities of 50-100. These include several boxcars made for the 1980 Presidential election, two or three cars made for the Strasburg Railroad, and an early set known as the "Four-Star Express". Readers are encouraged to send us data on pieces in their collections for reference in future editions. Once again, these products can be discerned by the seven-digit PVP/NBT code located somewhere on the car body or on the box.

THE GUINNESS WORLD RECORD-LENGTH LIONEL TRAIN

Edited from *The Lion Roars* newsletter of the Lionel Collectors Club of America, February-October 1981. Reprinted with permission of the LCCA.

In 1979, an Ohio Lionel enthusiast named Stewart Roberts was wandering around the Northland Mall in Columbus, Ohio when he glanced down the long empty corridor and commented how great it would be to set up track from one end to the other and run trains. This was the germination of an idea to make an attempt to run a world record-length Lionel train.

Roberts, who was also a fan of *Guinness' Book of World Records*, found that the book listed a record of 501 HO cars run by a New Jersey model railroad club. He decided that the use of the mall would enable him not only to exceed this record

(defined as a train traversing at least its own length) but to set the first record in a new category: most different trains run on a single loop at the same time. Guinness advised Roberts they would not expand the Model Train category for number of trains on a loop, but would accept his authenticated record for the longest train, if he could do it. The record is in terms of number of cars, not in actual feet and inches. Roberts and his merry band of "crazy" model railroaders decided on a goal of 1000 cars — in O Gauge this would result in a train four times longer than the previous 501-car record holder. Such a train would stretch nearly 1000 feet!

Late 1979 found Roberts seeking sponsors for the not-inconsiderable expense (he estimated $15,000) of the world-record attempt. The publicity inherent in the event prompted the Northland Mall to offer its enthusiastic support — with a catch. The run would have to be made late at night when the mall was empty. Lionel, too, recognized the good will such an event would promote, and offered to supply Roberts with all the track he would need. Lionel also said it would make the special cars Roberts wanted for the run, if he could find a sponsor.

This became the first hurdle Roberts' group had to overcome. He contacted dozens of commercial firms in hopes of obtaining a sponsor for the cost of the cars and rentals that were involved. In return, he offered unique decorating schemes on the cars, which could result in great publicity for the company and its products. But while many companies applauded his efforts and acknowledged the novelty of such an idea, none were willing to put up the needed capital. Finally, as 1979 turned into 1980, the group decided that "if it was going to be done, we'd have to put up the money." To their surprise a local bank came to the rescue, offering a large line of credit with the boxcars as security. The team would pay off the loan with the proceeds from sales of the special cars they would make for the record event.

Now things started to gain a momentum of their own. "A thousand problems needed to be solved," says Roberts. "I had to depend on many people to take charge of projects, come up with ideas, and lend a hand wherever needed." At its peak, the group consisted of about 50 Columbus-area model railroaders.

Naturally, one does not simply plunk down 1,000 boxcars and 25 engines on a track and expect the thing to work. A mind-boggling array of considerations required resolution: How many cars could be pulled, given the space available? How many and what kind of engines could be used? How many transformers were needed? How should they be wired? Should the cars have die-cast sprung trucks (better stability) or regular plastic trucks (lighter)? Should they have fixed couplers? What cars to use? Since they were no longer ordering cars directly from Lionel, Roberts' group now had to select boxcars from Lionel's 1980 production, and this involved questions of cost, timing and availability. They needed cars in sufficient quantity and with sufficient open space for the inscription.

The group finally decided on the handsome 9420 B & O Sentinel boxcar, which, fortunately, was the first of the scheduled 1980 boxcars to be produced. When 70 cases (840) of the B & O boxcars arrived in early May from Lionel, Roberts really began to feel as though the effort was coming together.

The team also purchased a case (12) each of various other 9400- and 9700-series boxcars (9400, 9402, 9405, 9413, 9414, 9415, 9416, 9739, 9754, 9768, 9770, 9782, 9783, and 9784). All 1008 cars were then sent via Frank Brown of N.C.D. Wholesale in Pennsylvania to Seymour Knight's Pleasant Valley Process shop in Cogan Station, Pa. There each was stamped (in red in the case of the 9420, in black or white as appropriate on the other cars):

GUINNESS
World's Longest
Model Electric Train
June 29, 1980
Columbus, Ohio

Many of these cars, particularly the 9420 B & O and the 9739 Rio Grande, show up today at various train meets. There is also a standard PVP logo stamped on the underside of the frame.

As it turned out, June 29 was not the date on which the record was achieved. More on that later.

One of the most important aspects of the entire operation was to characterize the engines and power supplies that would be used. "We had decided that twin-motored diesels with Magnetraction would maximize our pulling power and minimize decoupling and derailing problems," says Roberts. "So we asked Lionel's Pete Sappenfield for a dozen new 8850 Penn Central GG-1s, and we begged, borrowed or bought 20 new Fairbanks-Morse Trainmasters — mostly Chicago & North Westerns, with a few Southern Pacifics and Virginians."

At the same time Robert Rubin of the Troller Corp. in Chicago volunteered to aid the record attempt by supplying a dozen of his Troller 2001 power packs, the same type used in the New Jersey club's record run. There were also several ZWs and KWs supplied by members of the group.

The entire roster of engines and power packs was delivered to Bob Cloud, a friend of Roberts' and an officer of the TTOS, for calibration and testing. When Cloud finished this grueling work, every engine had been rated and ranked, and every transformer had been calibrated. The team knew precisely how much force was needed to get a car rolling, how many cars each engine could pull before slipping, how much current the engines would need at full load, and the exact capabilities of the Troller power packs.

Last but certainly not least, Lionel sent approximately one-half mile of O Gauge track. Members of the troupe were assigned the task of assembling the straight track into six-foot sections, which would lessen the setup time at the mall. O72 curve pieces were cut in half so that smooth wide-radius curves could be laid out. Local dealer John Howard soldered lead wires to the track at 100 locations.

At this point all the pieces of the project were coming together and the time was fast approaching to go for the gold. The last few days were spent doing interviews for local radio, TV and newspapers, along with a smattering of national news coverage. Cloud assembled the enormous lengths of wiring and extension cords that would be needed. Howard assembled some needed spare parts. Another local dealer, Bill Lott, got together track cleaner and rags. Other friends volunteered food and drinks.

After a party at Roberts' house on Saturday evening, June 28, 1980, this mass of humanity descended on Northland Mall to begin setting up. As the stores closed at 9:30 p.m., the last shoppers drifted out with quizzical looks at the 40 train nuts unloading tons of electric train equipment. Naturally, the mall was not about to compromise its profitable hours for a bunch of crazy Lionel railroaders, so the run had been scheduled for the wee hours of the morning on June 29.

One of the most daunting tasks was removing the 1008 boxcars from their boxes, checking for damages and fully operating trucks, then securing each coupler with a rubber band to prevent inadvertent opening.

By about 2:00 a.m., the 2000-foot loop of track was laid down and the power system wired up. Before setting up the long train, Roberts hauled out his prized 773 Hudson and Madison passenger cars for the inaugural run. The power packs were fired up and the 30-year old classic blasted off down the 900-foot straightaway and around the loop. Even at that late hour, the awe and magic of Lionel struck the assembled crowd, including many non-railroaders, like a thunderbolt. A loud cheer broke out.

After another test run of 110 of the B & O cars and two FM diesels went off without a hitch, the remainder of the boxcars and engines were placed on the track and at 3:20 a.m. the World's Longest Model Electric Train was set to go.

Now, though, those gremlins which bedevil all of us from time to time descended in force on Roberts and his troupe. "OVERLOAD!" The train had moved 12 feet. "OFF THE TRACK!" "OPEN!"

Despite the planning and the enthusiasm, "it was the longest night of my life," said Roberts. "Everything went wrong. It was dark, people were tired, nothing worked. The feelings of frustration and helplessness were overwhelming."

The team made 36 attempts with various train lengths — none succeeded. The 1000-car train's best attempt was 125 feet. Their best effort was a train of 660 cars, which broke 150 feet shy of the finish line. They called it quits at 8:30 a.m., packed up and headed home.

Roberts spent the next few days depressed and hard to live with. He went over all the aspects of the planning and execution. "Some of the problems," he says, "were easily solved — all it would take was more time, money, space, people, and energy — five things we were very short on. But within a week, everyone was talking about making another try, and everyone had suggestions."

A second attempt was set for July 26, 1980, and the new venue was to be Rickenbacker Air Force base. The team had decided on several crucial changes — to make the run in daylight, outdoors, and to run it on a straight track rather than a loop. Fewer engines would be used, spaced more evenly in the consist, and the track arrangement was rewired.

The Air Force agreed to rope off a half-mile of straight blacktop road on the base, but this presented its own set of unique problems for the railroaders. While crews worked on laying the track, getting the cars ready, and wiring the power system, another job was needed that wasn't required at the mall — leveling the roadbed. This task took quite a bit of time and effort. The blacktop was chipped away in some places and shimmed in others, and one six-foot bridge had to be built over a substantial dip in the road. None of the work was easy in the heat of a July Ohio afternoon.

Roberts' group decided to start conservative and try a train of 580 boxcars initially. At 2 p.m. they were ready to begin. The first run did not go well. One of the black GG-1s had overheated in the sun. Track spots had to be leveled better. Engines that were too close were redistributed. Some cars whose couplers were opening too frequently were removed from the train.

Now down to 525 boxcars (and one 9289 C & NW caboose), the crew readied their sixth attempt of the day. The train began to move. Spotters were hunched over watching the engines and the cars around them. Transformer operators from one end would sprint down to the other end after the train passed their blocks. Each carefully watched his pack for an overload. Many minutes went by as the train inched along. There was increasing excitement in the crowd as the huge consist continued to move smoothly.

Finally, it was over. The caboose had passed the point where the lead engine had started. It was a new world's record of 526 cars!

The team was instantly engulfed in emotions — joy, pride, relief. After a round of handshaking and backslapping, everyone pressed to try again with more cars.

Backing the train up to its original position proved the most difficult job of the day! The crews started putting an extra 225 cars on the back end, along with three more engines. This time they included all the other road name boxcars as well as 580 of the B & O Sentinel boxcars.

The 10 total engines used on this attempt were also later sent to PVP and stamped with the Guinness World Record insignia.

At 4:10 p.m. the 751-car train, stretching an astounding 670 feet, was ready to go. This time there was little doubt about the outcome — the grizzled veterans had fixed all the problems and knew what to watch for.

The shout of "BREAK!" brought the participants back to earth on the first two tries — they determined that there was a loose track wire in that area, and fixed it. The third time was the charm. The crowd, bigger than the one they drew at the mall in the middle of the night, let out a huge roar as the end of the endless train finally passed the starting point marker. It went all of one foot further while the operators at the far end shut down their transformers at different times, creating the world's longest model train wreck.

But no one cared. The celebration had started. The 751-car record had thoroughly smashed the old 501-car mark.

Sunburned, exhausted, and jubilant, the team said their goodbyes and packed up, ending a 13-month odyssey.

(*Editor's note:* In the 10 years since Stew Roberts made his record length run, no one has attempted to best the mark. As of now, his Guinness record still stands, although, unhappily, it has not been printed in the book for the last few years, apparently because of a Guinness policy to restrict the size of the book by dropping old records. The 751-car record did appear in the book for several years after 1981, however.)

CHAPTER 3

DEPARTMENT STORE SPECIALS

*L*ionel's policy of making special cars, engines or accessories for department and retail stores goes back at least to 1911 when Joshua Lionel Cowen authorized a special streetcar series (in Standard Gauge) for Maryland Electrical Supply Co., who at that time was a major Baltimore Lionel distributor. The streetcars were marked with Baltimore route names. In 1913 Lionel made specially marked sets for Montgomery Ward and F.A.O. Schwarz.

This type of marketing "bargain" between Lionel and the store chain or merchant is the theme that defines all the special production pieces Lionel has made through the years. The merchant would purchase a specially marked (almost always uncatalogued) train car or set usually bearing the store's company name. The merchant would then exclusively market and sell these sets, thereby obtaining enhanced public recognition, as well as keen interest from train enthusiasts. Since these sets were almost always inexpensive "starter" sets, the merchant would get its name permanently on many layouts of young railroaders. The unique cars or engines in the sets, not otherwise available through regular Lionel dealers, would attract the interest of train enthusiasts who may not normally have purchased such "starter" sets. In some cases the set would be identical to a regular-issue set, with only one specially-made car, bearing the company logos, substituted in for a standard car. In other cases the entire set would be unique, with none of the pieces regularly available.

Given our strict definition of *Special Production* (items made for train clubs, or items redecorated/stamped outside Lionel), the department store specials described in this chapter are not Special Production, even though they are certainly "special" train items. Strictly speaking, these items were made entirely by Lionel and available to the general public through the store. Therefore, we provided the detailed listings for all pieces produced since 1970 in Volume I of this Guide. But we will discuss and compile here the groups of cars and engines produced for the various retailers, for the benefit of our specialty-collecting friends. Many such cars and sets have

fascinating stories behind them. To complete the picture, the reader is referred to the uncatalogued section of the Sets chapter in this volume.

The large majority of the department and retail store specials made by modern Lionel are of the O27 Traditional Line variety. A notable exception is the JCPenney special engine series. The inexpensive O27 pieces are the cheapest for Lionel to make (hence the least expensive for the sponsor), and tend to be run on layouts.

As mentioned before, Lionel's department and retail store special items can be broken into two general categories: 1) *special sets* in which many or all of the pieces are customized for the individual store; and 2) *single customized cars* which are substituted into an otherwise regular-production set. In both cases the (uncatalogued) set is only available through the store, but it costs the sponsor less to have a single item produced rather than a full set.

The phrase "available only through the store" refers only to their initial retail sale. Within a few weeks of their initial release, such sets are often purchased by traders who seek to resell them at a premium on the open train-collecting market, and can then be found at many train meets and train stores.

In many cases, the contract arrangements between Lionel and the store involve reciprocal rights for Lionel to market much of the rest of its line to the public — in effect, for the duration of the contract, the store would become a Lionel outlet.

Some of the special retail store items produced by modern Lionel were "one-shot" special sets. These include the Mopar Express, the Nibco Express, and the Hawthorne sets. In addition, other stores like Kay-Bee Toys, Macy's, Shoprite Foods, Ace Hardware and Ford Autolite have sponsored special cars which have not been repeated to date.

On the other hand, Lionel has strong and continuing relationships with several retail chains in the United States. These stores are Lionel's main outlets for its bread-and-butter Traditional Line sets. Four of the most important such stores are Toys 'R' Us, True Value Hardware, Sears Roebuck and JCPenney. Each has sponsored the creation of many special sets and individual cars through the years, and the specialty collector can look for quite a variety of unique, special items made by Lionel for these companies.

One important note before we go into our descriptions of the sets from individual stores: Since most of these sets are O27/Traditional Line items, Lionel, especially in the early 1970s, was not too concerned about being consistent with the contents of any particular set (except for the special car). In other words, two boxes supposedly containing the same set marketed by Sears in those years might contain *different* complements of cars or road names. For example, one can find the 9141 BN gondola where a 9140 Burlington gondola was supposed to be. Lionel often switched cars like the 9010 Great Northern hopper, the 9011 Great Northern hopper, the 9020 UP flatcar, the 9140, 9141 and 9142 Republic Steel gondolas, and several of the early SP cabooses into and out of many of these early sets. It is difficult to establish the actual contents of the O27 sets from these years. We have relied on catalogue pictures and reports from people who own the sets.

If you have a set originally purchased from Sears or JCPenney during the 1970s, and you find your set does not match the description in our Sets chapter, please do not be surprised. We encourage you to contact us and describe your set in detail.

It is important to remember that all the specials discussed in this chapter were uncatalogued items, initially marketed only through the sponsoring store or chain.

On the other hand, Lionel has also created another entire class of "billboard" cars (refrigerator cars and hoppers, mostly) which *are* shown in Lionel's regular consumer catalogue and marketed through its normal distribution network.

TOYS 'R' US

Lionel maintains a strong relationship with Toys 'R' Us, the country's major toy retailing chain. Most of Lionel's Traditional Line sets, as well as some separate-sale and Collector items, are sold at Toys 'R' Us. The toy giant has also sponsored a special Lionel set each year since 1975. This limited edition consisted of a regular-issue Traditional set in which the Standard O27 short boxcar normally found in the set was replaced by a special Toys 'R' Us boxcar. This marketing scheme set the tone for later, similar offerings from other companies.

In the late 1970s and early 1980s, Lionel placed special short boxcars from the 9000 series in a variety of sets. All featured the Toys 'R' Us mascot, Geoffrey Giraffe, in one railroad guise or another. In two cases, it issued two different cars in the same year:

1975:	*9045 short 027 boxcar*
1976:	*9047 short O27 boxcar*
1976:	*9048 short O27 boxcar*
1977:	*9049 short O27 boxcar*
1977(-78?):	*9052 short O27 boxcar*
1979(-80?):	*9365 short O27 boxcar*
1981:	*9388 short O27 boxcar*

The customized sets in which the above cars appeared were:

The Thunderball Freight (1975)
The Black River Freight (1976-1977)
The Rock Island (1976)
The Steel Hauler (1977) and
The Midnight Flyer (1979-1981)

In 1978, Toys 'R' Us also sponsored a special version of the Timberline/Logging Empire set. The customization consisted of a special decal sheet, not a Toys 'R' Us car. At that time, Lionel was heavily marketing the inexpensive Logging Empire set, which featured snap-together train cars, buildings and accessories. It emphasized "hands-on" involvement for the youngsters. JCPenney and Sears also sponsored a variation of this set.

In 1982, Toys 'R' Us sold an improved Geoffrey giraffe car from the improved 6454-style boxcar mold. The upgraded boxcar (first the 7912, later the 7914 and the 16641) featured a track-tripped bobbing giraffe figure, fully operable sliding side doors, and excellent rivet detail reminiscent of the postwar 6454 short boxcar.

Lionel and Toys 'R' Us also settled on the Heavy Iron set in which to offer their special cars. This set can still be found at Toys 'R' Us today, long after it ceased being offered in its usual form by Lionel in 1983. The following three boxcars have been offered in the Heavy Iron set since 1982:

1982-84:	*7912 6454-style operating giraffe car*
1985-89:	*7914 6454-style operating giraffe car*
1990:	*16641 6454-style operating giraffe car*

Of the 10 special Toys 'R' Us boxcars, the 7912 and 7914 are the scarcest and most expensive, although none of the cars are particularly easy to find. Operators note: all the cars except the new 16641 have only one operating coupler.

TRUE VALUE HARDWARE

Following the Toys 'R' Us precedent, Lionel began producing specialty cars for the True Value hardware chain in 1976. Hardware stores have been Lionel outlets from the beginnings of Lionel. Lionel and True Value have maintained a working relationship for over two decades, one which appears productive with the recent release of three new special cars. True Value sells many Lionel products, but since the space allocated to trains is usually less than that of the big department and toy giants, the selection is not as complete. However, some fine old and new Lionel pieces can be found in True Value hardware stores, and some locations are actually licensed Lionel Service Stations.

True Value made two boxcars in the mid-1970s, which were found in special versions of the Rock Island Line set. There was a gap in production until 1986, when a 7930 True Value O27 boxcar appeared in a special version of the Freight Flyer set.

In 1987, Lionel revitalized and improved its line, at the same time improving its True Value line. Another short O27

Uncatalogued 1595 Sears Six Unit Diesel set from 1975: includes 8563 Rock Island Alco, 9043 Erie-Lackawanna boxcar, 9075 Rock Island caboose; 9020 Union Pacific flatcar; 9136 Republic Steel gondola; and 9013 Canadian National hopper.

boxcar (16207) appeared in 1988, but then True Value opted for the upgraded 6454-style boxcar (as did Toys 'R' Us) in 1989. The 1988-1990 boxcars have appeared in special versions of the Cannonball Express set. Here is the list of the six boxcars made for True Value. Operators note: only the two latest cars have two operating couplers.

1976: *9046 short O27 boxcar*
1977: *9053 short O27 boxcar*
1986: *7930 short O27 boxcar*
1988: *16207 short O27 boxcar*
1989: *16219 6454-style short boxcar*
1990: *16224 6454-style short boxcar*

SEARS ROEBUCK

In contrast to its dealings with True Value and Toys 'R' Us, which date only from the 1970s, Lionel's relationship with Sears Roebuck goes back at least to the 1920s, and perhaps earlier. Although the nature of the relationship changed between the postwar and modern eras (Lionel produced less for Sears), the links between Lionel and Sears have always been very tight. Many believe that Sears' Lionel train sales were exceedingly important to Lionel in the late 1960s and early 1970s; Sears represented a significant outlet for Lionel's important starter sets at a time when Lionel's own marketing ability had been weakened. A quick glance at the 1970-1973 period in the Sets chapter in this Volume, particularly the uncatalogued category, will show how Sears' sales supported Lionel's income during this crucial period.

The marketing and sales of Lionel cars and sets through Sears differs from most other retail arrangements in that it is principally a catalogue, and not a shelf display, operation. Sears department stores do not generally carry ready-to-sell Lionel sets on the floor. But the legendary Sears catalogue (the famous Christmas "Wish Book") devotes a page or two each year to Lionel sets, both regular-issue and special uncatalogued versions customized in some way for Sears. (Greenberg's use of the term "uncatalogued" refers to an item's absence in a *Lionel* consumer catalogue — the sets we are discussing here are splashed all over the pages of Sears' catalogues!)

C. O'Dell Collection; B. Greenberg photogr

Uncatalogued 11770 Sears Circus set from 1989: includes 18614 4-4-2 locomotive and tender, 16520 SP-type caboose, 16327 gondola and 16110 stock ◆ Catalogue numbers not on cars.

In the postwar era, the uncatalogued Sears sets occasionally ventured into the high-priced Collector sets market. The most famous example is the now-scarce 2347 Chesapeake and Ohio GP diesel set which came out in 1965. But most Lionel sets sold by Sears were either low- or medium-priced sets. Many classic pieces of postwar Lionel equipment began as Sears specials.

In the early to mid-1970s, Lionel chose not to create many specific specialty pieces. Consequently, the uncatalogued sets offered through Sears during this period consisted mostly of inexpensive Traditional Line sets. Lionel customized them by combining regular-issue rolling stock into sets in ways different from those listed in Lionel's regular catalogue, or by issuing regular sets with some added features like operating accessories or more track. It was easier for Lionel to do this, and make up special set boxes if necessary, than to undertake the planning and tooling for customized cars or engines.

Still, some of these pieces are now hard to find because of the small quantities produced in the early 1970s. And there are a few cases (particularly small steam engines on which Lionel would print unique numbers) where the piece was only available through Sears. These items are inexpensive steam engines, not collector classics such as the 2347 C & O.

Beginning in 1985 the Lionel/Sears marketing schemes changed. Lionel currently manufactures unique, uncatalogued sets marketed exclusively through Sears' stores. It is possible that Lionel could produce more higher-quality Collector items for Sears in the future. In 1985-1986, Lionel made the 7920 boxcar which bore the Sears corporate logo, so

far the first and only car to do so. The variety of unusual items made for Sears is astounding.

CHRONOLOGICAL HIGHLIGHTS OF SEARS ROEBUCK PRODUCTION (1970-1991)

1970: Sears teams up with the new MPC/Lionel with two uncatalogued starter sets using standard rolling stock. Many of the same sets (name/number) would contain different pieces. One unique engine, the **8043 Nickel Plate 2-4-2 Columbia**, shows up in a set which is not even in Sears' catalogue, much less Lionel's.

1971 and 1972: Two more unique-to-Sears small steam engines, the **8140 Southern 2-4-0** and the **8042 Pennsylvania 2-4-2**, head two more otherwise nondescript starter sets that are again not pictured in the Sears catalogue. The 8140 engine appears again in 1973, when as many as five distinct Sears sets are sold.

1973: A unique **8308 Jersey Central** 2-4-2 locomotive in black heads the Sears special version of the Blue Streak set. It is not clear why Lionel would have used this engine rather than the usual 8303 Jersey Central in blue, except that Sears probably wanted something different — a philosophy which guides Sears' marketing today.

1975: An interesting **8563 Rock Island Alco** in red is placed at the head of several sets. This engine does not appear in any Lionel paper.

1976: For the first time in the modern era, Sears catalogues no Lionel trains.

1978: Sears offers the Logging Empire set, as do JCPenney and Toys 'R' Us. Lionel is strongly marketing this inexpensive "hands-on" set through all its retail outlets.

1979-1984: A long period in which Sears offers no Lionel sets in its catalogue, except a duplicate of the regularly catalogued Black Cave Flyer in 1982. Lionel expanded its relationships with other stores and retailers.

1985: Sears highlights a special version of the Chessie System set with a **7920 Sears Centennial** boxcar, celebrating Sears' 100th anniversary. This is the one and only Lionel car to date with the Sears corporate logo on it. The word "Centenial" on the car is spelled incorrectly — without the third "n". Thousands go out the door this way.

1986: Sears re-releases the **7920** car, this time in a Nickel Plate special set, and this time with "Centennial" spelled correctly.

1987: Sears catalogues a Pennsylvania steam engine with the regular-issue PRR O27 streamlined passenger cars, but Lionel is unable to make them in time for the Christmas holidays. Sears cancels the arrangement.

1988: An interesting version of the Iron Horse Freight set appears in the Sears "Wish Book" containing a colorful **16209 Disney Magic** boxcar, which is hard to find now.

1989: The **11770 Sears Circus set** marks the first time Lionel has made a train for Sears in which all the pieces are unique to Sears. This colorful set contains a steam engine and tender, gondola, operating boxcar and caboose, none of which have their catalogue numbers on them. Sears also catalogues a set of the regular New York Central O27 passenger cars. But the engine pulling them is not the regular-issue 18606, but instead a special **8613 New York Central 4-4-2**.

1990: The Sears "Wish Book" shows a set of the regular Northern Pacific passenger cars, pulled by an **18616 Northern Pacific 4-4-2** steam locomotive not pictured anywhere else by Lionel.

JCPENNEY

Although it did not participate as much as Sears, Dallas-based JCPenney was also an important early modern era Lionel distributor. JCPenney marketed several intriguing sets. An important difference between the two stores, both of whom market their Lionel sets through catalogues, is that JCPenney has chosen a "Collector limited-edition" approach for many sets, rather than simply marketing mixed consists of Lionel's regularly catalogued stock. This is particularly true of JCPenney's "special engine series." As such, one usually finds some unusual and unique pieces in the JCPenney sets — an engine, or car, or additional accessories such as billboards or a play "environment."

Oddly, like Sears, modern Lionel has made only one car that actually has the JCPenney corporate logo on it — the 9054 boxcar from 1977.

But it is the unique engines and cars that are of interest to us here. To be precise, with the exception of the 9054 boxcar and a 9346 Wabash caboose, JCPenney's unique production has taken the form of special uncatalogued engines, which ultimately led to the beginning of the special engine series in 1980.

CHRONOLOGICAL HIGHLIGHTS OF JCPENNEY TRADITIONAL LINE SPECIAL SETS (1971-1987)

1971: JCPenney releases an otherwise nondescript set containing the unique 8022 Santa Fe Alco twin diesels. This rare, uncatalogued engine has an unknown, large number of variations, including one very rare version made, apparently, only for the

Year	No.	Road Name	Type	Popular Name	Quantity Made
1980	8006	ACL	4-6-4 Hudson	Silver Shadow	2000
1981	8104	Union Pacific	General-style	Golden Arrow	2000
1982	8272	Pennsylvania	EP-5	Congressional Special	5000
1983	8378	Wabash	FM Trainmaster	Bluebird	5000
1984	N O P R O D U C T I O N				
1985	8587	Wabash	GP-9	None	Unknown
1986	8615	L & N	2-8-4 Berkshire	Big Emma	3000
1987	18500	Milwaukee Road	GP-9	None	Unknown
1988	N O P R O D U C T I O N				
1989	18809	Susquehanna	RS-3	Susie-Q	3000
1990	18813	DM & IR	SD-18	None	Unknown

Figure 3.1

JCPenney store in Ann Arbor, Michigan. It is certainly Lionel's most unusual Alco, and the hardest one to pinpoint.

1973 and **1974:** JCPenney sponsors two Traditional Line sets headed by the unique **8311 Southern 0-4-0** steam switcher. This engine is not very easy to find today, and its 1973 set was one of the more advanced sets in the early period (it had eight pieces).

1977: A JCPenney version of the standard-issue Cargo Master set contains the **9054 JCPenney** short boxcar — still the only car with the JCPenney logo on it.

1978: JCPenney, like Sears and Toys 'R' Us, markets a regular edition Logging Empire set, with snap-together four-wheel rolling stock and many loads and parts.

1979: JCPenney produces the Wabash Deluxe Express, whose hard-to-find caboose, a **9346 Wabash**, is one of the strangest and most mysterious of Lionel's cabooses — like a ghost, this uncatalogued piece is reported to show up on occasion in regular sets in the years to follow.

1981: JCPenney's version of the standard Thunderball Freight set contains additional billboards.

1982: JCPenney releases an intriguing set called the Overland Freight which contains some regular rolling stock and some mysterious pieces, such as the gondola and the engine. With seven pieces, this is again one of Lionel's most extensive uncatalogued sets to date.

1985 and **1986:** JCPenney sells the standard Santa Fe Midland Freight set. In 1986 the set includes additional landscaping, figures, mats and a tunnel.

1987: An unexpected four-piece set called the "Timber Master" appears in the JCPenney catalogue. The focal point is the **18600 Atlantic Coast Line 4-4-2 Columbia,** a steam locomotive unique to JCPenney. Since 1987, JCPenney has released only standard Lionel sets.

THE JCPENNEY
SPECIAL ENGINE SERIES

Interesting as the above sets are, nothing has distinguished JCPenney's uncatalogued production more than this remarkable series of engines, which began in 1980 and continues today.

In 1980, Lionel and JCPenney apparently decided to offer something more expensive than a Traditional Line starter set to appeal to a growing market segment — the adult collector. Given its larger profit margin and a practically-guaranteed consumer audience, a "limited edition" top-of-the-line engine was a logical choice. JCPenney pursued this tactic with a vengeance.

Other than items made for the train clubs, these remarkable engines are (with a very few possible exceptions) the only collector-level uncatalogued pieces Lionel has made in the modern era.

The series started strong in 1980 with the attractive 8006 Atlantic Coast Line small Hudson, known as the Silver Shadow. Collectors immediately took notice and flocked to buy the new engine. Since then, each year's release has been eagerly awaited. Nine engines have been made through 1990 (none was offered in 1984 or 1988). Each was made in very limited quantities (usually less than 3000), and came with an acrylic display case and mount board. Three engines, the 1980 Silver Shadow, the 1983 Wabash "Bluebird" FM Trainmaster,

and the 1986 Lackawanna "Big Emma" steam locomotive have become collector classics and are difficult to find. Only the 1987 offering, a Milwaukee Road GP-9 which was also regularly catalogued, failed to elicit strong collector interest.

See *Figure 3.1* for the tabulation of this engine series. The reader will find the detailed listings for these engines in the motive power chapters of Volume I.

OTHER UNCATALOGUED
LIONEL DEPARTMENT AND
RETAIL STORE PRODUCTION

American Express

Lionel produced two uncatalogued sets for American Express: **1562 Fast Freight Flyer** in 1985, about which we know very little, and a **1608 General** set in 1986 with several interesting pieces. This resembled the James Gang set of 1980 and is one of Lionel's more desirable uncatalogued sets. Both sets were apparently marketed through flyers distributed by American Express Travel-Related Services. AmEx also offered a special edition of the **8210 Joshua Lionel Cowen** 4-6-4 small Hudson steam engine in 1982, which came with a display case. This engine is moderately scarce now.

Montgomery Ward

In the last 20 years, Lionel has marketed comparatively little through Montgomery Ward. In 1982 the store sold two regular-issue Lionel engines — the **8154 Alaska NW-2** switcher and the **8859 Conrail E-33** electric in collector-style display cases. In addition, in 1983 Montgomery Ward marketed one of the high-end Lionel sets, the Cross-Country Express, with an add-on landscaping kit. In other cases, Lionel marketed several standard-issue Traditional Line sets through Montgomery Ward.

Lionel Kiddie City (Lionel Leisure)

Many people are not aware that the old Lionel Corporation, which made the trains until 1969, still exists. It is in the toy retail field and owns a string of toy supermarkets called Lionel Kiddie City. Interestingly, these are the major competitors for Toys 'R' Us. Until 1990, when Richard Kughn bought the rights to the Lionel name, he paid a fee to the old Lionel Corporation for the privilege of using the Lionel name on its products. Fundimensions and Lionel Trains, Inc. have made many sets and special cars for Toys 'R' Us, but have made only a few special cars and sets for their former parent — Lionel Kiddie City. This was an inexpensive Steel Hauler set from 1977 containing the **9034 Lionel Leisure** short hopper. Another was the 1157 Wabash Cannonball from 1981. We know little of this set other than it included regular-issue rolling stock. Another little-known set was made in 1987 — the Lionel Lines Express.

Kmart

The large East Coast-based discount retail store offered a little **8507 2-4-0 Porter** engine in a 1975 set. Thereafter, Kmart catalogued nothing except regular-issue Lionel sets until 198

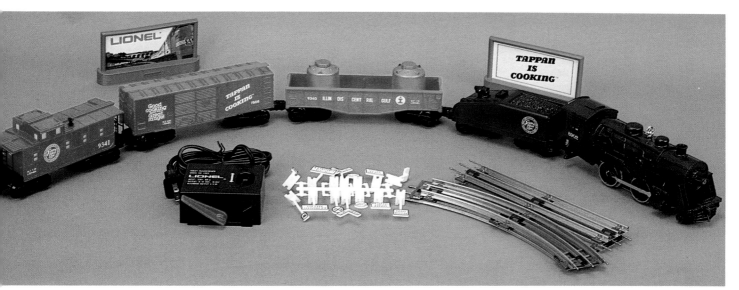

atalogued 1265 Tappan set from 1982: includes 8902 Atlantic Coast Line 2-4-0 locomotive and tender, 7908 Tappan boxcar, 9341 ACL caboose and 9340
G gondola.

when an odd **11771** set called the **Microracer** popped up, featuring a 2-4-0 steamer, tank car, SP caboose and a strange barrel ramp car with four Microracer cars and a canister. This is certainly one of Lionel's more interesting uncatalogued sets.

Tappan and Town House

These two sets, the **1265 Tappan** from 1982 and the **1658 Town House** from 1986, were sponsored by the Town House home appliances store near Chicago. They both used the ubiquitous 8902 Atlantic Coast Line 2-4-0 small steamer and matching 9341 SP caboose. The first set featured a **7908 Tappan short boxcar**, which the manager of Town House had convinced the Tappan Range Company into sponsoring; for the second set, Town House sponsored its own car — the **7931 Town House** boxcar. Mike Moore, proprietor of Town House, had tried to persuade other companies to sponsor sets from Lionel. The most notable case occurred in 1978, when the Frigidaire Company agreed to the idea. Lionel went so far as to create a prototype Frigidaire, short, white boxcar with blue lettering, to be included in a special set similar to the Trains 'N Truckin' sets from that year. But, because of a dispute over the decorating techniques, Frigidaire canceled the order. Unfortunately, a thief absconded with the prototype boxcar from Frigidaire's offices, a circumstance which did not sit well with Fundimensions. Since that time Lionel has insisted, in no uncertain terms, on the return of all its prototype pieces.

Anheuser-Busch

Lionel produced an unusual set in 1989 featuring a small steam engine, a billboard refrigerator car and an SP caboose, all of which were unnumbered specials lettered for Anheuser-Busch and Budweiser. This was the **11775 Anheuser-Busch** set designed to appeal to the adult train collectors and only available through the Anheuser-Busch catalogue. A follow-up uncatalogued **16225 Budweiser beer** vat carrier was released in 1990, also available only through the Anheuser-Busch gift catalogues. There may be more types of rolling stock in the future. The refrigerator car in the set (Lionel's catalogue number 16223) and the vat car were remakes, with slightly different graphics, of the 9850 Budweiser refrigerator car from 1973 and the 9193 Budweiser vat carrier in 1983, respectively, both of which were shown in Lionel's catalogues.

PACE

The newest trend in Lionel's marketing schemes seems to be its production of special sets for stores like PACE, a members-only discount warehousing outlet. Lionel made sets for PACE in 1989 (**11776**) and 1990 (**11784**), consisting of a regular Iron Horse set packaged with an additional "shoebox" containing extra track, switches and other layout accessories.

Costco

Costco, a West Coast competitor of PACE, joined forces with Lionel in 1990 and subsequently sold the **11785 Union Pacific Express** set. This contained unique rolling stock, none of which are shown in the Lionel catalogue. The set had a steam locomotive, boxcar, gondola, hopper and caboose — all lettered for the Union Pacific — as well as some desirable accessories.

7931 Town House boxcar from 1986 uncatalogued Town House set 1658.

Uncatalogued 11756 Lionel Freight Flyer set from 1988
Top shelf: **8902 ACL engine and tender.**
Bottom shelf: **16211 Hawthorne boxcar; 9341 Atlantic Coast Line caboose.**

R. LaVoie and M. Salnik Collections; B. Greenberg photograph

THE "ONE-SHOT" SPECIALS

Macy's

Despite the long and hospitable relationship between the old Lionel Corporation and Macy's department store in the pre-World War II era, modern Lionel has had little interaction with the New York-based department store. The only special set to appear on the market was the **11772 Freight Flyer** in 1989, which included a special **16221 Macy's** short boxcar with no number on it.

Kay-Bee Toys

In addition to marketing regular Lionel sets, Kay-Bee Toys invited Lionel to make a special version of the Freight Flyer set in 1986, which included a white **7932 Kay-Bee** short boxcar. Apparently these did not spark particular collector interest; no other Kay-Bee specials have appeared.

Ace Hardware

A special version of the Cannonball set for this hardware chain (a competitor of True Value) appeared in 1989. It featured a white **16220 Ace Hardware** short boxcar. So far this has been the first and only Ace Hardware special car and set.

Shoprite Foods

The special set made in 1988 for this North Jersey-based food store was an unusual first for Lionel. The set, an otherwise nondescript Freight Flyer set with the **16213 Shoprite** short boxcar in yellow, was the first one made by modern Lionel for a food store chain.

Hawthorne Home Appliances

Hawthorne Home Appliances sold the inexpensive **11756 Lionel Freight Flyer** set in 1987 with the rather scarce **16204 Hawthorne** short boxcar. The set was re-released in 1988 (same number) but this time with the similar **16211 Hawthorne** car.

Nibco

Lionel produced this higher-than-usual quality set **1264** for Nibco Plumbing Products in 1982. This interesting set consisted of the **8182 Nibco NW-2** switcher (one of the few special sets not headed by a steam engine), a standard boxcar and gondola, and the exclusive **6482 Nibco** SP caboose. A now-rare **7520 Nibco** Classic-type boxcar was offered separately later in the year.

Chrysler-Mopar

One of the most intriguing uncatalogued sets made in the modern era is set **11757**, made as a promotion for Chrysler Motors Genuine Parts (MOPAR) in 1987 and 1988. This scarce set was one of the few uncatalogued ones in the modern era to approach collector level. The pieces in it were available exclusively through the Chrysler-Mopar announcements, and included a desirable **Mopar Express** steam engine, boxcar, TOFC flatcar, gondola and caboose. In 1988, Lionel added a three-dome tank car. We have had reports of a 1989 Chrysler-Mopar version of the Amtrak Silver Spike set, in which the Alco engines have added "MOPAR EXPRESS" lettering. Although Chrysler published a flyer advertising the set, we are not sure if it was made and distributed, or if only normal Silver Spike sets were used. Further reader comments requested.

Ford

In 1971, Ford Motor Co. sponsored a special uncatalogued version of the Allegheny set which included the **9042 Autolite** short boxcar and several billboards, as well as a Ford Motorcraft Tuneup kit. Although the car was not catalogued in 1971, it did appear for separate-sale the next year. Since then, the policy regarding such corporate special cars has changed. No unique cars which appear in uncatalogued special sets for corporate customers are to appear in the Lionel catalogue. In other words, the sponsor is exclusively responsible for their advertising. Lionel has not repeated any special items for Ford since then.

Other companies have arranged with Lionel to supply standard sets for their stores as promotionals, such as McDonald's (1987) and United Model (1988).

M<small>ODERN</small> E<small>RA</small> L<small>IONEL</small> S<small>ETS</small>

◆ C H A P T E R 4 ◆

*L*ionel has produced more than 280 sets between 1970 and 1991. About two-thirds of these sets were illustrated and described in Lionel's consumer catalogues or its collector flyers and brochures. These we refer to as Lionel *Catalogued Sets*, and include *Canadian* and *separate-sale* sets. The remainder are called *Uncatalogued Sets*, and include most *Service Station* sets.

This chapter includes all known Lionel sets — catalogued and uncatalogued — arranged by year. We have dropped the prefix "6" which was used since 1971 by Fundimensions and its successors. Set values require more descriptive definitions than separate rolling stock and engines: **Mint** means untouched, original sets sealed in the box; **Excellent** applies to sets found with all the original components, but with obvious evidence of use. The rolling stock in sets termed **EXC** must be in at least excellent condition, the original box(es) must be present, and all parts, accessories and instruction sheets must be included.

The following letter(s) are shown at the end of each set description which describe its type and level:

T = Traditional Line Set*

C = Collector Line Set*

D = Department Store or Retail Special Set (always uncatalogued)

SSS = Service Station Set (usually uncatalogued)

CA = Canadian Distribution (set number has "T-" prefix)

SE = Separate-sale Set (no set box; no set number)

---

*Note: Lionel did not use the terms "Collector" or "Traditional" before 1979-1980; but because they are generally known descriptors of the level and quality of any given set, we have applied these terms to all the post-1970 listings to give the reader a feel for the nature of the set.

* *Asterisk found in listings indicates that the information within that listing was derived from Lionel catalogue only.*

C<small>ATALOGUED</small> S<small>ETS</small>

Just what are the criteria for a catalogued set? With the advent of the Service Station Special sets and the separate-sale sets, this is not an easy question to answer. The three requirements for determining whether a set is considered *catalogued* are: 1) The set had to appear in Lionel's consumer catalogue or collector brochures and could not have been categorized as a Service Station or separate-sale set; 2) the set must have been marketed as a complete set, regardless of what dealers have done with it since it came from the factory; and 3) the set must have included a set box when shipped from the factory. Catalogued sets which do not meet this third point are called "separate-sale" sets.

Lionel's catalogue record is moderately accurate. However, since each year's catalogue was prepared considerably before the sets' actual production, some production changes were made that are not reflected in the catalogue. In some cases, entire sets were catalogued but never made. This report is based on the catalogue record; when deviations are known we have reported the actual set components. If you note differences in your set(s) from those listed in this chapter, please write to us and describe the differences. For the uncatalogued sets we use the department store descriptions as a reference, as well as reports from our readers on actual set contents.

Canadian Sets: The Parker Brothers Connection

By Glenn Halverson

When you are a new company just putting your wares out for sale, it is only natural for you to ask where your markets may be. It is even more true that if you have taken over a struggling concern, you seek to expand your horizons a

Two scarce Type I Parker Brothers boxes. Sides and ends have Parker Brothers logo, front panel has small window without cellophane. These boxes are marked in pen rather than with labels, when they are marked at all. Often, the number will be preceded by a "T", the Canadian prefix for Lionel special production. Example: 9703 boxcar can be found in a box marked "T9703".

bit. That is just what the new makers of Lionel Trains — Fundimensions — tried to do as it began its struggle to rebuild a market fallen into stagnation. Lionel Corporation's lack of a firm marketing policy had resulted in poor decisions, which ultimately led to its demise as a manufacturer of toy trains.

Fundimensions had the advantage of the many resources offered by its parent company, General Mills, which has contacts and divisions all over the world. One place considered likely for Fundimensions marketing was Canada; and the Parker Brothers toy firm seemed a natural outlet for the new line of trains in that country. According to Dan Johns of Lionel, Parker Brothers never produced anything itself. All the trains, even the cars marketed only in Canada, were made in Mount Clemens, Michigan.

According to Fran Mauti, the Director of Customer Relations at Parker Brothers in Canada, the firm distributed Fundimensions trains between 1970 and 1974. Fundimensions train products were packaged in bilingual boxes, French and English, because the trains were intended only for the Canadian market. These trains were not featured in the regular Parker Brothers toy catalogues. Rather, Parker Brothers imported catalogues from the United States and listed the Fundimensions trains on its own price sheets for dealers.

Most of the trains marketed by Parker Brothers were identical to contemporary Fundimensions American products, but a few items were not — and that is where the special interest in the Canadian distribution lies. Some of these trains, such as the 8031 Canadian National GP-7 with large metal or all-plastic railings, the maroon 9143 Canadian National gondola, the maroon version of the 9063 GT caboose and

the tuscan 9065 CN caboose, were never marketed in th United States and are thus hard to find here. Most of th Parker Brothers efforts were aimed at large department stor accounts, such as Simpson-Sears, Ltd., the Canadian sub sidiary of Sears, Roebuck & Company.

The trains distributed by Parker Brothers in Canada fo separate-sale come in boxes which are similar to the regula Fundimensions Type I boxes. However, as a rule, the cel lophane window in these boxes is much smaller, th "whirlpool" Parker Brothers logo is present, and the boxes ar bilingual. When compared to Fundimensions' prosperity i the United States, the Canadian venture was not nearly a successful. The marketing efforts were not aggressive, so fe sets and individual items were distributed in Canada. As result, these trains are now difficult to find.

In 1971, Fundimensions put out a special train catalogu for the Parker Brothers distribution. This catalogue came i two forms: a regular 8-1/2" x 11" version somewhat similar t the American catalogue; and a smaller-sized catalogue, whic represents real production more accurately. The Canadia sets and individual cars are preceded in number by a "T" prefi instead of the universally ignored "6" prefix Fundimension used for its American distribution.

We have listed the Canadian sets by set number an name. Reader comments, corrections and/or additions ar requested. Most of the individual rolling stock and accessor pieces found in the American catalogue were also sold a separate-sale items in Canadian Parker Brothers-marke boxes. Clearly, the original box adds quite a bit of value to th car.

Separate-Sale Sets

The above heading may sound like a contradiction, but it really represents a marketing strategy first used in 1974 with the advent of the Spirit of '76 set and its matching special boxcars. Lionel's catalogues carried the legend, "All items sold separately, not as a set." Perhaps they were meant for separate-sale, but in fact these matching items were sold as sets by dealers. The separate-sale device freed Lionel from producing the exact numbers for each item, and from a need to produce a box for each set. For example, in both the Southern Crescent and Blue Comet sets, many more sets of cars were made than engines. In addition, the separate-sale ploy made it possible for Lionel to add other cars to the sets later, as indeed it did, especially with the extruded-aluminum passenger cars. Incredibly, 10 years passed between the introduction of the Southern Crescent and Blue Comet sets and the introduction of dining cars for them!

What are the criteria for separate-sale sets? 1) They must constitute a legitimate set, no matter in what order the items were produced. That means a locomotive, cars, and (for freights) a caboose; 2) they must have been marketed as separate-sale items. That leaves out such boxed sets as the Royal Limited, even though extra cars were issued separately later for that set. The definition of a separate-sale set is one without a "set" box — each item is individually boxed; and 3) they must be perceived by both collector and dealer as separate-sale items which combine into sets. That is why the Lionel Lines items constitute a separate-sale set, but the beer refrigerator cars, for example, do not. It is also why any one of the countless "road name" sets (such as Santa Fe cars or Wabash cars) and/or "type" collections of cars (such as all short gondolas or all three-dome tank cars) do not count as separate-sale sets. Collectors and dealers just do not think of those items as sets, and they are seldom found for sale together. However, the Lionel Lines items, at least partially, are often found together for sale. The "mint set," although not initially perceived as a separate-sale set, is now considered one (and the pieces are often found together now) because Lionel released an engine and caboose designed specially for it.

Since Lionel first introduced the separate-sale strategy in 1974, it has moved more aggressively each year into this type of marketing. In most cases thus far (with the possible exception of the Favorite Food Freight and the recent O27 passenger sets) these sets are considered exclusively Collector-level, and most are also limited editions. Each remains in demand today, and many are quite scarce. In fact, many are nothing less than the top sets modern Lionel has made.

This is not to say all Collector sets are separate-sale. Lionel still produces boxed Collector sets (which therefore have numbers), which most often do not include track or transformer, as most lower-priced Traditional sets do. And many of the components of the boxed Collector sets are in demand as well. But it seems Lionel has reserved the best sets that it makes for separate-sale sets. This gives the company maximum marketing freedom.

The listings in this chapter show sets which were meant for separate-sale but have matching components and, in many cases, additions in later years. The sets are listed by year with the locomotive and/or original components first. Later additions are then listed along with the year of their issuance. In practice, many dealers sell these matching components as sets, no matter what Lionel may have said or is saying. We have also indicated where these matching components are described in the literature. By definition, separate-sale sets are not boxed, and have no standard Lionel set numbers.

Uncatalogued Sets

By Michael A. Solly, with the assistance of
Paul Ambrose, Al Weaver and Louis A. Bohn

Uncatalogued sets comprise a category which is growing in importance to the collector. These are sets which are made for a wide variety of American businesses. The defining feature is that none have appeared in Lionel's regular consumer catalogue. For the most part, they consist of sets which were made by Lionel for a particular store or chain, such as Sears, JCPenney, and Toys 'R' Us. The manufacture of special sets for specific department store retailers is a long-standing tradition with Lionel, going back at least to 1911 and continuing today.

The list of uncatalogued sets is expected to grow in future editions of this Greenberg Guide. Much information is still to be learned and more sets continue to be discovered, but the picture becomes clearer with each report from our readers. Curiously, the Lionel uncatalogued sets we report seem to gravitate mostly towards the very low end of the price scale. Some of these sets can only be considered as cheap loss-leaders. There are a few important exceptions in which uncatalogued sets or pieces are at the "collector" level. In the last five years, Lionel seems to be placing more emphasis on special promotional sets and individual uncatalogued special cars than it did in the 16 years before. The variety is becoming greater with time, and Lionel is increasing the quantity of uncatalogued items it makes each year.

For the uncatalogued sets, Greenberg uses the following guidelines: 1) The set must never have appeared in a Lionel catalogue; 2) the set must have been marketed as a full set and include a set box; and 3) the set must not fit into the Service Station or separate-sale categories. (Service Station sets are for the most part uncatalogued, but they are a special type of set which we will discuss separately.)

These sets have been marketed to an astonishing array of American businesses, from American Express to Montgomery Ward. Lionel has also made them for special promotions, such as the Mopar, Hawthorne, Ford and Nibco Plumbing sets.

Each set has a set number, the name (if any) and the retail outlet for which the set was produced. Although our listing is extensive, it is not complete and we look forward to reader reports on sets not listed here. As far as we know, every set has an official Lionel number, but some of these sets also have catalogue numbers particular to the company selling them, such as Sears catalogue numbers, and we are missing the Lionel set numbers. We ask for reader assistance in this area as well. In quite a few cases, Lionel placed a special car in a regular set, so that the set box still carries the regular catalogue number. But Lionel itself assigned a different internal number to it! Where known, this book lists the set under the latter number to avoid confusion.

The reader will find the early modern era listings (1970 through 1975) quite confusing, because Lionel would place cars or engines in the sets based on what it had available in stock, not necessarily on how it was pictured or listed or marketed. Even today, Lionel Trains, Inc. prints a disclaimer on its very-low-end set boxes claiming that "colors or contents of sets may vary." Nonetheless, such set juggling was at its bewildering height in the early 1970s. Deciphering the actual contents of these inexpensive sets can be quite aggravating. We therefore enlist the aid of our readers to help in defining variations in our listed set contents wherever possible.

One final note: Lionel has also made many uncatalogued individual *pieces* (not sets) over the years. Examples include the special engine series made for JCPenney (see our tabulation of these fine engines in the Department Store Specials chapter and in the detailed listings in Volume I), and other specific cars like the Artrain tank car and the Tennessee World's Fair boxcar. These are not included here in the Sets chapter (some are mentioned in the Department Store Specials chapter) but all are described in full in Volume I.

The following uncatalogued sets are listed by their Lionel-assigned set numbers or their department store catalogue numbers. If you can clarify one of these uncatalogued sets for us, be sure to let us know the set number, the date and all the contents — even the lubricant, wires and instruction leaflets. Photographs of the set boxes are an immense help.

Service Station Sets

By John Kouba, with the assistance of Emil C. Vatter, Emil C. Vatter, Jr., C. Charles Lang and Michael A. Solly

From 1971 to 1978, Lionel issued a yearly Service Station set. The purpose of this set was to give authorized Service Stations a special set to be marketed only through their stores. With the advent of uncatalogued Collector sets in 1979, the practice was discontinued through 1985. It is possible that Fundimensions felt dealers were splitting up the sets, and the larger dealers, who were not necessarily authorized Service Stations, were cornering the market on the sets.

Both the 1971 and the 1972 sets have elicited controversy because their existence has been questioned. In fact, Service Station sets were made in both years. All the items from these two sets were subsequently available on the open market, which has created the difficulty.

Most collectors agree the 1973 Canadian Pacific set is the most prized, followed by the 1974 Rio Grande set and the 1977 Budd set.

The reader will notice many cars were catalogued separately in later years. Quite often there are differences between set cars and those available separately. Some interesting observations on Service Station sets:

(a) Some cars were sold separately but never catalogued such as the gray 9113 Norfolk & Western hopper, 9626 Erie Lackawanna boxcar, and 9138 Sunoco tank car. Since none of these are hard to find, Lionel must have produced them in large quantities. An alternative conclusion is that many of the original Service Station sets were in fact broken up for the individual cars.

(b) Some cars, though catalogued the next year, are hard to find. Examples include the 9723 Western Pacific boxcar, the 9724 Missouri Pacific boxcar (both from the 1973 set), and the 9166 Rio Grande caboose. Perhaps Lionel never ran them again, and those available come from broken sets. The production run for the separate-sale may also have been short.

(c) The 1972 set is the only one with a steam engine, the 8206, which was catalogued and available for four more years. The 1971 and 1972 sets are the only ones which came with track.

(d) The 1976 set comes with a green and yellow caboose which is true to the prototype. However, it does not match the engine. So, in response to collector demand, Fundimensions later introduced a black and gold caboose to match the locomotive. (This problem occurred again two years later, when the blue and yellow Santa Fe SD-18 locomotive was issued with a red and black 9274 ATSF caboose. Collector demand forced Fundimensions to issue a blue and yellow 9317 ATSF caboose. Thus, the 9274 is a scarce item.)

(e) There is no documentation of the Service Station sets made from 1971 to 1976, other than in bulletins distributed to the Service Stations themselves. In 1977 Lionel printed a flyer announcing the Budd Car set. In 1978 and for the sets for 1986 and beyond, Lionel has similarly announced its Service Station set in a special flyer. The 1991 set was shown in the consumer catalogue for the first time.

1986-1991 SERVICE STATION SETS

Since the 1986 takeover of Lionel by Richard Kughn, most significant change has occurred with the total revamping of the Service Station sets. Revived immediately by the new management, this series of uncatalogued sets is anything but warmed-over production that only the most ardent of collectors would ever bother to pursue.

Gone are the days when collectors would purchase a Service Station set, only to see Lionel reissue the same cars (and sometimes the engines) in the next year's catalogue with the same numbers and color schemes! As a result, collectors were offered little incentive to pursue one of these "uncatalogued" sets of trains. There were distribution and retail problems as well. In fact, by 1978, the concept had been abandoned because the larger Lionel dealers had been acquiring these sets and breaking them up for individual sale.

However, with the introduction of the 1632 Santa Fe Work Train by Lionel Trains, Inc. in 1986, collectors of Service Stations sets have seen renewed opportunity and significant improvements. These apply not only to the set's makeup, but to the construction and introduction of new products as well. Since then, Lionel has endeavored to introduce new features on many of the subsequent years' sets. Although many of the sets have found their way into the hands of other dealers or have been broken up for separate-sale — as they were before 1978 — the recent sets seem to remain intact more than they are separated. The usual non-Service Station dealer's practice is now to keep as many of the sets intact as possible and insist that the sets be sold intact. In that way, the dealer —

Uncatalogued 1971 Service Station Special set 1187, using generic set box.

B. Greenberg photograph

Service Station and non-Service Station alike — can dispose of the less desirable cars in the set as well as the "good" ones. Fortunately for collectors, the sets issued so far are excellent and desirable items.

The following is a discussion of each Service Station set released by Lionel Trains, Inc. since 1986.

THE 1986 SANTA FE WORK TRAIN SET

The Santa Fe Work Train, released in late November 1986, is based upon the highly successful catalogued New York Central Yard Chief set of 1985. A much more highly developed set, it comes in a rather plain white carton, as did the Yard Chief. That is where the resemblance ends. It is evident from the first examination of the Santa Fe set that Lionel Trains, Inc. wants to make a favorable impression upon collectors.

Lionel has chosen this set to introduce a colorful version of its new **tool car**, first seen in the B & O Freight set in 1986. Finished in red oxide (or tuscan) with yellow lettering, the tool car from the Santa Fe set boasts some interesting design changes from its predecessor, the bunk car (a version of which is also in the Santa Fe set). Lionel's die makers have changed

the side window scheme and added two door inserts, one in each end panel.

Lionel has heavily modified the sides of the bunk car with several major die changes: it has eliminated the holes for the clear marker lights used on bunk cars; the bunk car's four square windows are replaced by two eight-pane rectangular windows with sills; the ladder pattern is altered, leaving only rungs; gone also are the two reporting boards on the bunk car next to the left side of the door. Finally, Lionel has designed a new two-pane door with a small bottom step and long vertical grab-bars on either side of the door frame. Unlike the bunk car door, which is a solid piece, illuminated versions of the tool car door have frosted window inserts for illumination. In addition, frosted window inserts replace the clear ones of the bunk cars. All these changes make the tool car look distinctively different from its predecessor, though the roof and bottom pieces remain the same. The Santa Fe tool car still has a hole for the smokestack, and this piece and the brakewheel are packed separately to prevent breakage. On the new 19651 Santa Fe illuminated tool car, the smokestack hole is eliminated from the roof.

The finishing touch on the tool car — indeed, on all the cars — is the use of Standard O die-cast sprung trucks. The Standard O trucks cannot at this time be adapted to take pickups for light rollers, so their use negates any interior illumination, and the tool and bunk cars remain dark in this set. Prototypes for the bunk cars have been photographed in the mid-1960s on the Pennsylvania-Reading Seashore Lines; they resemble Lionel's model quite a bit. The tool car is certainly a fitting, handsome addition to one's maintenance train roster.

Another first in this Santa Fe set is the 6496 **work caboose** with Standard O trucks. The crane car, too, has the Standard O trucks. Most of Lionel's recent crane cars use the die-cast six-wheel passenger trucks; the Standard O trucks on this crane pose a problem because they couple too closely with other cars. Lionel should have provided a longer coupler shank for these trucks so that the couplers would extend further away from the body. Still, they do add a touch of class to an otherwise standard-fare car. The same is true of the otherwise bland caboose.

Another interesting quirk regarding the consist is that the 6272 **long gondola** is shown in Lionel's flyer carrying two black empty cable reels. These are packed separately in the set box. Inside the box containing the car, however, are three gray canisters identical to previous loads issued with other Lionel gondolas of the Fundimensions years. Apparently Lionel found that it had a large supply of these canisters in inventory and decided at the last minute to include these with the car as well. The box description for the car makes no mention of either load.

The 0-4-0 **steam switcher** engine included with the Santa Fe set is the second edition of the Lionel steam switchers with working smoke units and backup lights in the tenders. Unhappily, after making major improvements to the engine and the cars, Lionel ironically put the less expensive Symington-Wayne plastic trucks on the tender! There may be some physical explanation for this. First, steam engine tenders with metal trucks have always been equipped with six-wheel die-cast passenger trucks, which are far too large for this tender. The Standard O truck has never been modified into a version without the coupler. Secondly, the tender has a plastic bottom piece which may not be compatible with the screw-mounted Standard O trucks. Collectors might try to purchase Standard O trucks and mount them to the tender on this set, but some further modification may be necessary. Probably, shim washers will be necessary both inside and outside of the tender frame. The tender may also ride too high on Standard O trucks for the drawbar from the engine, and some way will have to be found to attach a drawbar to the front truck of the tender while eliminating the coupler. All these changes may have been too costly for Lionel to contemplate at this point.

The engine itself, however, is a work of art. Lionel obviously has taken great pains to ensure it is the best-looking as well as the best running steam switcher produced thus far. Upon first inspection, one notices that considerable hand work into smoothing off the casting seams from the die-cast boiler shell. The casting detail, rivets, etc. seem to be sharper than on previous models, giving the impression that the dies for this engine have been retooled. This attention to detail, combined with a first-class paint job, result in one of Lionel's finest steam switchers ever.

Another new feature listed in the brochure is a new type of **smoke unit**. This unit solves a problem which has plagued the smoke units ever since Lionel's first use of the modern fast-angle wheels for the rolling stock. By making the rolling stock easier to pull, Lionel has created a new problem for its smoke units. The effort required to pull the cars of a modern era train is far less than in the postwar era, and this results in the train operating at lower voltage, especially with the quieter and efficient can motors used in the modern switchers. Generally, Lionel's newer engines can pull three times the number of new cars at far less voltage than required by the older postwar cars. Apparently the Lionel engineers have overlooked the fact that the smoke units require a higher operating voltage than do the motors — hence, far less smoke is produced in modern era engines. One cure for this problem is for the operator to add several postwar cars with old-style wheels to the train consist to put more drag on the engine. The engine then needs a higher voltage which will, in turn, produce more smoke. This is hardly the ideal solution! The locomotive motors of modern era engines are good, but over extended periods of operation at high voltage serious motor problems are likely to develop.

The smoke problem seems to be solved by the new smoke units used in the 8516 New York Central switcher and the new Santa Fe locomotive. Lionel's engineers have lowered the smoke unit resistance in these engines. With as little as eight volts, these engines will send up volcanic, impressive puffs of smoke from their stacks. Of course, the operator will have to refill the smoke units with liquid smoke fluid more frequently, but that is a small price to pay for the agreeable smoking effect produced. Be careful not to overload the engine's pulling capacity; too much voltage could burn out the smoke unit. In addition, many operators caution against refilling the smoke unit when it is very hot, for the same reason. A load limit of 14 volts seems reasonable and safe for these switcher engines.

Nit-picking aside, the 1632 Santa Fe Service Station Special is a class act. The set has an excellent looking and operating engine with a vastly improved smoke unit, a new tool car, and Standard O trucks on the rolling stock. These features explain the set's enthusiastic reception by collectors and operators alike. It is no wonder that the set sold out quickly and has been in demand ever since.

THE 1987 SOUTHERN FREIGHT RUNNER SET

In 1987 the Southern Freight Runner made its debut with several original features: A GP-9 issued in the Southern's green color scheme; a coal dump car with Standard O trucks; and die-cast leaf-spring trucks on the N5C caboose.

With the set's operating **coal dump car**, Lionel has entered into a new era with operating cars fitted with the better-quality **Standard O trucks**. Like the crane car in the 1986 Service Station set, these trucks add a previously missing classiness to the rolling stock. In addition to the realism comes some much-needed weight and a lower center of gravity, necessary to improve riding traction and stability. With the Southern **N5C caboose**, Lionel has reintroduced a feature not seen since the glory days of the postwar period — the return of the die-cast leaf-spring trucks, complete with die-cast

G. Simbolt Collection; B. Greenberg photograph

ox cover and inside contents of uncatalogued 1972 Service Station Special set 1250, includes Type I and Type II boxes on rolling stock, and plain white boxes on others. Verified as original packaging.

couplers, roller assembly and plunger plates. While the leaf-spring trucks were used on other cabooses previously, they are all high-end models like the extended vision and wood-sided models. This is the first time they have appeared on the N5Cs. Although it has not received as much attention as its 1986 predecessor, the Southern Freight Runner set, as a whole, has been well received and sells well. It is now sought after by collectors interested in adding a high-quality set to their assortment.

THE 1988 VIRGINIA & TRUCKEE "DRY GULCH LINE" SET

The Virginia & Truckee "Dry Gulch Line" for 1988 is a resurrection of the General locomotive and passenger cars. Although the General is a popular Traditional Line engine, the Virginia & Truckee set holds no new surprises for the collector. Perhaps Lionel was biding its time for the 1989 set, which includes some truly eye-catching firsts.

For this set, Lionel has reissued the **General locomotive** with the new motor and electronic E-unit assembly that first appeared in the 1986 uncatalogued American Express General set. Lionel's plan may have been to phase-in train design improvements through its uncatalogued offerings (like the Service Station sets), and department store and credit card specials.

The Virginia & Truckee General sports smoke and an operating headlight. The vertically mounted DC motor, used in conjunction with the new micro-sized E-unit, produces a quiet and smooth-running model that glides effortlessly down the track. The use of a rubber tire, in lieu of Magnetraction, affords it positive traction as it moves over crossovers and turnouts. The simple black and gold paint scheme lends an elegant, if somewhat somber, air to the engine and tender.

The two **passenger cars** and the **baggage car** are painted in the Virginia & Truckee color scheme of the late 1800s. The striping and lettering represents some of Lionel's finest, and the metal truss rods add a fine, authentic touch. Like all the previous 1800-era passenger cars produced by Lionel, these are lighted.

For the beginning collector, the Virginia & Truckee represents some of Lionel's best creative work, offering high quality at a very reasonable price, as well as limited-edition Service Station status.

THE 1989 DESERT KING SET

If the Virginia & Truckee set of 1988 offers no new surprises, the 1989 Desert King is nothing but surprises — and all of them good ones! Every piece in it tells a story.

Reading the description on the plain white box or the preorder advertising sheet offers no clues as to what is contained inside. However, when one opens the set and examines its contents, it becomes readily apparent that Lionel has elevated the quality of its Service Station sets to a new high. Lionel considers this a Traditional Line set (as it does with all of them except the first two sets in 1971 and 1972), but these pieces are all certainly Collector-level. Let's take a look at each piece and see what it offers:

The **18608 Rio Grande engine and tender** mark the return of the 2025/675 steam locomotives not seen since 1952 production.

During the Korean War in 1952, these engines were made without the popular Magnetraction feature. So it is, too, with the Rio Grande. In lieu of Magnetraction, the engine employs a traction tire on one of its rear drive wheels. Another change in design is the electronic E-unit, necessary for the DC motor's operation. Thus, the Rio Grande is capable of running on either AC or DC power.

The 2466 tender also returns for the first time in the modern era. It includes wire railings, but lacks the old air-driven whistle system. The big news with the tender, however, is the return of the bar-end trucks, not seen on tenders since the glory days of postwar Lionel. The die-cast trucks add a considerable amount of weight to the tender, thereby giving it a lower center of gravity and assuring better "trackability." The more adventurous collectors will enjoy installing a postwar whistle system inside, since all the requisite holes are still in the frame. They will, however, have to replace the trucks with center-rail collector trucks to make the whistle operative. Still, it is gratifying to see the return of such high-quality trucks to the Lionel tender line.

With the return of the full valve gear and the die-cast bar-end tender trucks, Lionel is once again offering Collector features on Traditional Line engines. These distinctions, previously found only in the more expensive Collector pieces, are now available at greatly reduced prices.

Lionel has apparently decided to start reinstating some of its best features of the postwar period. And that is exactly what it has done with the remainder of the cars in the set.

By simply picking up the box, it is obvious that something is radically different with this **16616 D & RG searchlight car**. Closer inspection, after removing it from the carton, reveals the answer — die-cast leaf-spring trucks. Yes, another first for this set, and for the searchlight car series, as well.

The method of attaching these trucks is also unique. Rather than affixing the trucks to the car body with screws, a center post boss has been incorporated into the design of the trucks. The boss passes through the hole in the flatcar body, and then a round speednut is pressed down over the boss, securing the truck to the car and, more importantly, assuring that the truck will never come loose from the car body.

The car is attractively painted in the bright yellow and black D & RG colors. Had Lionel thought to add a hand-painted figure standing over the control panel, it could have made this beautiful car even more handsome. Of course, such a figure is readily available from parts dealers.

Finished in bright silver with gloss-black lettering, the **16105 D & RG three-dome tank car** body is quite handsome. The ends of the tank car are unique: they are unpainted, matte black plastic with the road name's letters and the car's number imprinted in silver — a nice touch. The car also rides on the deluxe Standard O sprung trucks, again a feature usually reserved for high-end Collector tank cars.

The only "ordinary" car in this set, the **16206 D & RG boxcar** is very impressive-looking. It is a crisp orange and black boxcar of the classic 9700-series mold (again, note the Collector-heritage, despite the number on the car!). The attention in manufacturing is evident with the painting of the roof; it is so precisely done, that at first glance it appears the roof is a separate piece from the body. There are no flash marks on the body, indicating that the paint masks have been skillfully applied in the painting process. This car, like the tank car, also rides on the improved Standard O trucks.

Bringing up the rear of this unique train set is the **16509 D & RG SP caboose**. Like the other pieces, several original

features await the collector. The handsome orange and black body has a completely detailed plastic underside showing the trusses, supports, rivets, air compressor, and battery box. It is an illuminated SP caboose, another not-often-seen touch usually reserved for the higher-level pieces.

The caboose rides on the new Type IX die-cast arch bar trucks — another first! Until now, there has never been an SP-type caboose made by Lionel with this type of truck. The 6657 Rio Grande SP caboose, last made in 1957, represents the last time any die-cast truck was used on an SP caboose. Twenty-two years later, Lionel re-enters the golden age of train building by bringing back this deluxe caboose.

In summation, the Desert King Service Station set represents one of the best values for collectors. Every piece in it reveals a historical first for the new Lionel. The quality of workmanship, attention to detail, and relatively low price add up to a great value for any collector looking to expand his roster of unique, high-quality rolling stock.

THE 1990 GREAT LAKES EXPRESS SET

This set is a mixture of the very old and the very new. Generally, four-car, O27-type passenger car sets, coupled with the remakes of the 2025 steam locomotive, do not elicit praise from serious collectors. Is their reaction justified? Hardly. Is the set worth getting? Definitely!

The picture on the box does not do the set any type of justice. At first glance, one sees the steam engine in Union Pacific Gray, followed by its 2046-type tender. Trundling behind are the respective four passenger cars that appear to be reissues of the current New York Central, Pennsylvania, Amtrak and Northern Pacific offerings. So what's new, you ask? Plenty!

Like the Desert King set of 1989, this set also has the work horse 2025 **steam engine** painted with a glossy finish. (Surprise — the picture on the box shows a definitely matte-finish engine and tender). To set it off, Lionel Trains, Inc. put a white stripe on the running board, and an "LL" logo enclosed in a rectangle with the corners scalloped on each side of the steam chest. White full-serif numbers are on the cab sides. Unfortunately, the firm has yet to put wire grab-rails along the sides of the boiler and attach them to the front of the cow-catcher, as was done on the premium postwar steamers. Another point of discontent is the unlighted red markers located on the face of the boiler front. Once Lionel realizes that the higher-priced locomotives do not end up in the hands of children, possibly the nice postwar marker lights can once again grace the tops of our locomotives — especially in Service Station sets.

Power for this steamer is supplied by a DC can motor, in lieu of the AC-type motor that graces the postwar locomotives. Harnessed to this is a solid-state DC reversing unit with its requisite lock-out switch. While all the wheels are die-cast, it is nevertheless disturbing that Lionel chooses to use a nylon-type of gear system for this type of locomotive — while retaining a brass pinion gear for the motor itself! It appears that Lionel is using a three-pole motor (the least expensive type of its kind). By switching to a five-pole, shaded DC motor, Lionel can considerably reduce the noise level of this little locomotive, as well as give it better speed control and smoother operation. Operators must break in this out-of-the-box engine for about

ox lid for the rare uncatalogued 1972 Service Station Special set 1250.

G. Simbolt Collection; B. Greenberg photograph

20 hours before the gears finally mesh better and the rough edges on the motor's armature have a chance to burnish out the rough spots. Until that is done, operators are in for a substantial racket. After that, however, it settles down and becomes more typical of DC can-type drive systems: q-u-i-e-t.

Another aspect not highlighted in the picture is that the 2046W-type tender has been converted to an oil-type tender to which Lionel has added chromed wire grab-rails on the back — a nice touch. Leaf-spring die-cast trucks, along with a die-cast metal coupler, are attached to the stamped-metal tender frame via horseshoe clips. The body of the tender appears to have been reworked: there is a Lionel logo within a rectangular box on the back end of the sides. On the back, the portholes have once again been opened. The original rectangular box with the tender designation is still there, only now it is devoid of any information.

There is a minor curiosity concerning the **tender trucks**: the axles of the tender trucks are swaged (i.e., grooved or ribbed) on one side. Lionel Trains, Inc. has elected to use the same axles found in the RailSounds tenders and boxcars. In RailSounds applications, a round magnet, which activates the transistor placed in front of it, is pressed onto the swaged portion of the axle. This tells the microprocessor how fast or slow the unit is traveling. In the absence of movement it resets and goes to the "idle" sound mode. Of course, this detail is not necessary here because this tender has no Rail-Sounds.

The **passenger cars** in this set are truly worth getting excited about. Lionel has decided to resurrect a color scheme that has not been seen on the Lionel Lines since the late 1940s: a medium matte-green body, with semi-gloss yellow trim on the windows and stripes. The lettering for the cars is done in a gloss white, and the names for the four cars are chosen to reflect the new area that the modern Lionel company lives in: Mt.Clemens (16027), Detroit (16028), Lansing (16029), and

Chesterfield (16030). The roofs of all four cars are painted in a matte, medium-gray finish, and the observation car sports a clear warning light in its rear roof section.

For this set of cars, Lionel has made up an entirely new set of window silhouettes. Instead of the black human-like form used in the postwar set, the windows display an etched "reverse image" and considerable detail. One thing missing from the modern image strips are the figures of men smoking, a possible concession to the times in which we live!

On the original 1948 cars, the doors and ends are a separate piece of metal, attached to the metal substructure that holds the lighting system and provides a place for the roof to attach via "ventilator" screws. Sadly, this favorable detailing is missing from the new issue. The doors on the current set are sealed off, as is the passageway between cars. To mount the roofs, Lionel uses two screws, driven up from the bottom, to secure the roof to the one-piece bodies. To replace a burned-out lamp, simply remove the two screws, lift off the roof and replace the bulb.

Lionel has avoided the "flickering-light-syndrome" by wiring the collector rollers on each truck together, instead of to each respective lamp in the car. Now, when the train travels over switches and crossovers, the lights burn steadily.

For all the cars in the set (except the observation car), Lionel has continued the recently revived practice of using the postwar-style die-cast passenger trucks with the attached die-cast couplers. The observation car lacks a coupler at the rear. It should also be noted that, in addition to the aforementioned die-cast coupler, Lionel has also made the coupler knuckle out of metal, too. All cars have the attendant finger lever for manual uncoupling. The trucks are finished in matte black. And judging from the crisp detail, it appears that the die for these has been reworked. Lionel Trains, Inc. has improved the overall appearance of this set considerably.

Furthermore, the added weight of the die-cast trucks helps the tracking ability of the cars, as well as providing a better ground circuit for the lighting system.

Since these are metal trucks, it is advisable to lubricate the axle points and journals in the trucks every so often. This helps eliminate squeaks as the train attempts to navigate your layout. Don't forget the tender's wheels and the lead and trail trucks on the engine, too. With the plastic-sided Delrin trucks, lubrication is not necessary.

So how does the Great Lakes Express rate in the Service Station sets line-up? If (and when) Lionel reinstates the wire handrails on the engine, as well as moves the marker lights back to their former place of honor, then its smaller steam locomotive sets will quickly move up in status. This sequence of events will capture all of the finest elements of the old manufacturing methods and unite them to the latest technology of new materials and sound systems that this current generation offers. One can only hope that a RailSounds-equipped engine (steam or diesel) will soon be offered in the Service Station series, which will constitute a new benchmark in quality for the Service Station series of sets.

LIONEL SETS LISTINGS

	GD	VG	EXC	MT

1970 Catalogued

1081 WABASH CANNONBALL: 8040 Nickel Plate 2-4-2 locomotive and tender; 9060 Nickel Plate SP caboose; 9020 Union Pacific flatcar; 9140 Burlington gondola or 9141 BN gondola; 4045 transformer; eight 5013 curved track; two sections 5018 straight track; new mechanical automatic uncoupler; lockon; wires; owner's maintenance and instruction manual. The 1970 catalogue pictures a Santa Fe flatcar in this set, but it was made with the 9020 UP. This set was the lowest-priced starter set in the 1970-71-72 Lionel line. *(T)* — — 60 100

1082 YARD BOSS: 8010 ATSF NW-2 switcher diesel; 9021 Santa Fe work caboose; 9140 Burlington gondola or 9141 BN gondola; 9010 Great Northern hopper; 4045 transformer; eight sections 5013 curved track; two sections 5018 straight track; new automatic uncoupler; lockon; wires; owner's maintenance and instruction manual. *(T)* — — 125 200

1083 PACEMAKER: 8041 New York Central 2-4-2 locomotive and tender; 9062 Penn Central SP caboose; 9020 Union Pacific flatcar; 9140 Burlington gondola or 9141 BN gondola; 9010 Great Northern hopper; 5020 90-degree crossover; 12 sections 5013 curved track; four sections 5018 straight track; 4045 transformer; train crew (three-figure set); foam building; 2911 smoke pellets; mechanical automatic uncoupler; lockon; wires; owner's maintenance and instruction manual. The 1970 catalogue shows an L & N gondola, an item never made. *(T)* — — 100 150

1084 GRAND TRUNK & WESTERN: 8042 Grand Trunk Western 2-4-2 locomotive and tender; 9040 Wheaties boxcar; 9063 Grand Trunk SP caboose; 9020 Union Pacific flatcar; 9010 Great Northern hopper; 9050 Sunoco tank car; 5149 uncoupling track;

	GD	VG	EXC	MT

eight sections 5013 curved track; three sections 5018 straight track; 4045 transformer; train crew (three-figure set); foam buildings; 2911 smoke pellets; lockon; wires; owner's maintenance and instruction manual. *(T)* — — 120 175

1085 SANTA FE EXPRESS DIESEL FREIGHT: 8020 Santa Fe Alco AA diesel; 9041 Hershey's boxcar; 9061 ATSF SP caboose; 9120 Northern Pacific TOFC flatcar; 9140 Burlington gondola or 9141 BN gondola; 9010 Great Northern hopper; 9050 Sunoco tank car; 5149 uncoupling track; 5020 90-deg crossover; 12 sections 5013 curved track; seven sections 5018 straight track; 4045 transformer; train crew (three-figure set); lockon; wires; owner's instruction and maintenance manual. *(T)* — — 200 300

1086 THE MOUNTAINEER: 8062 Great Northern Hudson 4-6-4 locomotive and tender; 9202 Santa Fe boxcar; 9164 Great Northern N5C caboose; 9120 Northern Pacific TOFC flatcar; 9130 quad hopper (catalogue states C & O but picture shows B & O, which is the way it was later made); L & N log dump; 5149 uncoupling track; eight sections 5013 curved track; seven sections 5018 straight track; 4090 transformer; train crew (three-figure set); 2911 smoke pellets; lockon; wires; owner's maintenance and instruction manual. It would have been interesting to see this large Hudson engine running around on a loop of O27 track! The engine, caboose and log dump cars from this set were never made. The other cars were. Catalogued but not manufactured. *(C)*
Not Manufactured

1087 MIDNIGHT EXPRESS: 8030 Illinois Central GP-9 diesel; 8031 Illinois Central dummy (pictured that way in the catalogue — this number was later assigned to the Canadian National GP-7; an Illinois Central GP-9 dummy was made, but as 8254); 9203 Union Pacific boxcar; 9160 Illinois Central N5C caboose; Penn Central communications satellite car (a car which was never made, but resembles the postwar satellite-carrying flatcars); 9120 Northern Pacific TOFC flatcar; 9130 B & O quad hopper; L & N log dump; 10 sections 5013 curved track; 11 sections 5018 straight track; 5121 remote switch (R); 5122 remote switch (L); 5149 uncoupling track; 4090 transformer; train crew (three-figure set); lockon; wires; owner's maintenance and instruction manual. Catalogued but not manufactured. *(C)*
Not Manufactured

1970 Uncatalogued

1091 SEARS SPECIAL: 8043 Nickel Plate 2-4-2 locomotive and tender; 9060 Nickel Plate SP caboose; 9140 Burlington gondola; 9011 Great Northern hopper. This set is not pictured in the Sears 1970 catalogue, and its 8043 engine is unique to Sears. We would like to hear from readers owning this set to determine how it was advertised, and how it may compare to the 79N97082 set below, which was catalogued. *(T, D)* — — 70 100

1092 (79N97081C) SEARS: 8042 Grand Trunk Western 2-4-2 locomotive and tender; 9063 Grand Trunk SP caboose; 9020 Union Pacific flatcar; 9140 Burlington gondola; 9010 Great Northern hopper; eight sections 5013 curved track; three sections 5018 straight track; uncoupling track; three figures; 2909 smoke fluid; 4045 transformer. There are at least three reported variations of this set (see 1971), and probably more. It is essentially similar to the regular-issue 1084 Grand Trunk Western set from 1970, except that a gondola replaced the Wheaties boxcar and the tank car was dropped. It was not unusual for Lionel to mix and

C. O'Dell Collection; B. Greenberg photograph

1183 The Silver Star catalogued set from 1971: Note unusual raised lettering beneath cab window.

	GD	VG	EXC	MT

exchange its O27 rolling stock between sets in this way throughout the early Fundimensions period. *(T, D)*

— — 100 150

79N97082C SEARS: 8040 Nickel Plate 2-4-2 locomotive and tender; 9060 Nickel Plate SP caboose; 9140 Burlington gondola; 9010 Great Northern hopper; two sections 5018 straight track; uncoupling unit; eight sections 5013 curved track; 4045 transformer; manual. This set is similar to the 1081 Wabash Cannonball set from 1970, the lowest-priced starter set in the 1970 line, except that there is a hopper in the Sears set in place of the flatcar in the regular set. In the Sears 1970 catalogue, the engine for this set is marked "243". Clearly Lionel was using a postwar-leftover engine when it took the picture for the catalogue! L. Bohn comment. *(T, D)* — — 60 100

1971 Catalogued

1081 WABASH CANNONBALL: 8040 Nickel Plate 2-4-2 or 8043 Nickel Plate 2-4-2 locomotive and tender; 9060 Nickel Plate SP caboose; 9020 Union Pacific flatcar; 9142 Republic Steel gondola; eight sections 5013 curved track; two sections 5018 straight track; mechanical uncoupler; 25-watt Trainmaster transformer;

	GD	VG	EXC	MT

2900 lockon; wires; instructions. Same set as in 1970 except gondola is changed — a policy not unusual for Lionel on these low-priced sets. *(T)* — — 60 100

1085 SANTA FE TWIN DIESEL: 8020 Santa Fe Alco A-unit only; 8021 Santa Fe B-unit; 9040 Wheaties boxcar; 9061 ATSF SP caboose; 9120 Northern Pacific TOFC flatcar; 9141 BN gondola; 9012 TAG hopper; 9050 Sunoco tank car; 4050 transformer; push-button electric uncoupling track; 12 sections 5013 curved track; seven sections 5018 straight track; 5020 90-deg crossover; foam model buildings; two figures; 2900 lockon; wires; instructions. Although it carries the same number, this set differs from the 1970 version: The boxcar and hopper changed identities, and this set has a Santa Fe A-B Alco, while the 1970 set had an A-A combination. Clark O'Dell comment. *(T)*

— — 200 300

1182 THE YARDMASTER: 8111 DT & I NW-2 diesel; 9090 Mini-Max boxcar; 9021 Santa Fe work caboose; 9142 Republic Steel gondola; 9300 Penn Central log dump; eight sections 5013 curved track; four sections 5018 straight track; mechanical uncoupler; 45-watt Trainmaster transformer; 2900 lockon; wires; instructions. The 1971 catalogue shows the caboose as a ◆ 9025

	GD	VG	EXC	MT

DT & I work caboose. It is possible the set comes both ways — Lionel was known to interchange the two cabooses often. *(T)*

— — 125 200

1183 THE SILVER STAR: 8141 PRR 2-4-2 locomotive and tender; 9062 Penn Central SP caboose; 9020 Union Pacific flatcar; 9142 Republic Steel gondola or 9141 Burlington Northern gondola; 9010 Great Northern hopper or 9011 Great Northern hopper; 12 sections 5013 curved track; four sections 5018 straight track; 5020 90-deg crossover; 4050 transformer; two figures; mechanical uncoupler; 2900 lockon; wires; instructions. Some sets came with mismarked 8041 locomotive. R. LaVoie comment. *(T)*

— — 60 100

1184 THE ALLEGHENY: 8142 C & O 4-4-2 locomotive and tender; 9040 Wheaties boxcar; 9064 C & O SP caboose; 9022 ATSF flatcar; 9141 BN gondola; 9012 TAG hopper; eight sections 5013 curved track; five sections 5018 straight track; 5149 push-button electric uncoupling track; 4050 transformer; two figures; foam model buildings; 2900 lockon; wires; instructions. This set came in two configurations: (A) With Wheaties boxcar for regular dealers; and (B) With Autolite boxcar in place of Wheaties car as a special for Autolite Car Parts stores in 1971 (see 1971 uncatalogued sets section). The Autolite car was offered in the regular catalogue in 1972 (pictured with this set but not actually offered with it, only for separate-sale). This meant the collectors who thought they were purchasing a limited-edition boxcar in 1971 when they bought the set in Autolite stores were unpleasantly surprised the next year! *(T)* — — 125 200

1186 CROSS COUNTRY EXPRESS: 8030 Illinois Central GP-9 diesel; 9200 Illinois Central boxcar; 9160 Illinois Central N5C caboose; 9121 L & N flatcar with dozer or scraper; 9135 N & W quad hopper; 9300 Penn Central log dump; 9250 Waterpoxy tank car; 10 sections 5013 curved track; 11 sections 5018 straight track; 5149 uncoupling track; 5121 remote switch (R); 5122 remote switch (L); 4090 transformer; mechanical uncoupler; two figures; 2900 lockon; wires; instructions. *(C)* — — 250 350

T-1171 CANADIAN NATIONAL STEAM LOCOMOTIVE: 8040 Canadian National 2-4-2 locomotive; 9065 Canadian National SP caboose; 9143 Canadian National gondola; eight sections 5013 curved track; two sections 5018 straight track; lockon; T-4045 transformer; wires; instructions. *(T, CA)*

— — 125 200

T-1172 YARDMASTER: 8010 ATSF NW-2 switcher; 9061 ATSF SP caboose; 9141 BN gondola or 9143 Canadian National gondola; 9010 or 9011 Great Northern hopper; eight sections 5013 curved track; four sections 5018 straight track; mechanical uncoupler; lockon; T-4045 transformer; wires; instructions. *(T, CA)*

— — 125 200

T-1173 GRAND TRUNK AND WESTERN: 8041 New York Central 2-4-2 or 8042 Grand Trunk Western 2-4-2 locomotive and tender; 9062 Penn Central SP caboose or 9063 Grand Trunk SP caboose; 9020 Union Pacific flatcar or 9022 ATSF flatcar; 9143 Canadian National gondola; 9012 TAG hopper; eight sections 5013 curved track; six sections 5018 straight track; lockon; T-4045 transformer; smoke fluid; wires; instructions. *(T, CA)*

— — 125 175

T-1174 CANADIAN NATIONAL: 8031 Canadian National GP-7 diesel with Type I railing and Hillside roller pickup; 9040 Wheaties short boxcar with Type IV body; 9065 Canadian National tuscan Type IV body SP caboose; 9120 green NP flatcar with plain white vans; 9012 TAG navy blue hopper; 9143 Canadian

National tuscan gondola; 12 sections 5018 straight track; eight sections 5013 curved track; T-5020 90-degree crossover in early Type I shrink-wrapped packaging; lockon; manumatic uncoupler; T-4045 transformer with black marbled plastic case; wires; bilingual instructions. G. Halverson Collection. *(C, CA)*

— — 350 450

1971 Uncatalogued

1092 (79C97105C) SEARS "SIX-UNIT": 8042 Grand Trunk Western 2-4-2 locomotive and tender; 9063 Grand Trunk SP caboose; 9020 Union Pacific flatcar; 9141 BN gondola; 9011 Great Northern hopper; four sections 5018 straight track; eight sections 5013 curved track; uncoupling unit; two figures; two canisters; smoke fluid; 50-watt transformer. The Sears catalogue shows two gondolas, but the description (hopper and gondola) does not match the picture. This set is similar to, but not the same as, the 1092 set listed under 1970. Sears catalogued the two versions with different numbers, but Lionel did not bother to change its number. There are two reported variations of this set: *(T, D)*
(A) As described. The 9020 flatcar here is the yellow version (D). C. Rohlfing Collection. — — 100 150
(B) Same as (A), but with a 9010 GN hopper instead of 9011; and the 9020 flatcar is the tuscan version (H). This version of the 9020 may be unique to this Sears set. Could also be a variation of the 1970 set, as implied by the number. T. Durbin Collection.

— — 120 180

1190 SEARS SPECIAL #1: 8140 Southern 2-4-0 locomotive and tender; 9060 Nickel Plate SP caboose; 9020 Union Pacific flatcar; 9140 Burlington gondola. The locomotive in this set is unique to Sears. The set is not pictured in the 1971 Sears catalogue, but is very similar (with the exception of the engine) to the "Five-unit" 79C97101C set which is catalogued. *(T, D)*

— — 75 125

1195 JCPENNEY SPECIAL: 8022 Santa Fe Alco diesel; 9021 Santa Fe work caboose; 9140 Burlington gondola; 9011 Great Northern hopper. The Santa Fe Alco heading this set is unique to JCPenney. *(T, D)* — — 200 300

1198: 8010 Santa Fe NW-2 switcher; 9021 Santa Fe work caboose (can be converted to a flatcar); 9142 Republic Steel gondola; 9011 Great Northern hopper; 12 sections 5018 straight track; 14 sections 5013 curved track; two 2110 graduated trestle sets (to create a figure-8 over-under layout); two canisters; two figures; 4150 Trainmaster transformer; manual uncoupler; lockon; wires; instructions. Came in a generic box with a sticker labeled "6-1198" and picturing the contents. We would be interested in hearing from other readers with this set to identify for whom it was made and how it was marketed. J. Merz Collection. *(T)*

— — 125 200

1199 FORD AUTOLITE: Same as regular-issue 1184 Allegheny set from 1971, except with the 9042 Ford Autolite boxcar in place of Wheaties boxcar. The set also included two special Autolite billboards and a Ford tuneup kit. See discussion under 1184 set. J. Brandon Collection. *(T, D)* — — 150 250

79C95204C SEARS SANTA FE DIESEL: 8020 Santa Fe Alco diesel; 9040 Wheaties boxcar; 9061 ATSF SP caboose; 9141 BN gondola; 9012 TAG hopper; 9050 Sunoco tank car; five sections 5018 straight track; 12 sections 5013 curved track; push-button remote track; 5020 90-deg crossover; two figures; three canisters; 4050 50-watt transformer. This set appears to be a "shortened" version of the 1085 Santa Fe Twin Diesel set which was shown in

GD VG EXC MT

he 1971 Lionel catalogue. This version is missing the NP TOFC latcar and the dummy Alco B-unit diesel. The Sears catalogue picture does not clearly identify the gondola or the short boxcar; but due to similarity with the Twin Diesel set, we infer the Sears et contained the 9040 Wheaties boxcar and the 9141 BN gondola. t is possible the gondola is a 9140 or 9142. The catalogue picture hows two hoppers, rather than one hopper and one gondola, which the description indicates and which is the way it was made. Obviously, Lionel was not too consistent in its set pictures or set ontents during this period. *(T, D)* — — 175 250

9C97101C SEARS "FIVE-UNIT": 8040 Nickel Plate 2-4-2 r 8043 Nickel Plate 2-4-2 locomotive and tender; 9060 Nickel Plate SP caboose; 9020 Union Pacific flatcar; 9141 BN gondola; wo sections 5018 straight track; eight 5013 curved track; 25-watt ransformer. This set is a variation on the regularly catalogued 081 Wabash Cannonball set for 1971, which is itself a variation f the Wabash Cannonball set catalogued in 1970. The only onsistency is in the engine and caboose — the other two cars can e any of the short gondolas, hoppers, flatcars or boxcars made in his period. Add $50 to prices for presence of 8043 locomotive. Notice how the Sears catalogue refers to "five units", counting the ngine's tender as one. *(T, D)* — — 75 100

187 SERVICE STATION SPECIAL: 8030 I.C. GP-9 diesel, ariation (A); 9200(F) Illinois Central boxcar; 9211(G) Penn Central boxcar; 9214(A) Northern Pacific boxcar; 9215(A) Norfolk & Western boxcar; 9230(A) Monon boxcar; 9160(B) Illinois Central N5C caboose; eight sections O curve track; 11 sections straight rack; 5502 remote-control section in older Hillside box, styrofoam packaging material by Myco; estimated production of 1,000. When sold, the set will carry a 35 percent premium over the value f the individual items only if the original set box is present. Set ame in generic set box with paper label. All rolling stock came n Type I boxes except locomotive, which came in postwar-type box vith Fundimensions label (the early plain 8030 box with double laps on the ends and a punch-through display piece on the side). n addition to being the first modern Service Station set (although ot widely advertised as such at the time), this intriguing set is ominated by no less than five classic-style boxcars of the 9200-eries. These boxcars are otherwise rarely found in sets. It is ossible there are variations in the contents of this set or its packaging. Further reader comments requested. G. Mueller Collection. *(C, SSS)* — — 450 550

972 Catalogued

081 WABASH CANNONBALL: 8040 Nickel Plate 2-4-2 ocomotive and tender; 9060 Nickel Plate SP caboose; 9020 Union Pacific flatcar; 9136 Republic Steel gondola; eight sections 5013 urved track; two sections 5018 straight track; mechanical uncoupler; 4125 transformer. This set was also offered in the 1972 CPenney catalogue unchanged from Lionel's version. L. Bohn omment. Note that Lionel continued to juggle the rolling stock n this set as related to earlier versions, while retaining the same umber. *(T)* — — 75 100

182 YARDMASTER: 8111 DT & I NW-2 diesel; 9025 DT & I vork caboose or 9061 ATSF SP caboose; 9136 Republic Steel ondola; 9013 CN hopper; 9300 Penn Central log dump; eight ections 5013 curved track; four sections 5018 straight track; mechanical uncoupler; 4125 25-watt Trainmaster transformer. ame as Yardmaster set from 1971, except the 9013 hopper eplaced the 9090 Mini-max car. Distributed in Canada as T-1272. he 1972 catalogue illustrates the engine in this set as "8112",

GD VG EXC MT

although the description lists 8111. 8111 is the way the engine was made — no 8112 engine was ever manufactured. R. Bicknese comment. *(T)* — — 100 150

1183 SILVER STAR: 8203 PRR 2-4-2 locomotive and tender; 9062 Penn Central SP caboose; 9020 Union Pacific flatcar; 9136 Republic Steel gondola; 9013 CN hopper; 12 sections 5013 curved track; four sections 5018 straight track; 5020 90-deg crossover; mechanical uncoupler; 4150 transformer. Distributed in Canada as T-1273. Although it has the same number as the 1971 set, Lionel changed the engine and two of the four cars. *(T)*
— — 75 100

1186 CROSS COUNTRY EXPRESS: 8030 Illinois Central GP-9 diesel; 9700 Southern boxcar; 9701 B & O boxcar; 9160 Illinois Central N5C caboose; 9121 L & N flatcar; 9111 N & W quad hopper; 9151 Shell tank car; 10 sections 5013 curved track; 11 sections 5018 straight track; 5149 uncoupling track; remote switches; figures; 4090 transformer. *(C)* — — 350 500

1280 KICKAPOO VALLEY & NORTHERN: 8200 Kickapoo dockside locomotive, no tender; 9067 Kickapoo bobber caboose; 9330 Kickapoo half-size coal dump car; 9030 Kickapoo half-gondola; eight sections 5013 curved track; two sections 5018 straight track; 50-watt transformer. Distributed in Canada as T-1280. There are no numbers on the cars in this set, except a molded "9330" on the bottom of the dump car. One of the most inexpensive sets ever made by Lionel, though its unusual characteristics meant it did not remain that way. *(T)* — — 100 150

1284 ALLEGHENY: 8204 C & O 4-4-2 locomotive and tender; 9040 Wheaties boxcar; 9064 C & O SP caboose; 9022 ATSF flatcar with stakes and load; 9141 BN gondola; 9012 TAG hopper; eight sections 5013 curved track; five sections 5018 straight track; 5149 uncoupling track; figures; whistle controller; 4150 transformer. This set is catalogued with the Autolite boxcar, but it did not come that way in 1972; it was made with the Wheaties boxcar. M. Solly comment. One original set is known to exist with a 9142 Republic Steel gondola substituted for the 9141 Burlington Northern gondola. J. R. Hunt comment. This set was also offered unchanged from the Lionel version in the 1972 JCPenney catalogue. L. Bohn comment. *(T)* — — 125 200

1285 SANTA FE TWIN DIESEL: 8020 Santa Fe Alco diesel; 8021 Santa Fe Alco B-unit dummy; 9700 Southern boxcar; 9061 ATSF SP caboose; 9122 Northern Pacific TOFC flatcar; 9140 Burlington gondola or 9141 BN gondola; 9012 TAG hopper; 9300 Penn Central log dump; 12 sections 5013 curved track; seven sections 5018 straight track; 5149 uncoupling track; 5020 90-deg crossover; figures; 4150 transformer. *(T)* — — 200 300

1287 PIONEER DOCKSIDE SWITCHER: 8209 Pioneer dockside locomotive and short tender; 9060 Nickel Plate SP caboose; 9136 Republic Steel gondola; 9013 CN hopper; nine sections 5018 straight track; eight sections 5013 curved track; manual switch; 4150 transformer. *(T)* — — 125 200

T-1173 GRAND TRUNK AND WESTERN: Same as T-1173 set from 1971.

T-1174 CANADIAN NATIONAL: 8031 Canadian National GP-7 diesel; 9703 CP Rail boxcar; 9065 Canadian National SP caboose; 9120 Northern Pacific TOFC flatcar; 9143 Canadian National gondola; 9013 CN hopper; 12 sections 5018 straight track; eight sections 5013 curved track; T-5020 90-deg crossover; lockon; T-4045 transformer; wires; instructions. *(C, CA)*
— — 350 450

	GD	VG	EXC	MT

T-1272 YARDMASTER: 8111 DT & I NW-2 switcher diesel; 9025 DT & I work caboose or 9061 ATSF SP caboose; 9136 Republic Steel gondola; 9013 CN hopper; 9300 Penn Central log dump; eight sections 5013 curved track; four sections 5018 straight track; mechanical uncoupler; 25-watt Trainmaster transformer. *(T, CA)* — — 100 150

T-1273 SILVER STAR: 8203 PRR 2-4-2 locomotive and tender; 9062 Penn Central SP caboose; 9020 Union Pacific flatcar; 9136 Republic Steel gondola; 9013 CN hopper; 12 sections 5013 curved track; four sections 5018 straight track; 5020 90-deg crossover; mechanical uncoupler; 4150 transformer. *(T, CA)* — — 60 100

T-1280 KICKAPOO VALLEY & NORTHERN: Same as 1280 American set. *(T, CA)* — — 100 150

1972 Uncatalogued

1290: 8140 Southern 2-4-0 locomotive and tender; 9060 Nickel Plate SP caboose; 9020 Union Pacific flatcar; 9136 Republic Steel gondola. This set does not appear in the 1972 Sears catalogue but is very similar to the 79N97101C set listed below, except for the engine. This engine is unique to Sears. *(T, D)* — — 75 125

1291 SEARS: 8042 Pennsylvania 2-4-2 locomotive with 1130T tender; 9062 Penn Central SP caboose; 9022 ATSF flatcar; 9141 BN gondola; 9012 TAG hopper; 4150 transformer; 12 sections 5013 curved track; four sections 5018 straight track; 90-degree crossover; manumatic uncoupler; lockon; wires. Generic set box with paste-on label. R. LaVoie Collection. We would be interested to know how this set was marketed; it is not shown in the 1972 Sears catalogue. *(T, D)* — — 75 125

79N97101C SEARS "FIVE UNIT": 8040 Nickel Plate 2-4-2 or 8043 Nickel Plate 2-4-2 locomotive and tender; 9060 Nickel Plate SP caboose; 9020 Union Pacific flatcar; 9136 Republic Steel gondola; two sections 5018 straight track; eight sections 5013 curved track; 25-watt transformer. Essentially a reissue of the Five-Unit set from 1971, except the gondola changed identity. *(T, D)* — — 75 100

79N9552C SEARS SIX UNIT STEAM: 8141 Pennsylvania 2-4-2 locomotive and tender; 9062 Penn Central SP caboose; 9020 Union Pacific flatcar; 9141 BN gondola; 9012 TAG hopper; 5020 90-deg crossover; four sections 5018 straight track; 12 sections 5013 curved track; canisters; 5025 manumatic uncoupler; 4150 transformer. *(T, D)* — — 80 125

79N9553C SEARS SIX UNIT DIESEL: 8020 Santa Fe Alco diesel; 9040 Wheaties boxcar; 9061 ATSF SP caboose; 9140 Burlington gondola; 9011 Great Northern hopper; 9300 Penn Central log dump; 5020 90-deg crossover; eight sections 5018 straight track; 12 sections 5013 curved track; canisters; 5025 manumatic uncoupler; 4150 transformer. Similar to the Santa Fe diesel set from 1971, but once again Lionel mixed up the rolling stock. *(T, D)* — — 175 250

1250 SERVICE STATION SPECIAL: 8206 New York Central 4-6-4 small Hudson locomotive; 9710 Rutland boxcar; 9709 State of Maine (BAR) boxcar; 9162 Pennsylvania N5C caboose; 9111 N & W quad hopper; 9707 Katy stock car; 9151 Shell tank car; eight O curved; 12 sections straight; production quantity not known. This little-known but high quality set marks the return of the small Hudson to Lionel's modern line. All the pieces

in this set were later catalogued for separate-sale, but reportedly less than 1000 boxed sets were made. *(C, SSS)* — — 500 600

1973 Catalogued

1380 U. S. STEEL INDUSTRIAL SWITCHER: 8350 U.S. Steel gas turbine; 9068 Reading bobber caboose; 9024 C & O flatcar; 9031 Nickel Plate gondola; eight sections 5013 curved track; 4350 DC power pack. The first Lionel set powered by DC *(T)* — — 75 100

1381 CANNONBALL: 8300 Santa Fe 2-4-0 locomotive and slope-back tender; 9061 ATSF SP caboose; 9024 C & O flatcar; 9031 Nickel Plate gondola; eight sections 5013 curved track; two sections 5018 straight track; 25-watt transformer. *(T)* — — 50 80

1382 YARDMASTER: 8111 DT & I NW-2 diesel switcher; 9025 DT & I work caboose; 9136 Republic Steel gondola; 9013 CN hopper; 9300 Penn Central log dump; eight sections 5013 curved track; four sections 5018 straight track; 25-watt transformer. *(T)* — — 100 150

1383 SANTA FE FREIGHT: 8351 Santa Fe Alco diesel; 9021 Santa Fe work caboose; 9136 Republic Steel gondola; 9013 CN hopper; 9300 Penn Central log dump; eight sections 5013 curved track; six sections 5018 straight track; 25-watt transformer. *(T)* — — 150 200

1384 SOUTHERN EXPRESS: 8302 Southern 2-4-0 locomotive and tender; 9066 Southern SP caboose; 9020 Union Pacific flatcar; 9136 Republic Steel gondola; 9013 CN hopper; 12 sections 5013 curved track; four sections 5018 straight track; 5020 90-deg crossover; 4150 transformer. *(T)* — — 100 150

1385 BLUE STREAK FREIGHT: 8303 Jersey Central 2-4-2 locomotive and tender; 9043 Erie-Lackawanna boxcar; 9069 Jersey Central SP caboose; 9020 Union Pacific flatcar; 9140 Burlington gondola; 9136 Republic Steel gondola; 9013 CN hopper; eight sections 5013 curved track; six sections 5018 straight track; 4150 transformer. *(T)* — — 125 175

1386 ROCK ISLAND EXPRESS: 8304 Rock Island 4-4-2 locomotive and tender; 9125 N & W auto carrier; 9070 Rock Island SP caboose; 9023 MKT flatcar; 9131 Rio Grande gondola; 9018 Reading hopper; eight sections 5013 curved track; six sections 5018 straight track; 4150 transformer. *(T)* — — 175 250

1387 MILWAUKEE SPECIAL: 8305 Milwaukee Road 4-4-2 locomotive and tender; 9500, 9502, and 9503 Milwaukee Road short Madison passenger cars; eight sections 5013 curved track; six sections 5018 straight track; 4150 transformer. Many other passenger cars were sold separately later as add-ons to this set. Price for boxed set only. *(C)* — — 300 350

1388 GOLDEN STATE ARROW: 8352 Santa Fe GP-20 diesel; 9126 C & O auto carrier; 9708 U.S. Mail boxcar; 9163 ATSF N5C caboose; 9135 N & W quad hopper; 9707 MKT stock car; 9152 Shell tank car; 4150 transformer; 10 sections 5013 curved track; 11 sections 5018 straight track; 5149 uncoupling track. An 8355 Santa Fe dummy GP-20 was offered for separate-sale as a match for this set. This is the top-of-the-line set for 1973. It is really a "Collector" set, although at the time Lionel did not use those terms. *(C)* — — 300 400

T-1173 GRAND TRUNK AND WESTERN: Same as T-1173 set from 1971 and 1972. *(T, CA)*

1380 U.S. Steel Industrial Switcher set from 1973-1975.

C. O'Dell Collection; B. Greenberg photograph

	GD	VG	EXC	MT

T-1174 CANADIAN NATIONAL: Same as T-1174 set from 1972. *(C, CA)*

T-1272 YARDMASTER: Same as T-1272 set from 1972. *(T, CA)*

T-1273 SILVER STAR: Same as T-1273 set from 1972. *(T, CA)*

T-1280 KICKAPOO VALLEY & NORTHERN: Same as T-1280 set from 1972. *(T, CA)*

1973 Uncatalogued

1390 SEARS SEVEN UNIT: 8310 Nickel Plate 2-4-0 locomotive and tender; 9040 Wheaties boxcar; 9060 Nickel Plate SP caboose 9020 Union Pacific flatcar; 9136 Republic Steel gondola; 9013 Canadian National hopper. This set is not pictured in the 1973 Sears catalogue. We are interested in hearing from readers as to how this set was marketed. *(T, D)* — — **80 120**

1392 (79C95224C) SEARS "EIGHT-UNIT": 8303 (or 8308) Jersey Central 2-4-2 locomotive and tender; 9043 Erie-Lackawanna boxcar; 9069 Jersey Central SP caboose; 9124 Penn Central flatcar with logs; 9020 Union Pacific flatcar; 9136 Republic Steel gondola with canisters; 9013 Canadian National hopper; 10 sections 5013 curved track; 12 sections 5018 straight track; two manual switches; 4150 transformer. This is an expanded version

of the regular Blue Streak Freight set. It apparently came with either the 8303 or 8308 engines. *(T, D)* — — **130 200**

1393 (79C95223C) SEARS "SIX-UNIT": 8351 Santa Fe Alco diesel; 9043 Erie Lackawanna boxcar; 9061 ATSF caboose; 9020 Union Pacific flatcar; 9136 Republic Steel gondola with canisters; 9013 Canadian National hopper; eight sections 5013 curved track; two sections 5018 straight track; 25-watt transformer. The hopper car here is not clearly identified in the catalogue, but it is either the 9013 CN or the 9011 Great Northern. *(T, D)*

— — **175 250**

1395 JCPENNEY: 8311 Southern 0-4-0 locomotive and 1130T-type tender; 9043 Erie Lackawanna boxcar; 9066 Southern SP caboose; 9024 C & O flatcar; 9140 Burlington gondola; 9013 Canadian National hopper; 9050 Sunoco tank car. The engine in this set is unique to JCPenney. *(T, D)* — — **100 150**

1350 SERVICE STATION SPECIAL: 8365 and 8366 Canadian Pacific F-3 diesels (powered and dummy); 9723 Western Pacific boxcar; 9724 Missouri Pacific boxcar; 9165 Canadian Pacific N5C caboose; 9113 N & W quad hopper available separately; 9725 Katy stock car; 8469 Canadian Pacific F-3 B-unit available separately (in 1974); estimated production: 2,500. Very hard to find as an intact set, and probably the most desirable of

	GD	VG	EXC	MT

all the Service Station sets due to the nostalgia appeal of the Canadian Pacific F-3s. These two diesels were actually made in less quantity than the original 2373 postwar engines on which they were based, so they may actually be more scarce than the postwar originals. *(C, SSS)* — — 1400 1700

1974 Catalogued

1380 U. S. STEEL INDUSTRIAL SWITCHER: Same as 1380 set from 1973. *(T)*

1381 CANNONBALL: Same as 1381 set from 1973. *(T)*

1382 YARDMASTER: 8111 DT & I NW-2 diesel switcher; 9025 DT & I work caboose; 9120 Northern Pacific flatcar (not a TOFC car, carries logs only); 9136 Republic Steel gondola; 9013 CN hopper; eight sections 5013 curved track; four sections 5018 straight track; transformer. Same as 1382 set from 1973, except the NP flatcar replaced the 9300 PC log dump. *(T)* — — 75 150

1383 SANTA FE FREIGHT: Same as 1383 set from 1973. *(T)*

1384 SOUTHERN EXPRESS: Same as 1384 set from 1973. *(T)*

1385 BLUE STREAK FREIGHT: Same as 1385 set from 1973. *(T)*

1386 ROCK ISLAND EXPRESS: Same as 1386 set from 1973. *(T)*

1388 GOLDEN STATE ARROW: 8352 Santa Fe GP-20 diesel; 9126 C & O auto carrier; 9301 U.S. Mail operating boxcar; 9163 ATSF N5C caboose; 9135 N & W quad hopper; 9707 MKT stock car; 9152 Shell tank car; transformer; 5149 uncoupling track; 10 sections 5013 curved track; 11 sections 5018 straight track. Same as 1973 Golden Arrow set, except a 9301 operating mail car is substituted for a 9708 non-operating U.S. Mail boxcar. An 8355 Santa Fe dummy GP-20 was offered for separate-sale as a match to this set. *(C)* — — 300 400

1460 GRAND NATIONAL: 8470 Chessie U36B diesel; 9126 C & O auto carrier; 9740 Chessie boxcar; 9167 Chessie N5C caboose; 9121 L & N flatcar; 9114 Morton Salt quad hopper; 9303 Union Pacific log dump; 9860 Gold Medal refrigerator car; 5121 remote switch (R); 5122 remote switch (L); 5149 uncoupling track; 5020 90-deg crossover; transformer; 23 sections 5018 straight track; 18 sections 5013 curved track. This was the top-of-the-line set in 1974 (along with 1487 listed next). A matching 8560 dummy C & O U36B was made the following year. *(C)* — — 325 450

1487 BROADWAY LIMITED: 8304 Pennsylvania 4-4-2 locomotive and tender; 9507, 9508, 9509 Pennsylvania short Madison passenger cars; eight sections 5013 curved track; six sections 5018 straight track; transformer. Many other passenger cars were sold separately later as add-ons to this set. Price for boxed set only. *(T, C)* — — 325 375

1489 SANTA FE DOUBLE DIESEL: 8020 Santa Fe Alco diesel; 8021 Santa Fe Alco B-unit dummy; 9042 Autolite boxcar; 9061 ATSF SP caboose; 9020 Union Pacific or 9024 C & O flatcar; 9140 Burlington gondola; 9136 Republic Steel gondola; 9013 CN hopper; eight sections 5013 curved track; six sections 5018 straight track; transformer. The catalogue picture for this set shows the 9042 Autolite boxcar, but it is also possible that a 9040 or 9043 boxcar were occasionally substituted. Reader comments invited. *(T)* — — 200 300

THE SPIRIT OF '76: Commemorative series, consumer catalogue: 1776 Seaboard U36B; 7601 Delaware boxcar; 7602 Pennsylvania boxcar; 7603 New Jersey boxcar; 7600 Spirit of '76 N5C caboose. Later additions in 1975 consumer catalogue: 7604 Georgia boxcar; 7605 Connecticut boxcar; 7606 Massachusetts boxcar; 7607 Maryland boxcar. Later additions in 1976 consumer catalogue: 7608 South Carolina boxcar; 7609 New Hampshire boxcar; 7610 Virginia boxcar; 7611 New York boxcar; 7612 North Carolina boxcar; 7613 Rhode Island boxcar. This was Lionel's first set to use the "separate-sale" marketing philosophy. *(C, SE)* — — 675 800

1974 Uncatalogued

1463 COCA-COLA SPECIAL: 8473 Coca-Cola NW-2 switcher; 9743 Sprite boxcar; 9744 Tab boxcar; 9745 Fanta boxcar; 9073 Coke SP caboose. Same as 1463 set described in Lionel's catalogue in 1975. The set was uncatalogued this year, then was catalogued in 1975. *(T)* — — 250 350

1492 (79N96185C) SEARS "SEVEN-UNIT": 8310 Jersey Central 2-4-0 locomotive and 1130-type tender; 9043 Erie Lackawanna boxcar; 9069 Jersey Central SP caboose; 9124 Penn Central flatcar with logs; 9136 Republic Steel gondola with canisters; 9013 Canadian National hopper; eight sections 5013 curved track; eight sections 5018 straight track; manual switch; bumper; uncoupler; 25-watt transformer. The locomotive in this set was also sold separately by Sears as 49N96462. *(T, D)* — — 90 120

1493 SEARS: Same as 1492, but with mailer. *(T, D)*

1499 JCPENNEY GREAT EXPRESS: 8311 Southern 0-4-0 locomotive and 1130-type tender; 9066 Southern SP caboose 9020 Union Pacific flatcar; 9136 Republic Steel gondola; 9013 Canadian National hopper. The set is similar to the 1384 Southern Express set from 1973, except for the engine. Note similarity to 1395 JCPenney set the year before. *(T, D)* — — 100 150

79N95223C SEARS "SIX-UNIT": 8351 Santa Fe Alco diesel; 9043 Erie Lackawanna boxcar; 9061 ATSF SP caboose; 9020 Union Pacific flatcar; 9142 Republic Steel gondola; 9013 Canadian National hopper; eight sections 5013 curved track; two sections 5018 straight track; uncoupler; 7-1/2-watt transformer. Essentially the same set as in 1973 but with some rolling stock switched. The Alco diesel in the set was also sold separately by Sears as 49N96461. *(T, D)* — — 175 250

79N96178C SEARS "FOUR-UNIT": 8310 ATSF 2-4-0 locomotive and slope-back tender; 9071 ATSF bobber caboose; short 9031 Nickel Plate gondola with canisters; eight sections 5013 curved track. The gondola in this inexpensive set is not clearly shown in the Sears catalogue, but since it is short we infer it is the Nickel Plate. The previous edition of this Guide erroneously listed the engine in this set as 8502, but the 8502 was not made until 1975. *(T, D)* — — 70 100

1450 SERVICE STATION SPECIAL: 8464 (powered) and 8465 (dummy) Rio Grande F-3 diesels; 9739 Rio Grande boxcar; 9166 Rio Grande SP caboose; 9144 Rio Grande gondola; 9117 Alaska quad hopper; 9863 REA refrigerator car; an 8474 Rio Grande F-3 B unit was also available separately later in 1974. Estimated set production 3000. This set is also in demand by collectors due to the popularity of the Rio Grande F-3s, reissues of the popular postwar 2379 models. *(C, SSS)* — — 400 500

1463 Coca-Cola Special set: Uncatalogued in 1974, and catalogued in 1975.

C. O'Dell Collection; B. Greenberg photograph

	GD	VG	EXC	MT

1975 Catalogued

1380 U. S. STEEL INDUSTRIAL SWITCHER: Same as 1380 set from 1973 and 1974. *(T)*

1381 CANNONBALL: Same as earlier 1381 sets except the 8502 Santa Fe 2-4-0 locomotive and tender replaced the earlier 8300 Santa Fe for this year. *(T)* — — 50 80

1383 SANTA FE FREIGHT: Same as 1383 set from 1974. *(T)*

1384 SOUTHERN EXPRESS: Same as 1384 set from 1974. *(T)*

1388 GOLDEN STATE ARROW: Same as 1388 set from 1974. It is a one-line listing in the 1975 catalogue. Not illustrated. *(C)*

1461 BLACK DIAMOND: 8203 PRR 2-4-2 locomotive and tender; 9043 Erie-Lackawanna boxcar; 9062 Penn Central SP caboose; 9020 Union Pacific flatcar; 9136 Republic Steel gondola; 9140 Burlington gondola; 9013 CN hopper; eight sections 5013 curved track; six sections 5018 straight track; transformer. This set carries a "1461" number although released in 1975. A planned 1974 release may have been delayed. *(T)* — — 90 130

1463 COCA-COLA SPECIAL: 8473 Coca-Cola NW-2 switcher; 9743 Sprite boxcar; 9744 Tab boxcar; 9745 Fanta boxcar; 9073 Coke SP caboose; eight sections 5013 curved track; two sections

5018 straight track; 4050 50-watt transformer; lockon; wires. Uncatalogued in 1974, but listed in the 1975 catalogue, though not illustrated. *(T)* — — 250 350

1487 BROADWAY LIMITED: Same as 1974 set, but not illustrated in 1975. *(T, C)*

1489 SANTA FE DOUBLE DIESEL: Same as 1489 Santa Fe Double Diesel set from 1974. As with the 1974 set, the catalogue pictures this one with the 9042 Autolite boxcar, but it is possible that other short O27 boxcars were used. Set also came with either the 9020 UP or 9024 C & O flatcar. Reader comments on original set contents would be welcomed. *(T)* — — 175 220

1560 NORTH AMERICAN EXPRESS: 8564 Union Pacific U36B diesel; 9129 N & W auto carrier; 9755 Union Pacific boxcar; 9168 Union Pacific N5C caboose; 9121 L & N flatcar; 9260 Reynolds quad hopper; 9303 Union Pacific log dump; 9861 Tropicana refrigerator car; two remote-control switches; 23 sections 5018 straight track; 18 sections 5013 curved track; 5020 90-deg crossover; 5149 uncoupling track. A dummy 8573 UP engine was made late in 1975. This unit, with horn, is very hard to find. Price for boxed set only. *(C)* — — 300 375

1581 THUNDERBALL FREIGHT: 8500 Pennsylvania 2-4-0 locomotive and tender; 9062 Penn Central SP caboose; 9020 Union Pacific flatcar; 9032 Southern Pacific gondola; 9011 Great North-

1489 Santa Fe Double Diesel set from 1975.

C. O'Dell Collection; B. Greenberg photograph

	GD	VG	EXC	MT
ern hopper; eight sections 5013 curved track; two sections 5018 straight track; transformer. *(T)*	—	—	60	100

1582 YARD CHIEF: 8569 Soo Line NW-2 diesel; 9044 Rio Grande boxcar; 9027 Soo Line work caboose; 9026 Republic Steel flatcar; 9140 Burlington gondola; 9011 Great Northern hopper; eight sections 5013 curved track; two sections 5018 straight track; transformer. *(T)*

	—	—	130	200

1584 N & W SPIRIT OF AMERICA: 1776 (8559) N & W GP-9 diesel; 9129 N & W auto carrier; 9708 U.S. Mail boxcar; 1776 N & W N5C caboose; 9135 N & W quad hopper; 9707 MKT stock car; 9153 Chevron tank car; 5149 uncoupling track; 10 sections 5013 curved track; 11 sections 5018 straight track; 4150 transformer. *(C)*

	—	—	275	350

1585 75TH ANNIVERSARY SPECIAL: 7500 Lionel 75th Anniversary U36B diesel; 7501 75th Anniversary boxcar; 7505 75th Anniversary boxcar; 7506 75th Anniversary boxcar; 7508 75th Anniversary N5C caboose; 7504 75th Anniversary quad hopper; 7502 75th Anniversary refrigerator car; 7503 75th Anniversary refrigerator car; 7507 75th Anniversary refrigerator car; no track or transformer. Nine-unit train commemorating Lionel's 75th anniversary. The set did not sell very well, and Lionel was forced to catalogue it for two more years. *(C)*

	—	—	250	300

	GD	VG	EXC	MT

1586 CHESAPEAKE FLYER: 8304 C & O 4-4-2 locomotive and tender; 9125 N & W auto carrier; 9064 C & O SP caboose; 9022 ATSF flatcar; 9131 Rio Grande gondola; 9016 Chessie hopper; eight sections 5013 curved track; four sections 5018 straight track; two canisters; transformer. *(T)*

	—	—	200	300

1587 CAPITOL LIMITED: 8304 B & O 4-4-2 locomotive and tender; 9517, 9518, and 9519 Baltimore & Ohio short Madison passenger cars; eight sections 5013 curved track; four sections 5018 straight track; transformer. Many other passenger cars were sold separately later as add-ons to this set. *(C)*

	—	—	300	350

1975 Uncatalogued

1577 LIBERTY SPECIAL: 8570 Liberty Special Alco; 9759 Paul Revere boxcar; 9760 Liberty Bell boxcar; 9761 George Washington boxcar; 9076 We The People SP caboose. This set appeared only in a late 1975 dealer flyer. *(T)*

	—	—	225	275

1594 SEARS: 8563 Rock Island Alco diesel; 9075 Rock Island SP caboose; 9020 Union Pacific flatcar; 9026 Republic Steel flatcar; 9140 Burlington gondola; 9016 Chessie hopper. D. Alcorn Collection. The engine and caboose in this set (and in 1595 set following) are unique to Sears. This set is not pictured in the 1975

Uncatalogued 1577 Liberty Special set from 1975.

C. O'Dell Collection; B. Greenberg photograph

	GD	VG	EXC	MT

Sears catalogue, and is similar to the 1595 set described below, which is catalogued. It is not clear why two similar sets were marketed with different numbers. The contents of the two sets are different, as confirmed by original owners. However, it *is* possible these are the same (1595) Sears catalogued sets with consists juggled, as was Lionel's habit at the time. Reader comments invited. *(T, D)* — — 175 250

1595 (79C9716C) SEARS "SIX-UNIT DIESEL": 8563 Rock Island Alco diesel; 9043 Erie-Lackawanna boxcar; 9075 Rock Island SP caboose; 9020 Union Pacific flatcar; 9136 Republic Steel gondola with canisters; 9013 Canadian National hopper; eight sections 5013 curved track; two sections 5018 straight track; uncoupler; 7-1/2-watt transformer. D. Danner Collection. See comments under 1594 above. The Rock Island Alco was sold separately by Sears as 49-97161. *(T, D)* — — 175 250

79C9715C SEARS "FOUR-UNIT": Same set as the Sears Four-Unit set (79N96178C) in 1974. It is possible, but not verified, that the 8502 ATSF 2-4-0 steamer headed the set this year, taking over for the 8310 used the year before. *(T, D)* — — 50 75

79C9717C SEARS "SEVEN-UNIT": Same set as 1492 (Sears 79N96185) from 1974, except the Penn Central flatcar in the

earlier set is replaced by the 9020 Union Pacific flatcar here. *(T, D)* — — 80 110

TOYS 'R' US THUNDERBALL FREIGHT: Same as regular-issue 1581 Thunderball Freight set from 1975, except special 9045 Toys 'R' Us boxcar replaced the 9011 Great Northern hopper. This was the first of many Lionel sets made for this giant toy retailing conglomerate. *(T, D)* — — 125 200

KMART SPECIAL: 8507 ATSF 2-4-0 locomotive and slope-back tender. Reader comments on other set components are requested. The engine in this set is unique to Kmart. *(T, D)*
NRS

1579 SERVICE STATION SPECIAL: 8555 and 8557 Milwaukee Road F-3 powered and dummy diesels; 9754 New York Central Pacemaker boxcar; 9758 Alaska boxcar; 9169 Milwaukee Road SP caboose; 9119 Detroit & Mackinac quad hopper; 9132 Libby's vat car; 8575 Milwaukee Road F-3 B-unit available separately; estimated production: 6,000. By this time, Lionel's pattern was to sell Service Station sets headed by F-3 diesels modeled on postwar favorites. But this set, made in greater quantities, did not quite measure up in sales as compared to the previous two years. Buyers should be aware of peeling decals on the noses of the F-3 diesels in this set. *(C, SSS)* — — 400 550

C. O'Dell Collection; B. Schwab photograph

1660 Yard Boss set from 1976. Although the bottom-of-the-line set in 1976, today it is somewhat hard to find.

	GD	VG	EXC	MT

1976 Catalogued

1384 SOUTHERN EXPRESS: Same as 1384 set from 1974-1975. *(T)*

1489 SANTA FE DOUBLE DIESEL: Same as the 1489 Double Diesel set in 1975. *(T)*

1581 THUNDERBALL FREIGHT: Same as 1581 set from 1975, except the caboose is upgraded to the 9172 Penn Central. *(T)*   — — 80 120

1582 YARD CHIEF: Same as 1582 set in 1975. *(T)*

1585 LIONEL 75th ANNIVERSARY SPECIAL: Same as 1585 Anniversary set in 1975. *(C)*

1586 CHESAPEAKE FLYER: Same as 1586 set in 1975. *(T)*

1660 YARD BOSS: 8670 Chessie gas turbine; 9179 Chessie bobber caboose; 9026 Republic Steel flatcar; 9032 Southern Pacific gondola; 4550 DC power pack; eight sections 5013 curved track. One set found with 9031 NKP gondola substituted for 9032 SP gondola. Probably one of Fundimensions' rarest engines and

caboose. T. Ladny Collection. This was the bottom-of-the-line 1976 set, but is rather hard to find today. *(T)*

— — 100 150

1661 ROCK ISLAND LINE: 8601 Rock Island 0-4-0 locomotive and tender; 9078 Rock Island bobber caboose; 9020 Union Pacific flatcar; 9033 Penn Central gondola; die-cut cardboard freight station; bridge and tunnel; eight sections 5013 curved track; two sections 5018 straight track; transformer. *(T)*

— — 95 125

1662 THE BLACK RIVER FREIGHT: 8602 Rio Grande 2-4-0 locomotive; 9077 Rio Grande SP caboose; 9026 Republic Steel flatcar; 9140 Burlington gondola; 9016 Chessie hopper; two canisters; 22 telephone poles and road signs; die-cut freight station; bridge and tunnel; trestle set; eight sections 5013 curved track; four sections 5018 straight track; transformer. *(T)*

— — 80 125

1663 AMTRAK LAKE SHORE LIMITED: 8664 Amtrak Alco A-unit diesel; 6403, 6404, 6405 and 6406 Amtrak O27 streamlined passenger cars; eight sections 5013 curved track; four sec-

1663 Amtrak Lake Shore Limited set from 1976-1977.

C. O'Dell Collection; B. Greenberg photograph

	GD	VG	EXC	MT

tions 5018 straight track; 4651 transformer. Three other passenger cars and a hard-to-find 8667 dummy B-unit Alco for this set were sold separately later. Price for boxed set only. Add $100 for B-unit. *(T, C)* — — **280 375**

1664 ILLINOIS CENTRAL FREIGHT: 8669 Illinois Central U36B diesel; 9139 Penn Central auto carrier; 9606 Union Pacific hi-cube boxcar; 9767 Railbox boxcar; 9178 ICG SP caboose; 9121 L & N flatcar; 9852 Miller refrigerator car; 5021 Manual LH switch; 2280 bumpers; 2317 drawbridge; 5149 uncoupling track; 12 sections 5013 curved track; nine sections 5018 straight track; two 5019s; six trestles; transformer. Set is pictured in catalogue with 9852 refrigerator car, but several substitute refrigerator cars are known to have come with original sets, e.g., 9854 Baby Ruth. C. Rohlfing comment. This set is also catalogued with the 9266 Southern quad hopper, but it came with the 9606 UP hi-cube boxcar. Further reader comments invited. *(C)* — — **375 500**

1665 NYC EMPIRE STATE EXPRESS: 8600 New York Central Hudson 4-6-4 locomotive and tender; 9772 Great Northern boxcar; 9174 P & E bay window caboose; 9266 Southern quad hopper; 9773 NYC stock car; 9159 Sunoco tank car. Set listed in

catalogue with eight 5013 curved track; 10 sections 5018 straight track, and transformer, but was actually produced without these items. C. Rohlfing comment. This was the top-of-the-line set in 1976, a true Collector set, although Lionel did not use those terms at the time. *(C)* — — **550 600**

1976 Uncatalogued

1693 TOYS 'R' US ROCK ISLAND SPECIAL: Same as regular-issue 1661 Rock Island Line set, except the special 9047 Toys 'R' Us boxcar replaces the 9033 PC gondola. *(T, D)* — — **140 200**

1694 TOYS 'R' US BLACK RIVER SPECIAL: Same as regular-issue 1662 Black River Freight from 1976, except the special Toys 'R' Us 9048 boxcar replaced the 9016 Chessie hopper. *(T, D)* — — **140 200**

1696 SEARS: 8604 Jersey Central 2-4-2 locomotive with 1130T-type tender; 9044 Rio Grande boxcar; 9069 Jersey Central SP caboose; 9020 Union Pacific flatcar; 9140 Burlington gondola; 9011 Great Northern hopper. This set is not pictured in the 1976

1662 The Black River Freight set from 1976-1978.

C. O'Dell Collection; B. Greenberg photograph

	GD	VG	EXC	MT

Sears catalogue. Reader comments as to how it was distributed would be appreciated. *(T, D)* — — 80 100

1698 TRUE-VALUE: Same as regular-issue 1661 Rock Island Line set, except with the special 9046 True Value boxcar replacing the 9033 PC gondola. The first set produced by Lionel for the hardware giant. *(T, D)* — — 140 175

1672 SERVICE STATION SPECIAL: 8666 Northern Pacific GP-9 diesel; 9775 Minneapolis & St. Louis boxcar; 9776 Southern Pacific "Overnight" boxcar; 9177 Northern Pacific bay window caboose; 9267 Alcoa Aluminum quad hopper; 9869 Santa Fe refrigerator car; 8668 Northern Pacific GP-9 dummy unit available separately. Because the 9177 caboose did not match the engine, collector demand forced Lionel to produce a matching black and gold caboose, the 9265, the next year. Estimated set production: 6,000. This was the first Service Station set to include Standard O sprung trucks on the rolling stock. C. Lang comment. *(C, SSS)* — — 300 375

	GD	VG	EXC	MT

1977 Catalogued

1585 LIONEL 75th ANNIVERSARY SPECIAL: Same as 1585 Anniversary set from 1975-1976. *(C)*

1586 THE CHESAPEAKE FLYER: Same as 1586 sets from 1975-1976. *(T)*

1661 ROCK ISLAND LINE: Same as 1661 set from 1976. *(T)*

1662 THE BLACK RIVER FREIGHT: Same as 1662 set from 1976. *(T)*

1663 AMTRAK LAKE SHORE LIMITED: Same as 1663 set from 1976. *(T)*

1664 ILLINOIS CENTRAL FREIGHT: Same as 1664 set from 1976. The set is mentioned in the 1977 catalogue, but not illustrated. *(T, C)*

1760 STEEL HAULERS: 8769 Republic Steel gas turbine; 9071 ATSF bobber caboose; 9020 Union Pacific flatcar; 9033 Penn Central gondola; 9016 Chessie hopper; Peterbilt tractor with

C. O'Dell Collection; B. Greenberg photograph

Uncatalogued 1796 JCPenney Cargo Master "Trains n' Truckin'" set from 1977. The boxcar is the only modern era Lionel car with the JCPenney corporate logo.

	GD	VG	EXC	MT

die-cast chassis and Penn Central markings; trailer; operating crane kit; pull cart; eight sections 5013 curved track; two sections 5018 straight track; DC power pack; die-cut factories and shed. Plastic loads include pipes, I-beams, engine blocks, culverts, posts, train wheels, crates with loads, warehouse skids (over 100 pieces). *(T)*

	—	—	125	200

Note: Both the 1760 and 1761 sets were part of a Lionel marketing campaign known as "Trains N' Truckin'." This was an attempt by the company to promote, in two of its inexpensive starter sets, a harmony between the two major modes of hauling merchandise in the United States. These sets may have had more loose pieces of miscellaneous cargo than any other Lionel sets.

1761 CARGO KING: 8770 EMD NW-2 switcher; 9021 Santa Fe work caboose, 9025 DT & I work caboose, or 9027 Soo Line work caboose; 9026 Republic Steel flatcar; 9032 Southern Pacific gondola; 9016 Chessie hopper; Mack (Santa Fe) and Peterbilt (UP or Ryder) tractors; two trailers; two operating crane kits; pull cart; eight sections 5013 curved track; four sections 5018 straight track; die-cut buildings; transformer. Plastic loads include cement blocks, barrels, wood stacks, I-beams, culverts, pipes, crates, warehouse skids, posts. *(T)*

	—	—	200	300

1762 THE WABASH CANNONBALL: 8703 Wabash 2-4-2 locomotive and tender; 9771 N & W boxcar; 9080 Wabash SP caboose; 9284 Santa Fe gondola; 9079 Grand Trunk hopper; 9851 Schlitz refrigerator car; canisters; 2110 graduated trestle set; 12 sections 5013 curved track; 14 sections 5018 straight track; transformer. This set has also been found with the 9853 Cracker Jack refrigerator car in place of the 9851 Schlitz, and the 9737 Central Vermont boxcar in place of the 9771 N & W boxcar. C. O'Dell comment. *(T)*

	—	—	170	250

1764 THE HEARTLAND EXPRESS: 8772 GM & O GP-20 diesel; 9187 GM & O SP caboose; 9283 Union Pacific gondola; 9855 Swift's refrigerator car; 9302 L & N searchlight car; 7808 Northern Pacific stock car; 5027 pair manual switches; 10 sections 5013 curved track; seven sections 5018 straight track; transformer. *(C)*

	—	—	275	300

1765 ROCKY MOUNTAIN SPECIAL: 8771 Great Northern U36B diesel; 9610 Frisco Hi-cube boxcar; 9789 Pickens boxcar;

1862 Workin' on the Railroad "Logging Empire" set from 1978.

C. O'Dell Collection; B. Greenberg photogr

	GD	VG	EXC	MT

9188 Great Northern bay window caboose; 9285 IC Gulf TOFC flatcar; 9286 B & LE quad hopper; 9189 Gulf tank car; 5125 pair remote switches; two 2290 bumpers; three-piece trestle; 5149 uncoupling track; nine sections 5013 curved track; 23 sections 5018 straight track; transformer. This was the top-of-the-line set in 1977. *(C)*

			400	480

THE SOUTHERN CRESCENT: Passenger set, consumer catalogue: 8702 4-6-4 Hudson; 9530 baggage; 9531 combine; 9532 Pullman; 9533 Pullman; 9534 observation (9500-series short Madison passenger cars). Later addition: 19001 diner, 1987 year-end brochure. *(C, SE)*

			675	800

THE MICKEY MOUSE EXPRESS: Diesel and hi-cube boxcar set, consumer catalogue: 8773 Mickey Mouse U36B diesel; 9660 Mickey Mouse, 9661 Goofy, and 9662 Donald Duck boxcars; 9183 Mickey Mouse N5C caboose. Later boxcar additions from 1978 consumer catalogue: 9663 Dumbo; 9664 Cinderella; 9665 Peter Pan; 9666 Pinocchio; 9667 Snow White; 9668 Pluto. Later additions from 1978 dealer brochure: 9669 Bambi; 9670 Alice In Wonderland; 9671 Fantasia; 9672 Mickey Mouse 50th Birthday. Very difficult to assemble. *(C, SE)*

			1700	2100

THE GENERAL: Consumer catalogue: 8701 General locomotive. Later additions from 1977 dealer year-end brochure: 9551 baggage; 9552 coach (General-style passenger cars); 9553 flatcar with horses. Full set also catalogued in 1978. *(C, SE)*

			225	275

	GD	VG	EXC	MT

1977 Uncatalogued

1790 LIONEL LEISURE STEEL HAULER: Same as regular-issue 1760 Steel Haulers set from 1977, except the special 9034 Lionel Leisure (Kiddie City) short hopper replaced the regular 9016 Chessie hopper. Also the die-cast Peterbilt truck in this set is lettered for Lionel Leisure. Interestingly, this is the only special car made for Kiddie City, the toy store chain still owned by the original Lionel Corporation. *(T, D)*

			200	300

1791 TOYS 'R' US STEEL HAULER: Same as regular-issue 1760 Steel Haulers set from 1977, except the special 9049 Toys 'R' Us boxcar replaced the 9016 hopper. *(T, D)*

			200	275

1792 TRUE VALUE: Same as 1698 Rock Island True Value set from 1976, except 9053 True Value boxcar replaces 9046 True Value boxcar. *(T, D)*

			140	175

1793 TOYS 'R' US BLACK RIVER FREIGHT: Same as 1694 set from 1976, except 9052 Toys 'R' Us boxcar replaces 9046 Toys 'R' Us boxcar. *(T, D)*

			140	200

1796 JCPENNEY CARGO MASTER: Same as regularly catalogued 1761 Cargo King set from 1977, except the special 9054 JCPenney boxcar replaced the 9016 hopper. While Lionel had made several earlier sets for JCPenney, this is the first time a special car had been made for the giant retailer with the JCPenney's logo prominently displayed. *(T, D)*

			225	325

1864 Santa Fe Double Diesel set from 1978-1979.

C. O'Dell Collection; B. Greenberg photograph

	GD	VG	EXC	MT

1766 SERVICE STATION SPECIAL: 8766 powered, and 8767 and 8768 dummy Budd RDC passenger cars; 8764 powered and 8765 dummy Budd units available separately; estimated production: 5,000. In considerable demand from collectors. Price for 8766, 8767 and 8768 only. *(C, SSS)* — — 400 450

1978 Catalogued

1662 BLACK RIVER FREIGHT: Same as 1662 set from 1976 and 1977. *(T)*

1760 TRAINS N' TRUCKIN' STEEL HAULERS: Same as 1760 set from 1977, except the hopper in this set may be the 9011 Great Northern rather than a 9016 Chessie. *(T)*

1761 TRAINS N' TRUCKIN' CARGO KING: Same as 1761 Cargo King set from 1977. *(T)*

1860 WORKIN' ON THE RAILROAD TIMBERLINE: 8803 Santa Fe 0-4-0 locomotive and slope-back tender; work caboose; operating crane car; operating log dump car; plastic operating log loading mill; four figures; throttle; eight sections 5013 curved track; two sections 5018 straight track; transformer.

The rolling stock in this set consists of snap-in superstructures supplied with three 9019 four-wheel flatcars; see discussion under 1862 below for details. The previous edition of this Guide erroneously listed the locomotive in this set, and the 1862 following, as an "8501". This does not exist. The engine which came with the sets was the 8803. M. Solly comment. *(T)*

— — 60 90

1862 WORKIN' ON THE RAILROAD LOGGING EMPIRE: 8803 Santa Fe 0-4-0 locomotive and slope-back tender; boxcar; work caboose; operating crane car; operating dump car with logs; flatcar with fences; 2721 log mill kit; 2722 barrel loader kit; four plastic workmen; throttle; 12 sections 5013 curved track; six sections 5018 straight track; 5020 90-deg crossover; transformer. All the freight cars in this set use the same frame: an unlettered flatcar body on which two four-wheel trucks are simulated in the sides of the frame, but single axles with two wheels are located at the inboard bearing on each simulated truck frame. All frames have a piece on the top surface to knock out to attach crane cab for crane car. Frames are all black, 8-3/16" long, without couplers. The couplers are non-operating with a snap-in plastic

	GD	VG	EXC	MT

arm. This flatcar is the basic 9019. The boxcar body, crane, flatcar fences, dump car supports and bin, and the work caboose body were all supplied as separate pieces so that the user could assemble them onto the flatcars in any way desired. Each of the pieces has a mold number prefixed by "9019". Decals were supplied to be installed on the rolling stock bodies by the purchaser. In this manner, Lionel essentially avoided several manufacturing steps and was thus able to offer the set at reduced prices. Versions (A) through (C) below were reissued in separate boxes with two four-wheel trucks with lettered frames, as in 9363 N & W dump car and 9364 N & W crane; see the dump car and crane car chapters in Volume I. Obviously, this has led to some considerable numbering confusion. J. Sawruk Collection and comments. This set was also offered for sale unchanged from the Lionel version in the 1978 JCPenney and Sears catalogues, and was also sold by Toys 'R' Us. L. Bohn comment. The following cars can be made by assembling the supplied superstructures to the flatcars in this set:

(A) Yellow cab with boom for crane car; IC decals. This car was reissued later without decals in a separate box. The flatcar was fitted with standard Symington-Wayne trucks, and was stamped with "N & W" lettering. The box is labeled "9364" but the car sides are stamped "9325".

(B) Flatcar with tan fence around perimeter. Issued later as the 9325 flatcar with standard trucks and "N & W" lettering on the car.

(C) Blue snap-on dump car body. This car was issued later in a separate box with standard trucks as the 9363 with the flatcar again lettered as the "9325 N & W".

(D) Red snap-on work caboose body with Santa Fe decals.

(E) White snap-on double-door short boxcar body (similar to the standard short 9040 boxcar body; part no. 9019-T-055A molded into roof). Doors molded open on one side and closed on other side. PC decals fit to right of doors; Penn Central decal fits to left of closed doors only. This car body was also used as the basis for a Toys 'R' Us car using different decals. Price for all. *(T)*

| | | — | — | 75 | 110 |

1864 SANTA FE DOUBLE DIESEL: 8861 Santa Fe Alco diesel; 8862 Santa Fe Alco dummy; 9035 Conrail boxcar; 9058 Lionel Lines SP caboose; 9014 Trailer Train flatcar; 9033 Penn Central gondola; 9018 DT & I hopper; eight sections 5013 curved track; six sections 5018 straight track; manual uncoupler; 2905 lockon and wire; 2717 extension bridge; transformer. The Trailer Train flatcar in this set is hard to find. The 9022 ATSF flatcar is sometimes seen in its place, and a 9059 Lionel Lines SP caboose is sometimes found in place of the 9058. *(T)*

| | | — | — | 180 | 275 |

1865 CHESAPEAKE FLYER: 8800 Lionel Lines 4-4-2 locomotive and tender; 9035 Conrail boxcar; 9058 Lionel Lines SP caboose; 9017 Wabash gondola; 9018 DT & I hopper; 9036 Mobilgas tank car; 2717 extension bridge; 2180 road sign set; eight sections 5013 curved track; six sections 5018 straight track; 2905 lockon and wire; manual uncoupler; 2909 smoke fluid; transformer. *(T)*

| | | — | — | 150 | 250 |

1866 GREAT PLAINS EXPRESS: 8854 CP Rail GP-9 diesel; 9729 CP Rail boxcar; 9057 CP Rail SP caboose; 9121 L & N flatcar; 9140 Burlington gondola; 9011 Great Northern hopper; 9036 Mobilgas tank car; 2717 extension bridge; 10 sections 5013 curved track; seven sections 5018 straight track; 5027 pair manual switches; transformer. Pictured in catalogue with 9121 L & N

flatcar and 9140 Burlington gondola, but has also been seen with 9124 Penn Central flatcar and 9136 Republic Steel gondola as substitutes. C. Rohlfing comment. *(T)*

| | | — | — | 300 | 400 |

1867 MILWAUKEE LIMITED: 8855 Milwaukee Road SD-18 diesel; 9216 Great Northern auto carrier; 9411 Lackawanna boxcar; 9269 Milwaukee Road bay window caboose; 9276 Peabody quad hopper; 9876 Central Vermont refrigerator car; 9277 Cities Service tank car. Limited Collector set with no track or transformer. *(C)*

| | | — | — | 350 | 425 |

THE BLUE COMET: Passenger set, consumer catalogue: 8801 4-6-4 Hudson; 9536 baggage; 9537 combine; 9538 Pullman, 9539 Pullman; 9540 observation (9500-series short Madison passenger cars). Later addition from 1987 year-end brochure: 19000 diner. *(C, SE)*

| | | — | — | 700 | 800 |

AMTRAK: Budd railcars, consumer catalogue: 8868 baggage; 8869 passenger; 8870 passenger; 8871 baggage. *(C, SE)*

| | | — | — | 500 | 600 |

1978 Uncatalogued

1892 JCPENNEY LOGGING EMPIRE: Same as regular-issue 1862 Logging Empire set. At this point, Lionel was making maximum effort to market the inexpensive Logging Empire (also known as "Workin' On The Railroad") sets through its own distributors and through the large retail outlet stores. *(T, D)*

| | | — | — | 75 | 110 |

1893 TOYS 'R' US LOGGING EMPIRE: Same as regular-issue 1862 Logging Empire set, but with special decal sheet. The decals were to be applied to the boxcar. *(T, D)*

79N98765C SEARS LOGGING EMPIRE: Same as regular-issue 1862 Logging Empire set. The engine in this set was depicted incorrectly as 8601, which was a Rock Island locomotive made two years before. The engine actually made for the Logging Empire sets was the 8803 Santa Fe 0-4-0, which is correctly shown in the Lionel 1979 Advance catalogue. *(T, D)*

| | | — | — | 75 | 110 |

1868 SERVICE STATION SPECIAL: 8866 Minneapolis & St. Louis GP-9 diesel; 9726 Erie Lackawanna boxcar; 9271 Minneapolis & St. Louis bay window caboose; 9213 Minneapolis & St. Louis quad hopper; 9408 Lionel Lines circus stock car; 9138 Sunoco tank car; 8867 Minneapolis & St. Louis dummy GP-9 diesel available separately; estimated production: 6,000. This was the last Service Station set made until 1986, when the practice resumed under Lionel Trains, Inc. Readily available both as a complete set and as individual components, even though at least half these sets were broken up. *(T, SSS)*

| | | — | — | 225 | 300 |

1979 Catalogued

1864 SANTA FE DOUBLE DIESEL: Same as 1864 set from 1978. *(T)*

1865 CHESAPEAKE FLYER: Same as 1865 set from 1978. *(T)*

1866 GREAT PLAINS EXPRESS: This is the same set as the 1866 Great Plains Express from 1978, except that this year the 9417 CP Rail boxcar replaced the earlier 9729 CP Rail boxcar, a circumstance which led to considerable unhappiness on the part of collectors. *(T)*

| | | — | — | 250 | 350 |

1960 MIDNIGHT FLYER: 8902 Atlantic Coast Line 2-4-0 locomotive and slope-back tender; 9339 Great Northern boxcar;

Santa Fe Famous American Railroad Series No. 1 from 1979, separate-sale.
Top shelf: **8900 4-6-4 Hudson and tender.**
Second shelf: **9322 ATSF hopper; 9880 Santa Fe reefer.**
Third shelf: **7712 Santa Fe boxcar; 9321 ATSF tank car.**
Bottom shelf: **9323 ATSF bay window caboose; 9348 Santa Fe crane.**

	GD	VG	EXC	MT

9341 ACL SP caboose; 9340 ICG gondola; eight sections 5013 curved track; two sections 5018 straight track; DC power pack; 2905 lockon and wire. This set currently ranks as the least expensive modern Lionel set. This was the first appearance of this ACL engine and caboose, which have both since had more lives than the proverbial cat. *(T)* — — 60 80

1962 WABASH CANNONBALL: 8904 Wabash 2-4-2 locomotive and tender; 9035 Conrail boxcar; 9080 Wabash or 9346 Wabash SP caboose; 9016 Chessie hopper; 9036 Mobilgas tank car; eight sections 5013 curved track; four sections 5018 straight track; AC transformer; 2905 lockon and wire. The 1979 catalogue pictures this set with a 9346 Wabash SP caboose, but some sets are reported with the 9080. This has led to some confusion. Further reader comments are invited as to the identity of the caboose in this set. *(T)* — — 90 140

1963 BLACK RIVER FREIGHT: 8903 Rio Grande 2-4-2 locomotive and tender; 9077 Rio Grande SP caboose; 9026 Republic Steel flatcar; 9136 Republic Steel gondola; 9016 Chessie hopper; 2717 extension bridge; eight sections 5013 curved track; six sections 5018 straight track; DC power pack; 2181 telephone poles; 2180 road sign set; manumatic uncoupler; 2905 lockon and wire. *(T)* — — 65 90

1964 RADIO CONTROL EXPRESS: Battery-powered (8901) Union Pacific 0-4-0 locomotive and tender; boxcar; work caboose; operating dump car; gondola; log-loading mill; barrel loader; 10 wide-radius track sections; pair manual switches. This strange set was meant to run by radio remote-control. The rolling stock was based on the snap-on superstructure idea introduced in the Logging Empire sets. Since it was battery-powered, the catalogue also showed some unusual two-rail special track for the set. It was probably because of these major departures from Lionel's norm that it was shown in the Toy Fair catalogue but never manufactured. *(T)* **Not Manufactured**

1965 SMOKEY MOUNTAIN LINE: 8905 Smokey Mountain locomotive; no tender; 9357 Smokey Mountain bobber caboose; 9330 Kickapoo small coal dump car; 9030 Kickapoo half-gondola; 2180 road sign set; eight sections 5013 curved track; two sections 5018 straight track; DC power pack. This inexpensive set was similar to 1972's Kickapoo Valley set (like that one, the cars have no numbers), and was probably issued to use up leftover pieces from that set. The catalogue pictures it with an ATSF bobber caboose, but the Smokey Mountain bobber caboose was made for it. *(T)* — — 60 90

	GD	VG	EXC	MT

1970 THE SOUTHERN PACIFIC LIMITED: 8960 Southern Pacific U36C diesel; 8961 Southern Pacific U36C dummy; 9732 Southern Pacific boxcar; 9320 Fort Knox bullion car; 9316 Southern Pacific bay window caboose; 9315 Southern Pacific gondola; 9881 Rath refrigerator car; 9313 Gulf tank car. Limited Collector set with no track or transformer. This set was shown in the Toy Fair catalogue but deleted from the regular consumer catalogue because it was a rapid sell-out. It is therefore (technically) uncatalogued, but most collectors think of it as catalogued. *(C)* — — 550 650

1971 QUAKER CITY LIMITED: 8962 Reading U36B diesel; 9734 BAR boxcar; 9231 Reading bay window caboose; 9332 Reading crane car; 9336 CP Rail gondola; 9338 Pennsylvania Power & Light quad hopper; 9882 NYRB refrigerator car; 9331 Union 76 tank car. Limited Collector set with no track or transformer. *(C)* — — 400 460

SANTA FE: Famous American Railroad Series No. 1, consumer catalogue: 8900 4-6-4 Hudson; 7712 Santa Fe wood-sided boxcar; 9323 ATSF bay window caboose; 9322 ATSF hopper; 9880 Santa Fe refrigerator car; 9321 ATSF tank car. Later addition from Collector's Accessory Center brochure, 1979: 9348 Santa Fe crane. *(C, SE)* — — 600 650

PENNSYLVANIA: Congressional Limited passenger set, consumer catalogue: 8952-8953 Pennsylvania F-3 AA-units, green; 9570 baggage; 9571 William Penn coach; 9572 Molly Pitcher coach; 9573 Betsy Ross vista dome; 9574 Alexander Hamilton observation; long extruded aluminum passenger cars. Later additions from 1979 Collector's Accessory Center brochure: 8970-8971 Pennsylvania F-3 AA-units, tuscan; 9575 Thomas Edison coach. Later additions from 1980 Fall Collector Center brochure: 8059 F-3 B-unit, green; 8060 F-3 B-unit, tuscan. Later additions from 1981 Fall Collector Center brochure: 8164 F-3 B-unit, green, with horn; 9569 Paul Revere combine. Later addition from 1983 Fall Collector Center brochure: 7208 John Hancock diner. The reason there are two sets of F-3 diesels listed is that collector pressure forced Lionel to make a set of PRR tuscan F-3s, which are non-prototypical, in order to match the tuscan stripes on the passenger cars. Price for cars with either set of ABA units. *(C, SE)* — — 1800 2100

1979 Uncatalogued

1990 MYSTERY GLOW MIDNIGHT FLYER: Same as regular issue 1960 Midnight Flyer set, but with glow decals, road signs and barrel loader. Set was made for Creative Group, a catalogue merchandising outfit. *(T, D)* — — 70 100

1991 JCPENNEY WABASH CANNONBALL DELUXE EXPRESS: 8904 Wabash 2-4-2 locomotive and 1130T-type tender; 9035 Conrail boxcar; 9346 Wabash SP-type caboose; 9325 N & W flatcar with fences; barrel loader kit; short bridge; graduated trestle set; billboards; telephone poles; 12 sections 5013 curved track; six sections 5018 straight track for a figure-8 over-under layout. The 9346 caboose in this set is hard to find. JCPenney's catalogue number for this set is "X920-1666A". The engine was also available in the JCPenney catalogue as "X920-1674A". L. Bohn comment. *(T, D)* — — 100 160

1993 TOYS 'R' US MIDNIGHT FLYER: Same as regular-issue 1960 Midnight Flyer set, except 9365 Toys 'R' Us boxcar replaces the standard Great Northern boxcar. *(T, D)* — — 90 140

1980 Catalogued

1050 NEW ENGLANDER: 8007 NY, NH & Hartford 2-6-4 locomotive; 9035 Conrail boxcar; 9380 NY, NH and Hartford SP caboose; 9140 Burlington gondola; 9036 Mobilgas tank car; eight sections 5013 curved track; four sections 5018 straight track; telephone poles; manumatic uncoupler; 2905 lockon and wire; 4060 transformer; DC power pack. The previous edition of this Guide erroneously listed the caboose in this set as the 9346. *(T)* — — 100 150

1052 CHESAPEAKE FLYER: 8008 Chessie 4-4-2 locomotive; 9037 Conrail boxcar; 9381 Chessie SP caboose; 9017 Wabash gondola; 9038 Chessie hopper; 9036 Mobilgas tank car; 2717 extension bridge; 2180 road sign set; eight sections 5013 curved track; six sections 5018 straight track; 4065 DC transformer; 2905 lockon and wire. Reported production: 10,000. *(T)* — — 120 160

1053 THE JAMES GANG: 8005 ATSF General locomotive and tender; 9541 Santa Fe baggage/combine car; 9306 ATSF flatcar; 9305 Santa Fe stock car; 2784 freight platform kit; four plastic figures; two horses; six telephone poles; eight sections 5013 curved track; four sections 5018 straight track; DC power pack; 2905 lockon and wire. This is one of Lionel's more desirable Traditional Line sets. *(T)* — — 220 250

1070 THE ROYAL LIMITED: 8061 Western Maryland U36C diesel; 9432 Postwar Years boxcar; 9328 Chessie bay window caboose; 9329 Chessie crane car; 9234 Radioactive Waste flatcar; 9818 Western Maryland refrigerator car; 9344 Citgo tank car. Limited Collector set with no track or transformer. *(C)* — — 400 500

1071 MID-ATLANTIC LIMITED: 8063 Seaboard SD-9 diesel; 9433 Golden Years boxcar; 9372 Seaboard bay window caboose; 9233 Lionel transformer flatcar; 9371 Lantic Sugar quad hopper; 9370 Seaboard gondola; 9369 Sinclair tank car. Limited Collector set with no track or transformer. *(C)* — — 375 450

1072 CROSS COUNTRY EXPRESS: 8066 TP & W GP-20 diesel; 9428 TP & W boxcar; 9309 TP & W bay window caboose; 2303 Santa Fe manual gantry crane; 9379 ATSF gondola; 9374 Reading quad hopper; 9232 Allis Chalmers car; 9373 Getty tank car; eight sections 5013 curved track; six sections 5018 straight track; 4060 DC transformer; 2905 lockon and wire. The top-of-the-line Traditional set for 1980, this sleeper surprised many collectors with its unusual quality pieces. Collectors may have been confused by the DC transformer in this set. Actually, the engine has a Type II AC-DC universal motor, so it can run on both types of power, but Lionel supplied a DC transformer in the set. At the time, it emphasized the "quiet" nature of DC power, especially as it related to the E-unit, and in 1980 Lionel was in the process of heavily promoting DC power. Note that every other Traditional Line set this year had a DC transformer. The engines in the other sets are not so versatile as this diesel, however — trying to run their DC can motors on AC power will quickly destroy them. *(T)* — — 425 550

1960 MIDNIGHT FLYER: Same as 1960 set in 1979. *(T)*

1963 BLACK RIVER FREIGHT: Variation on the 1963 set from 1979, this set has a 9011 GN hopper rather than a 9016 Chessie hopper, and also has a 9140 Burlington gondola in place of the 9136 Republic Steel gondola in the earlier set. It is quite possible there are other variations. *(T)* — — 65 85

Black Cave Flyer set from 1982 displayed on colorful play mat. There are no numbers on the cars.

C. O'Dell Collection; B. Greenberg photograph

	GD	VG	EXC	MT

TEXAS & PACIFIC DIESEL: 8067 Texas & Pacific Alco diesel; Missouri Pacific boxcar; 9276 Texas & Pacific SP caboose; 9378 Lionel derrick car; 9375 Union Pacific flatcar with fences; 9140 Burlington gondola; 9039 Mobilgas tank car; four sections 5018 straight track; eight sections 5013 curved track; telephone poles; road signs; 4060 transformer; 2905 lockon and wire. This set was catalogued but never manufactured. The diesel, boxcar, flatcar and caboose were never made, but the other three cars exist. Similar Alco diesels were made for the Quicksilver set in 1982. *(T)* **Not Manufactured**

UNION PACIFIC: Famous American Railroad Series No. 2, consumer catalogue: 8002 Union Pacific locomotive; 9419 Union Pacific boxcar; 9368 Union Pacific bay window caboose; 9366 Union Pacific quad hopper; 9811 Pacific Fruit Express refrigerator car; 9367 Union Pacific tank car. Later addition from 1980 Fall Collector Center brochure: 9383 Union Pacific TOFC flatcar. (C, SE)   —   —   600   725

THE TEXAS ZEPHYR: Burlington passenger set from consumer catalogue: 8054-8055 F-3 AA-units; 9576 Silver Pouch baggage; 9577 Silver Halter coach; 9578 Silver Gladiola coach; 9579 Silver Kettle vista dome; 9580 Silver Veranda observation; long extruded-aluminum passenger cars. Later additions from

1980 Fall Collector Center brochure: 8062 F-3 B-unit; 9588 Silver Dome vista dome. *(C, SE)*   —   —   1150   1400

JOSHUA LIONEL COWEN: Commemorative boxcar set, consumer catalogue: 9429 Early Years; 9430 Standard Gauge Years; 9431 Prewar Years; 9432 Postwar Years (sold in Royal Limited set); 9433 Golden Years (sold in Mid-Atlantic set). Later addition from 1980 Fall Collector Center: 9434 The Man boxcar. Later additions from 1982 Spring Collector Center brochure: 8210 Joshua Lionel Cowen 4-6-4 Hudson steam locomotive; 6421 Joshua Lionel Cowen bay window caboose. *(C, SE)*
—   —   650   800

CHESSIE STEAM SPECIAL: Passenger set, consumer catalogue: 8003 2-8-4 steam locomotive; 9581 baggage; 9582 combine; 9583 Pullman; 9584 Pullman; 9585 observation (9500- series short Madison passenger cars). Later addition from 1986 year-end brochure: 9586 diner. *(C, SE)*   —   —   800   900

ROCK ISLAND & PEORIA: General set, consumer catalogue: 8004 4-4-0 General steam locomotive. Later additions from 1981 consumer catalogue: 9559 combine; 9560 coach; 9561 coach; General-style passenger cars. *(C, SE)*
—   —   250   325

GD   VG   EXC   MT

1980 Uncatalogued

No confirmed uncatalogued sets have been found from 1980, but it is possible that the 1993 Toys 'R' Us Midnight Flyer set was repeated this year. Further comments invited.

1981 Catalogued

1050 NEW ENGLANDER: Same as 1050 set from 1980. *(T)*

1053 THE JAMES GANG: Same as 1053 set from 1980. *(T)*

1072 CROSS COUNTRY EXPRESS: Same as 1072 set from 1980. *(T)*

1150 L. A. S. E. R. TRAIN: 8161 L. A. S. E. R. gas turbine; 6504 L. A. S. E. R. Helicopter flatcar; 6505 L. A. S. E. R. satellite 2 tracking flatcar; 6506 L. A. S. E. R. security car; 6507 L. A. S. E. R. ALCM flatcar; L. A. S. E. R. train play mat; eight sections 5013 curved track; four sections 5018 straight track; 4065 DC power pack. There are no numbers on the cars in this set. This unusual train is reminiscent of Lionel's "S.A.M.A.T." (Space And Military Action Trains) of the early 1960s. *(T)*   —   —   **160   200**

1151 UNION PACIFIC THUNDER FREIGHT: 8102 Union Pacific 4-4-2 locomotive and tender; 9035 Conrail boxcar; 6432 Union Pacific SP caboose; 9017 Wabash gondola; 9018 DT & I hopper; eight sections 5013 curved track; six sections 5018 straight track; 2717 extension bridge; 2180 road sign set; AC transformer; 2905 lockon and wire; manumatic uncoupler. This set was also sold with two additional billboards by JCPenney in 1981. *(T)*   —   —   **100   150**

1154 READING YARD KING: 8153 Reading NW-2 switcher; 6420 Reading transfer caboose; 9378 Lionel derrick car; 6200 Florida East Coast gondola; 9448 ATSF stock car; 6300 Corn Products tank car; eight sections 5013 curved track; four sections 5018 straight track; AC transformer; 2905 lockon and wire; manumatic uncoupler. Top-of-the-line Traditional set for 1981. This sleeper contains some hard-to-find and desirable pieces. *(T)*   —   —   **250   325**

1158 MAPLE LEAF LIMITED: 8152 Canadian Pacific SD-24 diesel; 9440 Reading boxcar; 9441 Pennsylvania boxcar; 6433 Canadian Pacific bay window caboose; 6508 Canadian Pacific crane car; 6103 Canadian National hopper; 6305 British Columbia tank car. Limited Collector set with no track or transformer. *(C)*   —   —   **500   575**

1160 GREAT LAKES LIMITED: 8151 Burlington SD-28 diesel; 9436 Burlington boxcar; 9387 Burlington bay window caboose; 9385 Alaska gondola; 9384 Great Northern operating hopper; 9437 Northern Pacific stock car; 9386 Pure Oil tank car. Limited Collector set with no track or transformer. *(C)*   —   —   **430   500**

1960 MIDNIGHT FLYER: Same as 1960 set from 1979-1980. *(T)*

1963 BLACK RIVER FREIGHT: Same as 1963 set from 1979-1980. *(T)*

NORFOLK & WESTERN: Passenger set, "Sneak Preview" brochure and consumer catalogue: 8100 4-8-4 steam locomotive; 9562 baggage; 9563 combine; 9564 coach; 9565 coach; 9566 observation (long extruded-aluminum passenger cars). Later addition from 1981 Fall Collector Center brochure: 9567 vista dome. Later addition from 1982 Fall Collector Center brochure: 7203 diner. Later addition from 1991 Stocking Stuffer brochure: 19108 full vista dome car. *(C, SE)*   —   —   **1700   2000**

ALTON LIMITED: Passenger set, "Sneak Preview" brochure and consumer catalogue: 8101 4-6-4 Hudson steam locomotive; 9554 baggage; 9555 combine; 9556 Pullman; 9557 Pullman; 955 observation (9500-series short Madison-style passenger cars). Later addition from 1986 year-end brochure: 9599 diner. *(C, SE)*   —   —   **800   95**

FAVORITE FOOD FREIGHT: Diesel and freight set, consumer catalogue: 8160 Burger King GP-20; 6449 Wendy's N5 caboose; 7509 Kentucky Fried Chicken refrigerator car; 7510 Re Lobster refrigerator car; 7511 Pizza Hut refrigerator car. Late additions from 1982 consumer catalogue: 7512 Arthur Treacher refrigerator car; 7513 Bonanza refrigerator car; 7514 Taco Bel refrigerator car. *(T, SE)*   —   —   **250   32**

GREAT NORTHERN: Famous American Railroad Series N 3, consumer catalogue: 3100 Great Northern 4-8-4 steam locomotive; 9449 Great Northern boxcar; 6438 Great Northern bay window caboose; 6102 Great Northern quad hopper; 9819 Western Fruit Express refrigerator car; 6304 Great Northern tank ca Later addition from 1981 Fall Collector Center brochure: 945 Great Northern stock car. *(C, SE)*   —   —   **700   82**

1981 Uncatalogued

1153 JCPENNEY THUNDERBALL FREIGHT: Same a regular-issue 1151 Union Pacific Thunder Freight set from 1981 except this version comes with two billboards (Lionel F-3 and Bab Ruth). The 1981 JCPenney catalogue also listed an unusual number of regular-issue Lionel accessories for sale, including th gateman, Rico station, sawmill, crane, and crossing gate. *(T, D)*   —   —   **120   17**

1157 LIONEL LEISURE WABASH CANNONBALL: 890 Wabash 2-4-2 steam locomotive and tender; 9376 Soo Line boxca 9058 or 9059 Lionel Lines SP caboose; 9325 N & W flatcar; 935 Pennzoil tank car. Set apparently made for exclusive distributio through Lionel Leisure Kiddie City stores. Other details ur known. We are asking for independent confirmation of the exist ence of this set and its contents.   **NR:**

1159 TOYS 'R' US MIDNIGHT FLYER: Same as regular issue 1960 Midnight Flyer set from 1979-1981, except for this se the special 9388 Toys 'R' Us boxcar replaces the 9339 Grea Northern boxcar. M. Didier comment. *(T, D)*   —   —   **90   14**

1982 Catalogued

1053 JAMES GANG: Same as 1053 set from 1980 and 1981. *(T*

1150 L. A. S. E. R. TRAIN: Same as 1150 set from 1981. *(T*

1151 UNION PACIFIC THUNDER FREIGHT: Same a 1151 set from 1981. *(T)*

1154 READING YARD KING: Same as 1154 set from 1981 *(T, C)*

1155 CANNONBALL FREIGHT: 8902 ACL 2-4-0 locomotive and tender; 9035 Conrail boxcar; 9341 ACL SP caboose; 9033 Pen Central gondola; play mat; manual barrel loader; two 271 billboards; 2180 road sign set; 2181 telephone poles; DC powe pack; eight sections 5013 curved track; four sections 5018 straigh track; 2905 lockon and wire. This set has an 1100-series numbe but was not catalogued until 1982. There may have been som delay from a planned 1981 release. *(T)*   —   —   **60   9**

	GD	VG	EXC	MT

1252 HEAVY IRON: 8213 Rio Grande 2-4-2 locomotive and tender; 9339 Great Northern boxcar; 9077 Rio Grande SP caboose; 9020 Union Pacific flatcar; 9031 Nickel Plate gondola; 2180 road sign set; 2309 mechanical crossing gate; eight sections 5013 curved track; four sections 5018 straight track; 4850 AC transformer; 2905 lockon and wire. *(T)* — — 100 140

1253 QUICKSILVER EXPRESS: 8268 Texas & Pacific Alco diesel; 8269 Texas & Pacific Alco dummy; 7200, 7201 and 7202 "Quicksilver Express" O27 streamlined passenger cars; 2311 mechanical semaphore; eight sections 5013 curved track; four sections 5018 straight track; AC transformer; 2905 lockon and wire. See the Factory Errors and Prototypes chapter for what may be the prototype for this set. *(T)* — — 300 400

1254 BLACK CAVE FLYER: 8212 Black Cave 0-4-0 locomotive and tender; 7905 Black Cave boxcar; 6478 Black Cave SP caboose; 6203 Black Cave gondola; play mat; die-cut cave scene; glow-in-the-dark decals; DC power pack; 2905 lockon and wire; eight sections 5013 curved track; two sections 5018 straight track. The cars in this set have no numbers on them. *(T)* — — 100 150

1260 THE CONTINENTAL LIMITED: 8266 Norfolk & Western SD-24 diesel; 9461 Norfolk Southern boxcar; 9738 Illinois Terminal boxcar; 6900 Norfolk & Western extended vision caboose; 6202 Western Maryland gondola; 6106 Norfolk & Western quad hopper; 7301 Norfolk & Western stock car. Limited collector set with no track or transformer. This set marked the first appearance of Lionel's extended vision caboose. *(C)* — — 525 600

SOUTHERN PACIFIC: "Daylight" passenger set, Spring Collector Center brochure and consumer catalogue: 8260 and 8262 F-3 AA-units; 9589 baggage; 9590 combine; 9591 coach; 9592 coach; 9593 observation (long extruded-aluminum passenger cars). Later additions from 1982 Fall Collector Center brochure:: 8261 F-3 B-unit; 7204 diner. Later addition from 1983 Collector Preview brochure: 8307 4-8-4 steam locomotive. Later additions from 1983 Fall Collector Center brochure: 7211 vista dome. Later addition from 1990 Stocking Stuffer brochure: 19107 full vista dome. The most expensive and difficult-to-assemble Lionel set in the modern era. Price for cars, ABA diesels, and the 8307 locomotive. *(C, SE)* — — 3700 4200

1982 Uncatalogued

1261 BLACK CAVE FLYER: Same as regular-issue 1254 Black Cave Flyer set, except with an added dynamite shack. This set was marketed to Montgomery Ward and Service Merchandise. The regular Black Cave Flyer was also sold by Sears as 49N95211. *(T, D)* — — 100 150

1262 TOYS 'R' US HEAVY IRON: This is the same as the regular-issue 1252 Heavy Iron set, but the GN boxcar is replaced by the special 7912 Toys 'R' Us operating giraffe boxcar, which was also one of the first recreations of the fine postwar 6454 short boxcar. Although it has "1252" on the box, Lionel's records list this set as "1262". *(T, D)* — — 200 300

1263 (XU671-0701A) JCPENNEY OVERLAND FREIGHT: (Number unknown) 0-4-0 Atlantic Coast Line locomotive and slope-back tender; 9339 Great Northern short boxcar; 9341 ACL SP caboose; red gondola with white lettering; 9016 Chessie hopper; 9036 Mobilgas tank car; 2717 extension bridge; 2309 mechanical crossing gate; 2311 semaphore; 14 road signs; 10 telephone poles; 16 track sections; two billboards; power pack. Not only is

this one of the more extensive Lionel uncatalogued sets to date, but it has two undefined train items, at least according to the JCPenney catalogue. The 0-4-0 engine has the ACL logo, but no known Lionel 0-4-0 engine came as an ACL. Nor is the fact that the description lists the engine with smoke consistent with features of known ACL engines. The gondola pictured is also strange. It is red with white lettering, but the pattern is not consistent with the only similar gondola made at the time — the 6206 C & IM. It is also possible it is a 9017 Wabash. It is possible this unusual set actually came with regular-issue pieces and the pictured items were never made. L. Bohn comments. Comments from owners of this set would be appreciated. *(T, D)* NRS

1264 NIBCO EXPRESS: 8182 Nibco NW-2 switcher; 9035 Conrail boxcar; 6482 Nibco Express SP caboose; 9033 Penn Central gondola; two special billboards. The engine and caboose are unique to this set, made as a special promotion for Nibco Plumbing products. Note that an extremely scarce 7520 Nibco classic boxcar was issued later, not as part of the set, although today they are often found together. This sort of special promotion set began increasing in frequency at this point in Lionel's history. The set was made in 1981, but distributed in 1982. Regular readers of our Guides will find a picture of this set on p. 29 of the first edition of this book (*Greenberg's Guide to Lionel/Fundimensions, 1970-1985*). *(T, D)* — — 175 225

1265 TAPPAN SPECIAL: 8902 Atlantic Coast Line 2-4-0 locomotive and tender; 7908 Tappan boxcar; 9341 Atlantic Coast Line SP caboose; 9340 Illinois Central Gulf gondola; two billboards; road signs; 4660 DC transformer; eight sections 5013 curved track; two sections 5018 straight track; lockon; estimated production: 6,000 sets. The Tappan number for this set is "88-1036-10". Sponsored by Mike Moore of Town House Appliances in Chicago, who also sponsored the similar 1986 Town House set. The Town House/Lionel special sets have been a tradition in the Chicago area since the mid-1970s. *(T, D)* — — 100 150

1983 Catalogued

1252 HEAVY IRON: Same as 1252 set from 1982. *(T)*

1253 QUICKSILVER EXPRESS: Same as 1253 set from 1982. *(T)*

1351 BALTIMORE & OHIO: 8315 B & O General locomotive and tender; 7217, 7215 and 7216 Baltimore & Ohio General-style passenger cars; station platform; five telephone poles; eight sections 5013 curved track; six sections 5018 straight track; 4065 DC power pack; 2905 lockon and wire. *(T)* — — 250 350

1352 ROCKY MOUNTAIN FREIGHT: 8313 Santa Fe 0-4-0 locomotive and tender; 7909 L & N boxcar; 6430 Santa Fe SP caboose; 9020 Union Pacific flatcar; eight sections 5013 curved track; four sections 5018 straight track; play mat; 4065 DC power pack; 2905 lockon and wire. *(T)* — — 60 100

1353 SOUTHERN STREAK: 8314 Southern 0-4-0 locomotive and tender; 7902 ATSF boxcar; 6434 Southern SP caboose; 6207 Southern gondola; 6115 Southern hopper; five telephone poles; 2180 road sign set; 2717 extension bridge; eight sections 5013 curved track; six sections 5018 straight track; DC power pack; manumatic uncoupler; 2905 lockon and wire. *(T)* — — 70 100

1355 Commando Assault Train set from 1983.

C. O'Dell Collection; B. Greenberg photograph

	GD	VG	EXC	MT

1354 NORTHERN FREIGHT FLYER: 8375 C & NW GP-7 diesel; 6428 C & NW transfer caboose; 9236 C & NW derrick car; 9399 C & NW coal dump car; 6206 C & IM gondola; 6113 Illinois Central hopper; 6522 C & NW searchlight car; 2311 mechanical semaphore; 2309 mechanical crossing gate; 2181 telephone poles; 2180 road sign set; 12 sections 5013 curved track; seven sections 5018 straight track; 5020 90-deg crossover; AC transformer; 2905 lockon and wire. This is the top-of-the-line Traditional set for 1983, '84 and '85. *(T)* — — **275 350**

1355 COMMANDO ASSAULT TRAIN: 8377 U. S. Marines gas turbine; 6435 Marines transfer caboose; 6561 Marines cruise missile flatcar; 6562 Marines flatcar w/crates; 6564 Marines flatcar w/tanks; play mat; eight sections 5013 curved track; two sections 5018 straight track; 14 soldier figures; operating supply depot kit; 4065 DC power pack; 2905 lockon and wire. The set comes with decals to be applied to the cars — the rolling stock comes with no numbers when found new-in-the-box. Price for new should include an unused decal sheet. *(T)*

— — **160 200**

1361 GOLD COAST LIMITED: 8376 Union Pacific SD-40 diesel; 9290 Union Pacific operating barrel car; 9468 Union Pacific boxcar; 6904 Union Pacific extended vision caboose; 6114 C & NW quad hopper; 9888 Green Bay & Western refrigerator car; 6357 Frisco tank car. Limited collector set with no track or transformer. *(C)* — — **800 1000**

NEW YORK CENTRAL: Twentieth Century Limited passenger set, 1983 Collector Preview and consumer catalogue: 8370 and 8372 F-3 AA-units; 8371 F-3 B-unit; 9594 baggage; 9595 combine; 9596 coach; 9597 coach; 9598 observation (long extruded-aluminum passenger cars). Later addition from 1983 Fall Collector Center brochure: 7207 diner. Later addition from 1984 Spring Preview brochure: 8206 4-6-4 Hudson. Price for cars and ABA diesels, not Hudson. *(C, SE)* — — **1300 1600**

SOUTHERN: Famous American Railroad Series No. 4, consumer catalogue: 8309 2-8-4 Southern steam locomotive; 9451 Southern boxcar; 6431 Southern bay window caboose; 6104 Southern quad hopper; 9887 Fruit Growers Express refrigerator

02 Chessie System set from 1984-1985. 1984 catalogue incorrectly pictures the 8403 engine as 8402.

C. O'Dell Collection; B. Schwab photograph

	GD	VG	EXC	MT

car; 6306 Southern tank car. Later addition from 1983 Fall Collector Center brochure: 7304 Southern stock car. *(C, SE)*

			740	800

LIONEL LINES: Diesel freight set, Fall Collector Center brochure: 8380 Lionel Lines SD-28 diesel; 9239 Lionel Lines N5C caboose; 9849 Lionel refrigerator car. Later addition from 1982 Fall Collector Center brochure: 5712 Lionel Electric Trains wood-sided refrigerator car (actually the first piece of the set made, predates all others). Later additions from 1984 Spring Collector Center brochure: 6214 Lionel Lines gondola; 6313 Lionel Lines tank car. Later addition from 1986 year-end brochure: 5733 Lionel Lines bunk car. Later addition from 1987 year-end brochure: 19303 Lionel Lines quad hopper. Later addition from 1990 consumer catalogue: 16323 Lionel Lines TOFC flatcar. The 9492 boxcar from 1986 is sometimes considered part of this set. Very difficult set to assemble. This set was prompted by the unauthorized painting of Lionel rolling stock in this manner by a small new England firm. *(C, SE)*

			700	900

1983 Uncatalogued

1346 MONTGOMERY WARD CROSS COUNTRY EXPRESS: Same as regular-issue 1072 Cross-Country Express set made originally in 1980, complete with the DC power pack. The Montgomery Ward catalogue number for this set is 48T21012. An additional landscaping kit, 48T21325, was also available through Montgomery Ward. This included a grass mat, tunnel, 12 assorted trees, eight-figure set, and material for earth or roads. L. Bohn comments. *(T, D)*

			475	600

1349 TOYS 'R' US HEAVY IRON: Same as 1262 Heavy Iron set listed under 1982, with special 7912 car. (T, D)

1362 LIONEL LINES EXPRESS: 8374 Burlington Northern NW-2 switcher; 7902 Santa Fe short boxcar; 6427 Burlington Northern caboose; 9020 union Pacific flatcar; 6207 Southern short gondola with two canisters; telephone poles; road signs; two billboards (MPC model kits and Lionel F-3); eight sections 5013 curved track; four sections 5018 straight track; transformer; lock and wires. This set, using all regularly-catalogued pieces (includ-

B. Dyson Collection; B. Schwab photograph

1451 Erie Lackawanna Limited set: Catalogued in 1984, but not produced until 1985.
Top shelf: 6906 extended vision caboose; 8458 SD-40.
Second shelf: 6118 covered quad hopper; 9474 boxcar.
Third shelf: 7303 long stock car; 6210 long gondola.
Bottom shelf: 6524 crane car.

	GD	VG	EXC	MT

ing two from the Southern Streak set), was a little-known exclusive sold only through the Lionel Leisure-Kiddie City stores. L. Caponi comment. — — **120 150**

1984 Catalogued

1351 BALTIMORE & OHIO: Same as 1351 set from 1983. *(T)*

1352 ROCKY MOUNTAIN FREIGHT: Same as 1352 set from 1983. *(T)*

1353 SOUTHERN STREAK: Same as 1353 set from 1983. *(T)*

1354 NORTHERN FREIGHT FLYER: Same as 1354 set from 1983. *(T, C)*

1355 COMMANDO ASSAULT TRAIN: Same as 1355 set from 1983. *(T)*

	GD	VG	EXC	MT

1402 CHESSIE SYSTEM: 8403 Chessie 4-4-2 locomotive and tender; 6485 Chessie SP caboose; 6211 C & O gondola; 7401 Chessie stock car; 6312 C & O tank car; five telephone poles; 2180 road sign set; eight sections 5013 curved track; four sections 5018 straight track; transformer; 2905 lockon and wire; manumatic uncoupler. The catalogue incorrectly pictures the engine as 8402. This set was sold unchanged by JCPenney in 1985. *(T)*
— — **140 200**

1403 REDWOOD VALLEY EXPRESS: 8410 Redwood Valley General locomotive and tender; 6912 Redwood Valley SP caboose; 6574 Redwood Valley short crane car; 6573 Redwood Valley small log dump car; 6575 Redwood Valley flatcar with fences; barrel loader kit; five telephone poles; 2180 road sign set; eight sections 5013 curved track; four sections 5018 straight track; DC power pack; 2905 lockon and wire; manumatic uncoupler.

	GD	VG	EXC	MT

This inexpensive starter set was a derivative of the Workin' On The Railroad sets from 1978. *(T)* — — 190 225

1451 ERIE LACKAWANNA LIMITED: 8458 Erie-Lackawanna SD-40 diesel; 9474 Erie-Lackawanna boxcar; 6906 Erie-Lackawanna extended vision caboose; 6524 Erie-Lackawanna crane car; 6210 Erie-Lackawanna gondola; 6118 Erie quad hopper; 7303 Erie stock car. Limited Collector set with no track or transformer. This set was catalogued in 1984 but not made until 1985 due to delays in Mexican production. An 18202 Erie-Lackawanna dummy SD-40 was sold in 1989. Price for boxed set only. *(C)* — — 650 750

PENNSYLVANIA: Famous American Railroads Series No. 5, consumer catalogue: 8404 6-8-6 S-2 Pennsylvania steam locomotive; 9456 Pennsylvania automobile boxcar; 9476 Pennsylvania boxcar; 6908 Pennsylvania N5C caboose: 6123 Pennsylvania quad hopper; 6307 Pennsylvania tank car. Later addition from 1989 holiday brochure: 19510 Pennsylvania stock car. *(C, SE)* — — 700 800

UNION PACIFIC: Passenger set, consumer catalogue: 8480 and 8482 F-3 AA units; 8481 F-3 B unit; 9545 baggage; 9546 combine; 9547 observation; 9548 coach; 9549 coach; 7210 diner (long extruded aluminum passenger cars). *(C, SE)* — — 1000 1200

1984 Uncatalogued

TOYS 'R' US HEAVY IRON: Same as 1262 Heavy Iron set listed under 1982, with special 7912 car. *(T, D)*

1985 Catalogued

1353 SOUTHERN STREAK: Same as 1353 sets from 1983-1984. *(T)*

1354 NORTHERN FREIGHT FLYER: Same as 1354 sets from 1983-1984. *(T, C)*

1402 CHESSIE SYSTEM: Same as 1402 set from 1984. *(T)*

1403 REDWOOD VALLEY EXPRESS: Same as 1403 set from 1984. *(T)*

1451 ERIE LACKAWANNA LIMITED: Same as 1451 set from 1984. *(C)*

1501 MIDLAND FREIGHT: 8512 Santa Fe 0-4-0 locomotive; 6494 AT & SF bobber caboose; 6576 ATSF short crane car; 6258 ATSF gondola; 6150 ATSF hopper; eight sections 5013 curved track; two sections 5018 straight track; five telephone poles; DC power pack; 2905 lockon and wire. Also offered in the 1985 and 1986 JCPenney Christmas catalogues unchanged from the Lionel version, but in 1986 the set came with extra materials: two 25" x 50" mats, large cardboard tunnel, trees, people, road signs and landscaping; these items apparently made by Life-Like O Scale products. L. Bohn comment. *(T)* — — 80 120

1502 YARD CHIEF: 8516 New York Central 0-4-0 locomotive and tender; 5735 NYC bunk car; 6916 NYC work caboose; 6579 NYC crane car; X6260 NYC gondola; 6529 NYC searchlight car. The catalogue pictures numbers as 6127 bunk car, 6325 crane car and 9247 searchlight car, but actual numbers were 5735, 6579 and 6529, respectively. C. Rohlfing comment. This set came with no track or transformer. *(T)* — — 225 300

1552 BURLINGTON NORTHERN LIMITED: 8585 Burlington Northern SD-40 diesel; 6234 BN Standard O boxcar; 6235 BN Standard O boxcar; 6236 BN Standard O boxcar; 6237 BN

Standard O boxcar; 6238 BN Standard O boxcar; 6913 BN extended vision caboose. This set, in which all the boxcars match except for numbers, was Lionel's first entry into the realm of "unit trains." It is also the first Lionel set to feature all Standard O freight cars. Limited Collector set with no track or transformer. An add-on 6239 boxcar was sold in 1986, and a dummy 18208 SD-40 (numbered 8586) was announced in the 1991 Stocking Stuffer brochure. *(C)* — — 550 600

ILLINOIS CENTRAL: "City of New Orleans" passenger set, consumer catalogue: 8580 and 8581 F-3 AA-units; 8582 F-3 B-unit; 7220 baggage; 7221 combine; 7222 coach; 7223 coach; 7224 diner; 7225 observation (long extruded-aluminum passenger cars). Also catalogued in 1987. *(C, SE)* — — 1200 1400

1985 Uncatalogued

1506 SEARS CENTENNIAL: Identical to 1984-85 Chessie System regular-catalogue set, except Chessie short stock car is replaced by special edition 7920 Sears Centennial O27-style short boxcar. Sears catalogue number is 49C95339C. The car in this set had its logo misspelled "CENTENIAL" — this can even be discerned in the Sears catalogue. Note: The car reappeared in 1986, but in a Nickel Plate Special set, and this time the spelling was correct. *(T, D)* — — 200 275

1512 JCPENNEY MIDLAND FREIGHT: Same as regularly-catalogued 1501 Midland Freight set. JCPenney catalogue number is "XU671-1816A". *(T, D)*

1549 TOYS 'R' US HEAVY IRON: Same as Heavy Iron sets from Toys 'R' Us in previous years (1982-1984), except this year the 7914 Toys 'R' Us operating Geoffrey Giraffe car is used as the store special. Note: this set was also available, unchanged (including number) from Toys 'R' Us in 1986, 1987, 1988 and 1989. *(T, D)* — — 220 270

1986 Catalogued

1501 MIDLAND FREIGHT: Same as 1501 set from 1985. *(T)*

1502 YARD CHIEF: Same as 1502 set from 1985. *(T)*

1602 NICKEL PLATE SPECIAL: 8617 Nickel Plate 4-4-2 locomotive; 7926 Nickel Plate boxcar; 6919 Nickel Plate SP caboose; 6254 Nickel Plate gondola with canisters; 6137 Nickel Plate hopper; five telephone poles; 14 road signs; 2309 mechanical crossing gate; eight sections 5013 curved track; four sections 5018 straight track; lockon; 4045 transformer. This set has frequently been used as a department store special and as a merchandise premium set without change. *(T)* — — 140 200

1615 CANNONBALL EXPRESS: 8625 Pennsylvania 2-4-0 locomotive; 7925 Erie Lackawanna boxcar; 6921 Pennsylvania SP caboose; 6585 Pennsylvania flatcar; 6177 Reading hopper; five telephone poles; 14 road signs; 2905 lockon and wire; 2717 extension bridge; eight sections 5013 curved track; four sections 5018 straight track; DC power pack; manumatic uncoupler. *(T)* — — 85 95

1652 B & O FREIGHT: 8662 B&O GP-7 diesel; 6918 B & O SP caboose; 9335 B & O operating log dump car; 6138 B & O quad hopper; 6314 B & O tank car; 5739 B & O tool car. Limited collector set with no track or transformer. Although there were technically no boxed Collector sets catalogued in 1986, most hobbyists view this set as a collector-level item. It is certainly the top-of-the-line set offered in 1986. *(C)* — — 200 250

S. Goodman Collection; B. Schwab photogr

Separate-sale Lionel Lines set (not shown: 16323 flatcar with two vans from 1990). Lionel continues to add to this set today.
Top shelf: 5712 reefer from 1982; 8380 SD-28 from 1983.
Second shelf: 5733 bunk car from 1986; 9492 boxcar from 1986; 9849 reefer from 1983.
Third shelf: 16318 flatcar (not technically part of set); 6313 tank car from 1983-84; 16615 searchlight (not technically part of this set).
Bottom shelf: 19303 quad hopper from 1987; 6214 gondola from 1984-85; 9239 N5C caboose from 1983.

	GD	VG	EXC	MT

JERSEY CENTRAL: "Miss Liberty" commemorative, consumer catalogue: 8687 Jersey Central Fairbanks-Morse diesel; 7404 Jersey Central boxcar; 6917 Jersey Central extended vision caboose. *(C, SE)* — — 475 600

WABASH: Fallen Flags Series No. 1, consumer catalogue: 8610 4-6-2 Wabash steam locomotive; 7227 diner; 7228 baggage; 7229 combine; 7230 Pullman; 7231 Pullman; 7232 observation (9500-style short Madison passenger cars). Also catalogued in 1987. This set was a slow seller at the beginning, partly because of a poor photo in the 1986 catalogue, but it later became very valuable. *(C, SE)* — — 1200 1400

B & A HUDSON AND STANDARD O CARS: 8606 Boston & Albany Hudson; 6232 Illinois Central Standard O boxcar; 6920 Boston & Albany Standard O caboose; 6907 New York Central Standard O caboose; 6233 Canadian Pacific Standard O flatcar; 6231 Railgon Standard O gondola; 6134 Burlington Northern two-bay ACF hopper; 6135 Chicago & North Western two-bay ACF hopper; 6230 Erie-Lackawanna Standard O refrigerator car. This (technically uncatalogued) set was marketed together by Lionel in a late-1986 direct mail flyer; and, although it contains two cabooses, is often found as a separate-sale set today. There is, however, a wide fluctuation in buy-sell prices. *(C, SE)* — — 2500 3100

1986 Uncatalogued

1512 JCPENNEY MIDLAND FREIGHT: Same as regularly-catalogued 1501 Midland Freight set and the 1512 JCPenney set from 1985, except this time JCPenney offered extra landscaping materials, known as an "environment"): two 25" x 50" mats,

large cardboard tunnel, trees, people, road signs and landscaping these items apparently made by Life-Like O Scale products JCPenney catalogue number is "XU671-1980A". L. Bohn comment. *(T, D)* — — 100 14(

1602 JCPENNEY NICKEL PLATE ROAD: Presumabl the same as the regular-issue Nickel Plate set. Further detail requested. *(T, D)* NR!

1606 SEARS CENTENNIAL: Identical to 1986 Nickel Plate Special regularly-catalogued set, except Nickel Plate short boxca is replaced by special edition 7920 Sears Centennial O27-style short boxcar. Similar in concept to the 1985 Sears set except the baseline set changed. The special 7920 car had the word "CENTENNIAL" correctly spelled this time. Sears catalogue numbe is 49N95204C. *(T, D)* — — 180 250

1608 AMERICAN EXPRESS GENERAL SET: 863(Western & Atlantic General-style locomotive; 7241 coach and 7242 baggage/combine Western & Atlantic General-style passenger cars; 6587 Western & Atlantic flatcar; 7312 Western & Atlantic short stock car. Similar to regularly-catalogued General set of 1977-78, except with an extra stock car. This set marked an interesting first for Lionel, and previewed the more intriguing and complex uncatalogued sets that would soon follow. It is the first uncatalogued set (other than the Coke and Liberty Special sets, which were at any rate announced in Lionel flyers) in which all the pieces are unique to this set. As a result this is one of the more desirable uncatalogued Lionel sets, and is quite hard to find. *(C, D)* — — 300 35(

1658 TOWN HOUSE SET: 8902 Atlantic Coast Line 2-4-(locomotive and tender; 7931 Town House boxcar; 9341 Atlantic

Great Northern Fallen Flags Series No. 3 separate-sale set from 1988.
Top shelf: 18302 EP-5 electric with Magnetraction.
Second shelf: 19401 long gondola; 19205 double-door automobile boxcar.
Third shelf: 19304 covered quad hopper; 19505 refrigerator car.
Bottom shelf: 19402 crane car; 19703 extended vision caboose.

M. Solly Collection; B. Schwab photograph

	GD	VG	EXC	MT

Coast Line SP caboose; 4660 DC transformer; eight sections 5013 curved track; two 5018 straight track; lockon. Special promotion set for Town House Appliances store of Niles, Illinois. Essentially the same as earlier Tappan set from 1982, but without the extra gondola. *(T, D)* — — **100** **140**

1685 TRUE VALUE FREIGHT FLYER: Same as regularly-catalogued 91687 Freight Flyer set from 1987, except that a special 7930 True Value short boxcar replaced the 9035 Conrail boxcar. The Freight Flyer set itself was not regularly catalogued until 1987, so that this set actually predates it, as do the 1658 Town House set and the 1686 Kay-Bee set listed in this section. Apparently Lionel liked the possibilities of this inexpensive DC set, so it released it as the Freight Flyer in 1987. *(T, D)* — — **100** **150**

1686 KAY-BEE FREIGHT FLYER: Same as regularly-catalogued 91687 Freight Flyer from 1987, except this set has the

	GD	VG	EXC	MT

7932 Kay-Bee short boxcar instead of the 9035 Conrail boxcar. This is the one and only special made for Kay-Bee Toys. *(T, D)* — — **90** **140**

1632 THE SANTA FE WORK TRAIN: 8635 ATSF 0-4-0 switcher; 5745 ATSF bunk car; 6496 ATSF work caboose; 6593 ATSF crane car; 6272 ATSF gondola; 5760 ATSF tool car. This is the 1986 Service Station Special set, reviving this series after a seven-year absence. Very strong seller as an intact set. *(T, SSS)* — — **245** **270**

1987 Catalogued

11700 CONRAIL LIMITED: 18200 Conrail SD-40 diesel; 17201 Conrail Standard O boxcar; 17602 Conrail Standard O wood-sided caboose; 17501 Conrail Standard O flatcar; 17401 Conrail Standard O gondola; 17002 Conrail ACF hopper; 17301 Conrail Standard O refrigerator car. Limited Collector set with no track or transformer. The pieces in this set are among the first modern Lionel cars made with five-digit numbers. Some set boxes

Western Maryland Fallen Flags Series No. 4 from 1989. All are separate-sale items.
Top shelf: **18501** Western Maryland NW-2 switcher.
Second shelf: **19214** WM boxcar; **19511** WM reefer.
Third shelf: **19403** WM gondola; **19601** North American tank car.
Bottom shelf: **19704** WM extended vision caboose; **19404** WM TOFC flatcar.

S. Goodman Collection; B. Schwab photograph

	GD	VG	EXC	MT

for the Conrail Limited come marked "1986" rather than "1987". J. Nowaczyk comment. *(C)* — — **600** **700**

11701 RAIL BLAZER: 18700 Rock Island 0-4-0 switcher; 16200 Rock Island boxcar; 16500 Rock Island bobber caboose; 16300 Rock Island flatcar with fences; 16304 Rail Blazer gondola in orange; trackside snap-together crane; two cable reels; five telephone poles; 20-piece crate load; eight sections 5013 curved track; two sections 5018 straight track; manumatic uncoupler; 4065 DC power pack; lockon. *(T)* — — **80** **100**

11702 BLACK DIAMOND: 18800 Lehigh Valley GP-9 diesel; 16501 Lehigh Valley SP caboose; 16609 Lehigh Valley derrick car; 16305 Lehigh Valley ore car; 16608 Lehigh Valley searchlight car; mechanical semaphore; five telephone poles; 14 road signs; eight sections 5013 curved track; six sections 5018 straight track; manumatic uncoupler; 4050 transformer; lockon. This was the top-of-the-line Traditional set in 1987. *(T)* — — **270** **320**

61602 NICKEL PLATE SPECIAL: Same as 1602 set from 1986. The "6" prefix designates that the set was originally made before the 1987 numbering system change-over. *(T)*

61615 CANNONBALL EXPRESS: Same as 1615 set from 1986. *(T)*

91687 FREIGHT FLYER: 8902 Atlantic Coast Line 2-4-0 locomotive; 9035 Conrail boxcar; 9341 ACL SP caboose; 9033 Penn Central gondola; two white canisters; eight sections 5013 curved track; two sections 5018 straight track; manumatic uncoupler; DC power pack; lockon. The Freight Flyer served as the least expensive bottom-of-the-line Traditional set from 1987 through 1990. It has also been used as the basis for many inexpensive uncatalogued special sets in recent years. The unusual number (a "9" or a "6" prefix) for this and a few later sets was used to designate older rolling stock (pre-1987) reissued in a post-1987 set (five-digit system). The set was based on several uncatalogued sets, using this engine and caboose, made for Town House, Kay-Bee and True Value in 1986. Hence the "16" portion of the number. *(T)* — — **55** **65**

PENNSYLVANIA: O27 passenger set, consumer catalogue: 18602 4-4-2 steam locomotive; 16000 vista dome; 16001 coach; 16002 coach; 16003 observation; 16009 combine (1988) (short 027 streamlined passenger cars). Later additions from 1988 consumer catalogue: 18901 and 18902 Alco AA diesel pair. Later addition from 1989 consumer catalogue: 16022 baggage. Later addition from 1990 consumer catalogue: 16031 diner. Price with cars and one engine. *(T, SE)* — — **250** **300**

MILWAUKEE ROAD: Fallen Flags Series No. 2, consumer catalogue: 18500 Milwaukee Road GP-9; 19204 Milwaukee Road

	GD	VG	EXC	MT

boxcar; 19701 Milwaukee Road N5C caboose; 19400 Milwaukee Road gondola; 19302 Milwaukee Road quad hopper; 19500 Milwaukee Road refrigerator car; 19600 Milwaukee Road tank car. Later addition from 1990 Stocking Stuffers brochure: 19515 Milwaukee Road stock car. *(C, SE)* — — **400 500**

THE MINT SET: Bullion car set from 1987 consumer catalogue: 18300 Pennsylvania GG-1 locomotive; 19702 PRR N5C caboose. Also includes bullion cars released earlier and later: 7515 Denver (1982); 7517 Philadelphia (1982); 7518 Carson City (1983); 7522 New Orleans (1985); 7530 Dahlonega (1986); 9320 Fort Knox (1979); 9349 San Francisco (1980); 19406 West Point (1991). *(C, SE)* — — **1000 1200**
Note: There are three Special Production bullion cars, two made by the TCA. The 9319 TCA car in blue, made in 1979, exists in sufficient quantities to sometimes considered part of this set. A very rare variation of the 7522 New Orleans car, with added white lettering on the windows, also exists, made for the 1986 convention banquet. This car, however, was made in such small numbers that it is not generally considered part of the larger set. Add $250 to the set price for each of these cars if they are included. Another overprinted 7518 Carson City bullion car was made in 1984 for the Inland Empire Train Collectors Association of California, but this too is not generally considered part of the set.

1987 Uncatalogued

11750 MCDONALD'S NICKEL PLATE SPECIAL: Same as regular-issue 6102 Nickel Plate Special set, but marketed through a contest at McDonald's. 1,100 made. J. Kouba comment. *(T, D)*

11751 (49C95171C) SEARS PENNSYLVANIA PASSENGER TRAIN: 18602 Pennsylvania 4-4-2 locomotive and tender; 16000, 16001 and 16003 Pennsylvania O27 streamlined passenger cars; eight sections curved track; two sections straight track; five telephone poles; 4050; lockon; wires. All the rolling stock in the set is also available for separate-sale. According to our sources, Lionel made this set, which comes in a white box with a brown and white paste-on label, for Sears for Christmas sales in 1987. The sets could not be made ready in time, so Sears canceled the arrangement after the sets were made. To dispose of the sets, Lionel distributed them to its major wholesale dealers by apportionment. Apparently a few did make it to Sears; however, reader J. Luce reports ordering it through Sears before Christmas 1987, and receiving it the following February. The carton carried two shipping labels, one to Sears and a second to a freight company in Ohio. *(T, D)* — — **160 200**

11752 JCPENNEY ACL TIMBER MASTER: 18600 Atlantic Coast Line 4-4-2 locomotive with slope-back tender; 9341 Atlantic Coast Line SP caboose; 6585 Pennsylvania flatcar with fences; eight sections 5013 curved track; two sections 5018 straight track; extension bridge; telephone poles; DC power pack. The engine in this set is unique to JCPenney. JCPenney catalogue number is "XU671-2970A". R. Sigurdson comment. *(T, D)* — — **110 140**

11753 KAY-BEE RAIL BLAZER: Same as the regular-issue 11701 Rail Blazer set except with the 7932 Kay-Bee boxcar substituted for the normal 16200 Rock Island boxcar. This is unusual because the Rail Blazer set was color-coordinated in red, so the white Kay-Bee car would look a little out of place. H. Hogue Collection. *(T, D)* — — **130 160**

11756 HAWTHORNE FREIGHT FLYER: 8902 Atlantic Coast Line 2-4-0 locomotive with slope-back tender; 16204 Hawthorne short boxcar; 9341 ACL SP-type caboose; eight sections 5013 curved track; two sections 5018 straight track; DC transformer; lockon and wires. Essentially a bare-bones version of the Freight Flyer — just the engine, caboose and boxcar. Comes in a plain white box with generic Lionel sticker picturing the Hawthorne boxcar. Made as a promotion for the Hawthorne Home Appliances & Electronics Store. This set was re-released in 1988 (same set number) but with a 16211 boxcar. R. LaVoie and M. Salnick Collections. *(T, D)* — — **100 120**

11757 CHRYSLER MOPAR EXPRESS: 1987, 18605 Mopar Express 4-4-2 locomotive with square-back tender; 16205 Mopar boxcar; 16507 Mopar Express SP caboose; 16311 Mopar Express TOFC flatcar; 16310 Mopar Express gondola. There are no numbers on any of the set components except "1987". This set is one of the more advanced uncatalogued sets Lionel has made, other than its own Service Station sets. This promotional set for Chrysler Motors Genuine Parts ("MOPAR") has become very hard to find, and many of its components are desirable pieces, particularly the tank car and the TOFC flatcar. This set can be considered to approach "Collector" level. It was repeated in 1988 with an add-on tank car. Price is for 1987 set without tank car. *(T, D)* — — — **300**

11704 THE SOUTHERN FREIGHT RUNNER: 18802 Southern GP-9 diesel; 16504 Southern N5C caboose; 16607 Southern coal dump car; 16402 Southern quad hopper; 16102 Southern tank car. This is the 1987 Service Station Special set. In 1991, Lionel released a 19405 Southern crane car and a 19409 Southern flatcar, both of which go well with this set. *(T, SSS)* — — **240 270**

1988 Catalogued

11701 RAIL BLAZER: Same as 11701 set from 1987, although the 16304 gondola changed color from orange to red between 1987 and 1988 production. *(T)* — — **75 95**

11703 IRON HORSE FREIGHT: 18604 Wabash 4-4-2 locomotive; 16201 Wabash boxcar; 16505 Wabash SP caboose; 16309 Wabash gondola; 4045 transformer; 2311 mechanical semaphore; eight sections 5013 curved track; four sections 5018 straight track; lockon; manumatic uncoupler; wires. This set has also been reported with an identically-decorated Wabash 4-4-2 elongated Columbia, except numbered "8213" rather than "8604". "8213" would not be consistent with Lionel's post-1986 numbering sequence. May be a prototype or an error. Further reader comments invited. J. Zerbinos Collection. *(T)* — — **125 150**

11705 CHESSIE SYSTEM UNIT TRAIN: 18201 Chessie SD-40 locomotive; 19700 Chessie extended vision caboose; 17100 Chessie ACF three-bay hopper; 17101 Chessie ACF three-bay hopper; 17102 Chessie ACF three-bay hopper; 17103 Chessie ACF three-bay hopper; 17104 Chessie ACF three-bay hopper. This set is a "unit train" of matching ACF hopper cars. Limited Collector set with no track or transformer. *(C)* — — — **530**

11707 SILVER SPIKE: 18903 and 18904 Amtrak Alco AA locomotive pair; 16013, 16014, and 16015 Amtrak O27 streamlined passenger cars; eight sections 5013 curved track; four sections 5018 straight track; 4045 transformer; manumatic uncoupler; lockon and wires. This was the top-of-the-line Tradi-

	GD	VG	EXC	MT

tional set from 1988. A 16023 coach (1989) and a 16033 baggage car (1990) were sold later as add-ons to this set. *(T)*
— — — 375

61602 NICKEL PLATE SPECIAL: Same as 1602 set from 1986. *(T)*

61615 CANNONBALL EXPRESS: Same as 1615 set from 1986. *(T)*

91687 FREIGHT FLYER: 8902 ACL 2-4-0 locomotive; 9001 Conrail boxcar; 9341 ACL SP caboose; 9033 Penn Central gondola; eight sections 5013 curved track; two sections 5018 straight track; DC power pack; lockon; manumatic uncoupler; wires. Other than a change in the boxcar, this is the same as the 1987 set. *(T)*
— — — 65

GREAT NORTHERN: Fallen Flags Series No. 3: 18302 Great Northern EP-5 electric locomotive; 19205 Great Northern double-door boxcar; 19703 Great Northern extended vision caboose; 19402 Great Northern crane; 19401 Great Northern long gondola with coal load; 19304 Great Northern covered hopper; 19505 Great Northern refrigerator car. *(C, SE)*
— — 420 475

1988 Uncatalogued

11708 TOYS 'R' US MIDNIGHT SHIFT: Same as regular-issue 11708 Midnight Shift set from 1989. Note that as with some earlier sets, Lionel "pre-released" this item first to Toys 'R' Us, then included it in the regular catalogue the next year. The odd result is that all the rolling stock in the set are marked "BLT 1-88" even though the set did not "formally" come out until 1989. *(T, D)*
— — — 120

11756 HAWTHORNE FREIGHT FLYER: See 11756 uncatalogued set from 1987.

11757 CHRYSLER MOPAR EXPRESS: Same as 11757 Mopar Express set from 1987, except this set included an add-on 16106 Mopar Express three-dome tank car. There is another difference in the two sets involving their availability, according to reader John Kouba. Chrysler's policy, after the set sold well in 1987, was to offer the 1988 set (which had the tank car) only to purchasers of 1988 Chrysler automobiles, not as a promotional give-away as it had been in 1987. This was to be through a direct mailing to purchasers of record. As a result, sets from 1988 can be distinguished from those in 1987 (in addition to the tank car) by the presence of a mailing carton with the requisite postage on it. It may also be assumed that the 1988 set is generally scarcer than the 1987 set. See other comments under 1987. *(T, D)*
— — — 425

11759 JCPENNEY AMTRAK SILVER SPIKE: Same as regular-issue 11707 Silver Spike set from 1988. JCPenney's catalogue number is "HD-671-3762A". *(T, D)*
— — — 375

11761 JCPENNEY IRON HORSE: Same as regular-issue 11703 Iron Horse Freight set. This set was also available in 1989. *(T, D)*
— — 125 150

11762 TRUE VALUE (COTTER) CANNONBALL: Same as 61615 Cannonball Express set from 1986-1988, except in this case a 16207 True Value short boxcar replaces the Erie Lackawanna boxcar. This set, intended to celebrate True Value's 40th anniversary, was repeated in 1989 with the same Lionel set number, although the True Value boxcar changed. Cotter owns True Value. *(T, D)*
— — — 150

11763 UNITED MODEL "FREIGHT HAULER": Identical to the JCPenney Timbermaster set from 1987 (see 11752) except a freight load from the Rail Blazer set was included. United Model is a hobby distributor headquartered in Wheeling, Illinois. *(T, D)*
— — — 150

11764 (49N95178) SEARS IRON HORSE FREIGHT: Identical to 1988 Iron Horse catalogued set, except Wabash short boxcar was replaced by 16209 Sears "Disney Magic" short boxcar. R. Sigurdson comment. *(T, D)*
— — — 300

11765 SPIEGEL SILVER SPIKE: Identical to regular 11707 Silver Spike set from 1988, except packaged with four additional 5013 curved track and a 90-degree crossover to permit a figure-8 layout. *(T, D)*
— — — 400

11767 SHOPRITE FREIGHT FLYER: Regular-issue 91687 Freight Flyer set except with the 16213 Shoprite short boxcar in place of the 9001 Conrail boxcar. A first special for the large East Coast food chain. *(T, D)*
— — — 140

11706 THE VIRGINIA & TRUCKEE DRY GULCH LINE: 18702 Virginia & Truckee General-style locomotive and tender; 16012 baggage/combine; 16010 coach; and 16011 coach (General-style passenger cars). This is the 1988 Service Station Special. *(T, SSS)*
— — — 240

1989 Catalogued

11703 IRON HORSE FREIGHT: Same as 11703 set from 1988. *(T)*

11707 SILVER SPIKE: Same as 11707 set from 1988. *(T)*

11708 MIDNIGHT SHIFT: 18900 Pennsylvania gas turbine; 16511 Pennsylvania bobber caboose; 16315 Pennsylvania flatcar with fences; 16313 Pennsylvania short gondola with cable reels; 16400 Pennsylvania short hopper; eight sections 5013 curved track; two sections 5018 straight track; 2309 mechanical crossing gate; 20-piece crate load; five telephone poles; DC transformer; manual uncoupler; wire and lockon. This set had been released the year before as an uncatalogued Toys 'R' Us set, and Lionel did not change the number. This explains why all the cars in the set are marked "BLT 1-88". *(T)*
— — — 120

11710 CP RAIL FREIGHT: 18203 CP Rail SD-40 diesel; 17200 Canadian Pacific Standard O boxcar; 19705 CP Rail extended vision caboose; 17500 Canadian Pacific Standard O flatcar; 17400 CP Rail Standard O gondola; 17000 SCLAIR three-bay ACF hopper; 17300 Canadian Pacific Standard O refrigerator car. Limited Collector set with no track or transformer. *(C)*
— — — 500

61602 NICKEL PLATE SPECIAL: Same as 1602 set from 1986-1988. *(T)*

61615 CANNONBALL EXPRESS: Same as 1615 set from 1986, with an interesting twist: In the 1989 catalogue, the small picture of the set shows an orange 7925 Erie Lackawanna short boxcar. This appears to be a very rare pre-production run of the car which somehow found its way into a few sets. It has been confirmed to exist. See the 7925 entry in the Factory Errors and Prototypes chapter. *(T)*
— — — 90

91687 FREIGHT FLYER: Same as 91687 set from 1988. *(T)*

AMTRAK: Passenger set: 18303 Amtrak GG-1 electric locomotive; 19100 baggage; 19101 combine; 19102 coach; 19103 vista dome; 19104 diner; 19106 observation (long extruded-aluminum

catalogued 11771 Kmart Microracers set from 1989.

R. LaVoie Collection; B. Greenberg photograph

	GD	VG	EXC	MT

Amtrak passenger cars). Later addition from 1989 Stocking Stuffers brochure: 19105 full vista dome car. *(C, SE)*

— — — 900

NEW YORK CENTRAL: Passenger set: 18606 New York Central 2-6-4 steam locomotive; 16016 baggage; 16017 combine; 16018 coach; 16019 vista dome; 16020 coach; 16021 observation (short O27 streamlined passenger cars). Later addition from 1991 consumer catalogue: 16041 diner. *(T, SE)*

— — — 290

WESTERN MARYLAND: Fallen Flags Series No. 4: 18501 Western Maryland NW-2 switcher; 19214 WM boxcar; 19704 WM extended vision caboose; 19404 WM TOFC flatcar; 19403 WM gondola; 19511 WM refrigerator car; 19601 North American tank car. The engine in this set is a deluxe version which recreated the excellent features of early postwar NW-2 switchers. *(C, SE)*

— — — 475

1989 Uncatalogued

11762 TRUE VALUE (COTTER) CANNONBALL: Same as 61615 Cannonball Express set from 1986-1988, except in this case a 16219 True Value short boxcar replaces the Erie Lackawanna boxcar. This is a higher-quality 6454-style short boxcar. Lionel used the same set number here as it did in 1988, even though the boxcar changed. True Value has released three different boxcars in succession three years in a row — 1988-1990. *(T, D)*

— — — 160

11770 (49GY95280) SEARS CIRCUS: 18614 Sears Circus 4-4-2 locomotive and square-back tender; 16520 Sears Circus SP-type caboose; 16327 Sears Circus short gondola with two canisters; 16110 Sears Circus operating short stock car; eight

	GD	VG	EXC	MT

sections 5013 curved track; four sections 5018 straight track; transformer. Lionel began capitalizing on a perceived interest in circus trains in 1989 and 1990. Lionel was to catalogue a circus set of its own in 1990. Both the Lionel and Sears versions have sold well. This Sears set also marks another intriguing milestone: it is the first time in the 19 years of Lionel's modern era that a Sears set was made in which all the pieces were unique to that set. *(T, D)*

— — — 190

11771 KMART MICRORACERS: 18704 Lionel Lines 2-4-0 locomotive and slope-back tender; 16508 Lionel Lines SP caboose; 16325 Microracers barrel ramp flatcar with four Microracer autos; 16108 Microracers short tank car. An unusual special for Kmart, the first one Lionel has made for it since 1975. All the pieces in this set are unique to Kmart. R. LaVoie Collection. *(T, D)*

— — — 90

11772 MACY'S FREIGHT FLYER: Same as regular-issue Freight Flyer set 91687, except with a special 16221 Macy's boxcar in place of the usual 9001 Conrail boxcar. The Macy's special car is extremely hard to find. *(T, D)* — — — 300

11773 (49GY95281) SEARS NEW YORK CENTRAL PASSENGER SET: 18613 New York Central 4-4-2 locomotive and square-back tender; 16018 coach; 16019 vista dome; 16021 observation (O27 streamline passenger cars); eight sections 5013 curved track; four sections 5018 straight track; transformer. This set used three of the six regular-issue separate-sale New York Central passenger cars catalogued in 1989, but the engine was a surprise special unique to Sears. It was not the 18606 NYC locomotive that Lionel catalogued with the set. To make matters worse, the Sears catalogue picture shows an 18602 (Pennsylvania) engine with an ACL tender. *(T, D)* — — — 225

GD   VG   EXC   MT

11774 ACE HARDWARE CANNONBALL: Same as regular-issue Cannonball Express set, except with a special 16220 Ace Hardware short boxcar replacing the Erie Lackawanna boxcar. A first special for the nationwide Ace Hardware chain. *(T, D)*

—   —   —   175

11775 ANHEUSER-BUSCH SET: 18617 Adolphus III (Anheuser-Busch) 4-4-2 locomotive and slope-back tender; 16524 Anheuser-Busch SP-style caboose; 16223 Budweiser refrigerator car; two "This Bud's For You!" billboards; eight sections 5013 curved track; four sections 5018 straight track; manual uncoupler; smoke fluid; 4851 transformer. Also known as the "Beer Train". A 16225 Budweiser vat car was released in 1990 as an add-on to this set. This is the third set in 1989 in which all the rolling stock is unique to the set — an indication that Lionel is becoming more bold with its uncatalogued production. *(T, D)*

—   —   —   275

11776 PACE IRON HORSE: Same as regular-issue Iron Horse Freight set in 1989 except with an added "bonus pack" shrink-wrapped with the set. The pack contained an additional 10 sections of 5018 straight track, two extra sections 5013 curved track, a pair of manual switches, road signs, telephone poles, and a 2717 short extension bridge. Pace is a members-only discount retailing outlet.

—   —   —   175

11758 THE DESERT KING: 18608 Rio Grande 2-6-4 locomotive and tender; 16206 Denver & Rio Grande boxcar; 16509 Denver & Rio Grande SP caboose; 16616 Denver & Rio Grande searchlight car; 16105 Denver & Rio Grande tank car. This is the popular 1989 Service Station Special. *(T, SSS)*

—   —   —   250

1990 Catalogued

11703 IRON HORSE FREIGHT: Same as 11703 set from 1988. *(T)*

11713 SANTA FE DASH-8 40B FREIGHT: 18206 Santa Fe Dash-8 40B diesel; 17202 Santa Fe boxcar with RailSounds; 17502 Santa Fe Standard O TOFC flatcar; 17402 Santa Fe Standard O gondola; 17003 Du Pont two-bay ACF hopper; 17108 Santa Fe three-bay ACF hopper; 17302 Santa Fe Standard O refrigerator car with End-Of-Train (EOT) device; RailSounds activation button. Limited Collector set with no track or transformer. This is the first set to feature a Dash-8 diesel, and the first Lionel freight set ever without a caboose. The EOT device and RailSounds were switched between the boxcar and refrigerator car after the catalogue was released. *(C)*

—   —   —   575

11714 BADLANDS EXPRESS: 18705 Neptune 0-4-0 switcher; 16329 Southern Pacific short flatcar; 16040 Southern Pacific baggage/combine passenger car; 16630 Southern Pacific stock car; eight sections 5013 curved track; two sections 5018 straight track; four-figure set; DC transformer; lockon and wires. *(T)*

—   —   —   90

11715 LIONEL 90TH ANNIVERSARY: 18502 Lionel Lines GP-9 diesel; 19219 Lionel Lines boxcar with RailSounds; 19220 Lionel Lines boxcar; 19221 Lionel Lines boxcar; 19222 Lionel Lines boxcar; 19223 Lionel Lines boxcar; 19708 Lionel Lines bay window caboose. Limited Collector set with no track or transformer. Originally catalogued with the RailSounds in the engine, Lionel found it could not fit it there and so placed it in the 19219 boxcar for production. Lionel did not produce a set in its Fallen Flags series this year, offering this set instead. The 90th Anniversary set was a moderately slow seller. *(C)*

—   —   —   450

GD   VG   EXC   MT

11716 LIONELVILLE CIRCUS SPECIAL: 18716 Lionelville Circus General-style locomotive and tender; 16522 Circus N5C caboose; 16629 Lionelville operating elephant car; 16628 "LAUGHTER" operating cop-and-hobo gondola; eight sections 5013 curved track; four sections 5018 straight track; 4060 transformer; telltale pole; uncoupler. A 16638 short animated stock car was released as an add-on in 1991. *(T)*

—   —   210

11717 CSX FREIGHT: 18810 CSX SD-18 diesel; 16518 Chessie bay window caboose; 16627 CSX log dump car; 16406 CSX quad hopper; 16626 CSX searchlight car; 16112 DOWX tank car; 12 sections 5013 curved track; 13 sections 5018 straight track; two 12754 graduated trestle sets for a figure-8 over-and-under layout; remote control track; 12773 freight platform kit; five telephone poles; 14 road signs; 4060 transformer; lockon and wires. This is the top-of-the-line Traditional set for 1990. *(T, C)*

—   —   —   250

61602 NICKEL PLATE SPECIAL: Same as 1602 set from 1986-1989. *(T)*

61615 CANNONBALL EXPRESS: Same as 1615 set from 1986-1989. *(T)*

91687 FREIGHT FLYER: Same as 91687 set from 1988. *(T)*

NORTHERN PACIFIC: Passenger set: 18609 Northern Pacific 2-6-4 steam locomotive; 16034 baggage; 16035 combine; 16036 coach; 16037 vista-dome; 16038 coach; 16039 observation (short O27 streamlined passenger cars). The set was also catalogued in 1991. *(T, SE)*

—   —   —   300

1990 Uncatalogued

11777 (49N95265) SEARS LIONELVILLE CIRCUS: Same as 11716 regular-issue Lionelville Circus set from 1990. *(T, D)*

—   —   —   210

11778 (49N95264) SEARS BADLANDS EXPRESS: Same as 11714 regular-issue Badlands set from 1990. Lionel also marketed this same set (it is actually a set in a mailer box) with the same number to Toys 'R' Us. *(T, D)*

—   —   —   90

11779 (49N95267) SEARS CSX FREIGHT: Same as 11717 regular-issue CSX Freight set from 1990. *(T, C, D)*

—   —   —   250

11780 (49N95266) SEARS NORTHERN PACIFIC PASSENGER SET: 18616 Northern Pacific 4-4-2 locomotive and slope-back tender; 16035 combine; 16037 vista dome; and 16039 observation (short O27 streamlined passenger cars); eight sections 5013 curved track; four sections 5018 straight track; transformer. In the same fashion as it had done the year before with its NYC passenger special set, Sears took three of the six regular-issue cars from the separate-sale Northern Pacific passenger train from 1990 and placed them behind a steam locomotive which was made uniquely for Sears. The steam engine Lionel catalogued with the set was the 18609. *(T, D)*

—   —   —   250

11781 TRUE VALUE CANNONBALL: Same as True Value sets from previous years except here Lionel used the 16224 short 6454-style special True Value boxcar. This was the third special True Value boxcar made in three years. *(T, D)*

—   —   —   150

11783 TOYS 'R' US HEAVY IRON: Same as Toys 'R' Us Heavy Iron sets from previous years (see 1982 and 1985), but this year a new 16641 operating Geoffrey giraffe short boxcar was created. Note: Toys 'R' Us also marketed the Badlands Express

11713 Santa Fe Dash-8 set from 1990, the first modern freight set with no caboose.
Top shelf: **18206** Dash-8 40B diesel.
Second shelf: **17108** three-bay ACF hopper; **17202** boxcar with RailSounds.
Third shelf: **17003** two-bay ACF hopper; **17302** Standard O refrigerator with EOT device.
Bottom shelf: **17502** TOFC flatcar; **17402** Standard O gondola.

M. Solly Collection; B. Schwab photographer

	GD	VG	EXC	MT

set this year (probably the 11778 set listed above under Sears). *(T, D)* — — — 220

11784 PACE IRON HORSE: Essentially the same as the 11776 set released in 1989, with slight changes in the contents of the bonus pack. *(T, D)*

11785 COSTCO UNION PACIFIC EXPRESS: 18622 Union Pacific 4-4-2 locomotive and square-back tender; 16226 Union Pacific short boxcar; 16528 Union Pacific SP caboose; 16336 Union Pacific gondola with canisters; 16408 Union Pacific short hopper; 12730 girder bridge; 12706 barrel loader building kit;

12714 automatic crossing gate; steam shovel kit; five telephone poles; 14 road signs; 12 sections 5013 curved track; eight sections 5018 straight track; 90-degree crossover for figure-8 layout; transformer. This set, one of the more complete uncatalogued sets from Lionel, contains all unique pieces — none was regularly catalogued. The set matches the consist of the regular-issue Nickel Plate Special set, down to the color of the bodies, but each piece is lettered for the Union Pacific. An unusual feature about the set is that all the rolling stock, including the engine, has the "1" dropped from the beginning of the catalogue number on the pieces. Lionel misspelled the store's name as "Cosco" on both the

GD   VG   EXC   MT

carton and the instruction sheet. Costco is a West Coast wholesale outlet. T. Watson Collection. Note: the descriptions for the individual cars in the set were received too late to include in Volume I. *(T, D)* — — — 300

11712 THE GREAT LAKES EXPRESS: 18611 Lionel Lines 2-6-4 locomotive and tender; 16027 Mt. Clemens combine; 16028 Detroit coach; 16029 Lansing coach; 16030 Chesterfield observation (O27 streamlined passenger cars). This good looking set was the 1990 Service Station Special. *(T, SSS)*

— — — 275

1991 Catalogued

11703 IRON HORSE FREIGHT: Same as 11703 set from 1988-1990. *(T)*

11714 BADLANDS EXPRESS: Same as 11714 set from 1990. *(T)*

11716 LIONELVILLE CIRCUS SPECIAL: Same as 11716 set from 1990. *(T)*

11720 SANTA FE SPECIAL: 18706 Santa Fe 2-4-0 locomotive and tender; 16227 Santa Fe short boxcar; 16529 ATSF SP-type caboose; 16114 Hooker short tank car; eight sections 5013 curved track; four sections 5018 straight track; manual uncoupler; DC transformer; lockon and wires. This is the bottom-of-the-line Traditional set for 1991. *(T)* **CP**

11721 MICKEY'S WORLD TOUR TRAIN: 18707 Mickey's World Tour '92 2-4-0 locomotive; 16642 Goofy operating boxcar; 16530 Mickey's World Tour SP-type caboose; 16339 Mickey's World Tour gondola; eight sections 5013 curved track; six sections 5018 straight track; 2717 extension bridge; five telephone poles; 14 road signs; DC transformer; lockon and wires. *(T)* **CP**

11722 GIRL'S TRAIN: 18014 Lionel Lines 2-6-4 locomotive and tender; 19234 New York Central boxcar; 19235 Katy boxcar; 19712 Pennsylvania N5C caboose; 19410 NYC gondola with four canisters; 19317 Lehigh Valley quad hopper; eight sections 5013 curved track; five sections 5018 straight track; uncoupler track; 4851 pink transformer; lockon and wires. This set is a near-exact remake of the famous 1957 Lionel Girl's Train. The new set has, of course, different numbers. The rolling stock has new Standard O sprung trucks rather than the bar-end trucks used on the postwar versions. The engine in the modern set does not have the Magnetraction found on its 1957 predecessor (it has a rubber traction tire), and the tender does not have the mechanical whistle used on the postwar version. The changes to the engine were announced later in 1991, and the features are therefore not correctly listed in the engine description (18014) in Volume I. *(C)* **CP**

11723 AMTRAK MAINTENANCE TRAIN: 18815 Amtrak RS-3 diesel; 16702 Amtrak bunk car; 16645 Amtrak work caboose with searchlight; 16644 Amtrak crane car; 16643 Amtrak coal (ballast) dump car; 16340 Amtrak flatcar with stakes. Catalogued in 1991 but never manufactured. This interesting set, intended to be the top of the Traditional Line in 1991, was a victim of Lionel's new policy not to make sets whose orders do not meet a minimum total. **Not Manufactured**

11726 ERIE LACKAWANNA FREIGHT: 18906 Erie-Lackawanna RS-3; 16229 Erie Lackawanna enclosed auto car-

GD   VG   EXC   MT

rier; 19243 (TBD) Clinchfield boxcar; 16535 Erie-Lackawanna bay window caboose; 16350 CP Rail flatcar with load; 19414 Boston & Maine long gondola with coil covers; 16116 U.S. Army tank car; telephone poles; road signs; 12 sections 5013 curved track; seven sections 5018 straight track; remote uncoupling track; 5020 90-degree crossover for oval layout; AC transformer; sound button; lockon. This set was devised in early 1991 as a replacement for the 11723 Amtrak Maintenance set. Intended to be the top of the Traditional Line in 1991. Note: The announcement and descriptions for this set were received too late in 1991 for the detailed car listings to be included in Volume I. **CP**

61602 NICKEL PLATE SPECIAL: Same as 1602 set from 1986-1990. Note that by 1991, this was the only remaining catalogued set which contained pre-1986 rolling stock. *(T)*

SANTA FE: Passenger set: 18100 powered Santa Fe F-3 diesel A; 18101 Santa Fe dummy B; 18102 Santa Fe dummy A with RailSounds; 19109 baggage; 19110 combine; 19111 diner; 19112 coach; 19113 vista-observation (long extruded-aluminum passenger cars). The vista-observation car in this set is a new design for Lionel. Later addition from 1991 Stocking Stuffer package: 18103 dummy B-unit. *(C, SE)* **CP**

FRISCO: Fallen Flags Series No. 5: 18504 Frisco GP-7 diesel; 19229 Frisco boxcar with RailSounds; 19230 Frisco double-door automobile boxcar; 19710 Frisco extended vision caboose; 19408 Frisco gondola with coil covers; 19519 Frisco stock car; 19602 Johnson tank car. There was a 16333 Frisco flatcar with load sold separately in 1991 which many people have added to the set. The coil-cover gondola was a new design for Lionel. *(C, SE)* **CP**

ILLINOIS CENTRAL: Passenger set: 18620 Illinois Central 2-6-2 steam locomotive; 16042 baggage; 16043 combine; 16044 coach; 16045 vista dome; 16046 coach; 16047 observation (short O27 streamlined passenger cars). *(T, SE)* **CP**

11719 THE COASTAL FREIGHT: 18814 Delaware & Hudson RS-3 diesel; 16525 Delaware & Hudson bay window caboose; 16335 New York Central TOFC flatcar with long van; 16407 Boston & Maine quad hopper; 19324 Delaware & Hudson refrigerator car; 16109 Baltimore & Ohio tank car. This is the 1991 Service Station Special, and for the first time in the modern era, Lionel included it in the regular consumer catalogue. *(T, SSS)* **CP**

1991 Uncatalogued

Note for 1991: Lionel and the retailers do not usually advertise these special trains sets until near the end of the year. Both Sears and JCPenney release Christmas catalogues in which these sets are usually pictured. So information on 1991 uncatalogued sets was not available at the time of this writing.

1992 Catalogued

11724 GREAT NORTHERN*: 1992; F-3 ABA diesel with RailSounds; 19116 baggage car "1200"; 19117 combine car "1240"; 19120 observation "1192"; 19118 passenger car "1212"; 19119 vista dome car "1322". Available for separate-sale from Lionel's 1992 Book One catalogue. **CP**

$\cdot$ CHAPTER 5 $\cdot$
MODERN ERA ACCESSORIES

By Roland E. LaVoie

Nowhere was postwar Lionel's commitment to quality better demonstrated than with operating accessories, those little animated joys which seemed destined to last forever. One of the main reasons for this durability was the dependence of these accessories upon solenoid relays and rugged vibrator motors for their operation. Take an old Lionel accessory out of its box after it has been unearthed from a 30-year stay in a dusty attic and, likely as not, the mechanism will operate perfectly. It is not unusual to see even prewar accessories in active use on layouts, day after day.

Building something to last is commendable indeed, but Lionel's commitment to durability in its accessories posed a very unusual marketing problem for the fledgling Fundimensions firm in 1970. The firm found itself in competition with its own past! How could Fundimensions expect people to buy its accessories when so many of the old ones were still out there working perfectly?

The obvious answer to that question was to build new kinds of accessories. Even here, the engineering excellence of the old Lionel Corporation seemed to haunt Fundimensions at every turn. For every reissue of the old accessories which was improved, such as the 2494 rotating beacon (which worked much better than its 394 and 494 predecessors), other reissues emphasized the inexperience of the firm at making these toys.

Thus, it took quite a while for Fundimensions to find its own niche for its accessory line, and even longer to get out of the shadow of its illustrious past. Many of the earliest accessories were direct copies of the older line with subtle differences. These were produced in very limited quantities and are well worth seeking today. In fact, Fundimensions had a copious supply of leftover production which it re-packaged into its own boxes! Thus, it is quite possible to find a 2154 blinking crossing signal which is absolutely identical to the postwar version but is packed in a Type I Fundimensions box. Only when these supplies were exhausted, around the beginning of

1972, did Fundimensions market its own lines — and even then these were no different from their predecessors except cosmetically. How many collectors know that the postwar 252 crossing gate and its Fundimensions 2152 successor can only be told apart by the gate prop at the end of the gate? It is metal in postwar production and black plastic in Fundimensions production. The bases of the 2152 gates even carry 252 Lionel Corporation markings!

The first stirrings of Fundimensions' individuality came in 1973, when the firm began selling scale O Gauge building kits. This is quite understandable, given the long background of model building possessed by the Craft Master and Model Products Corporation people who ran Lionel at that time. These attractive kits have been a staple of the Lionel line ever since that year. However, it was not until 1976 that Fundimensions introduced accessories which could truly be called its own — and it did so with a vengeance. One accessory, partly derivative from older forms, was the 2127 diesel horn shed, which worked from a 9-volt battery through a speaker hidden in a shack shaped like the one used for the 2126 whistling freight shed, also introduced (or re-introduced, if you prefer) that year. The others were original in every way. One was an ingenious 2175 Sandy Andy ore tower kit which used a system of weights to dump coal into a little ore car which traveled down a rack and dumped its contents into a waiting coal car. It was a devil to keep in adjustment, but it was amusing when it worked. Another was a coaling station kit which dumped coal into a car underneath the building.

The most original of the accessories, however, was a fully-operating 2317 automatic drawbridge. This terrific accessory used the same operating principles as the fabled 313 bascule bridge of the early postwar years, but it added the dimension of an over-and-under layout. If a train on the upper track approached an open drawbridge, it would stop until the bridge was lowered, a bell ringing all the while. If the train were on the lower level and encountered a closed drawbridge, it would stop until the bridge was raised. The accessory could be wired for continuous operation using insulated tracks or contactors. Although difficult to hook up, this was a fine accessory which brought great action to a layout and looked handsome.

But the lure of nostalgia proved too strong for Fundimensions to resist. In 1980, the fine 454 sawmill was revived by the firm, using the number 2301. This was the first revival of the truly magnificent and complex accessories from the glory days of the Lionel Corporation, and it sold very well. Also revived that year was a manual version of the old 282 gantry crane, and operators realized that a remote-control version could not be far behind. The meticulously detailed O Gauge switches were once again made in 1980, and in the next year the popular oil derrick made its appearance.

The year 1982 was accessory-heaven, as a steady parade of resurrections began apace. In that year, the colorful animated newsstand and the imposing icing station appeared. A nice revival of the old 256 freight station appeared as the 2129 in 1983, as well as the American Flyer oil drum loader, the 2316 remote control gantry crane, the 2315 overhead coaling station, and the 2318 operating control tower. Most of these accessories were delayed in production by Lionel's move to Mexico, but that only whetted the collector and operator appetite for more. In 1984, more followed. The good die-cast bumpers reappeared in two colors, the dwarf signal made an appearance, and the old 356 operating freight station and 445 operating control towers came out as the 2323 and 2324, respectively. No new accessories of this type were announced for 1985 or 1986, perhaps to give Lionel time to produce those already announced and to catch its collective breath after the production delays the firm experienced in 1983 and 1984.

Then came the new 1987 catalogue and a whole raft of revivals and new accessories. This was the first year during which the management of the modern era had revived accessories produced in the modern era itself. In an attempt to show that old wine can indeed be sold in new bottles, Lionel Trains, Inc. reintroduced many accessories in new and much brighter colors. This makes sense in the marketing arena, because color sells toy trains more than anything else. The 2318 operating control tower was reintroduced as the 12702 with new colors. The black 2140 banjo signal found new life as the 12709 in tuscan coloring; the attractive and scarce 2285 engine house kit was revived as the 12710; the good old 2175 Sandy Andy ore loader tower was resurrected in new colors; the 2152 crossing gate became the 12714 with a new gray base; the lighted and unlighted plastic bumpers have changed color from black to tuscan; and the 2314 twin searchlight tower reappeared in gray and bright orange.

Several new offerings appeared in 1987. First, there was a brand new solid state transformer, the MW, which gave Lionel's trains the most power available since the days of the old KW and ZW models. To the delight of operators and collectors alike, a new magnetic gantry crane like the old 282R made an appearance in attractive Erie-Lackawanna colors. The operating diesel fueling station of the postwar years also returned, and a brand new set of billboards and frames was developed.

Perhaps it is easy to chastise the current Lionel management for relying on the old tried and true Lionel accessories so much, but when the company has had a good thing going for it, one cannot blame anybody for sticking to a successful

formula. With few exceptions, the operating accessories have been very brisk sellers. In addition, there have been some technical innovations worthy of praise. In the modern operating gantry cranes and overhead coal loaders, the rugged but ponderous and noisy Lionel AC electric motors have been replaced by quiet, efficient AC/DC can motors which work more smoothly, never need lubrication (though the gears do) and use fewer volts than their predecessors. This means that more accessories can be activated on less power, not to mention the maintenance-free features.

In 1988, Lionel hit the accessory jackpot again. Several attractive building kits were released, among them the scarce grain elevator and coaling station. An ingenious roadside diner with a smoke unit was introduced, new designs for the whistle and diesel horn sheds were being produced, and revivals of the mail pickup set and microwave relay tower were made. The old animated newsstand was cleverly redesigned as an animated refreshment stand.

One of the most impressive operating accessories ever made by Lionel, in any era, appeared in 1989. The Union Pacific intermodal crane had an instant impact on Lionel layouts across the country. It provides a purpose for Lionel's TOFC flatcars and for the highly detailed tractor-trailer models Lionel introduced in 1989 and 1990. Like the real railroads, Lionel had finally formed a partnership with the trucking industry.

The years 1988 and 1989 also marked the advent of RailScope: a revolutionary miniature television camera system mounted in an engine, providing operators a unique engineer's-eye view of their own layouts.

Lionel Trains, Inc.'s most recent offerings demonstrate it is not slowing its pace to both reintroduce old favorites and create its own new gadgets. A burning switch tower variation of the old postwar operating tower appeared in 1990. That year also saw the release of the handsome 12759 floodlight tower, two versions of an illuminated extension bridge with rock piers, a 12763 single signal bridge, and another version of the smoking roadside diner.

In 1991, Lionel concentrated all its resources for the production of one of the most amazing train accessories ever — the 12782 lift bridge. Lionel Trains, Inc. proceeded where the old Lionel Corporation never trod — the 213 lift bridge had been catalogued in 1950 but never put into mass production; only a prototype was made. The modern version is a monster 2-1/2 feet long and 1-1/2 feet high.

Will there be further revivals of older Lionel operating accessories? If you need convincing that this will indeed be so, just look through the Lionel catalogues of the middle to late 1950s. There you may view the big water tower, the culvert loader and unloader, the overhead gantry signal, the barrel and coal ramps, the helicopter launching station, and many many other candidates for revival. Will there be entirely new accessories added to the Fundimensions line? The intermodal crane provides a strong affirmative answer to that question.

The tradition lives on. Only in 1985 did one accessory finally disappear from the catalogue after a continuous 50-year run in one form or another. This was the operating gateman, a little fellow who rushed out of his shack as the train went by, swinging his lantern mightily. From 1935 to 1984, this accessory was produced in 45, 045, 45N, 145, and

2125 whistling shed from 1971 only, leftover postwar motor, light works only when whistle blowing; **2126**, unlighted small diode motor, door windows indicate 1978 or older.

2145 configurations. It was truly the toy train equivalent of the Ford Model "T"! Despite the gateman's disappearance, this accessory has been too much a part of Lionel tradition to remain unproduced for long — and, in 1987, the gateman returned from his brief vacation sporting bright new colors — a light tan base, a butternut yellow shack, and a bright red roof. This long-lived and popular little fellow returned to uphold one of the great truths about Lionel Toy Trains: "Not just a toy... A tradition!"

ACCESSORIES LISTINGS

	GD	VG	EXC	MT

1355 TRAIN DISPLAY CASE: 1983.

	—	—	—	40

2110 GRADUATED TRESTLE SET: 1971-87; 22 pieces graduated from 3/16" to 4-3/4" high.
(A) Dark brown trestles; Type I box; leftover postwar pieces; came with postwar instruction sheet.

	5	7	12	15

(B) Light gray trestles; Type II or III packaging.

	5	7	10	12

2111 ELEVATED TRESTLE SET: 1971-87; 10 piers, 4-3/4" each.
(A) Dark brown trestles; leftover postwar pieces; Type I packaging.

	5	7	12	15

(B) Light gray trestles; Type II or III packaging.

	5	7	10	12

2113 TUNNEL PORTALS: 1984-87; gray plastic stonework; "LIONEL" and circular "L" logo molded into portal.

	—	—	5	6

2114 PASSENGER STATION: 1972-75; white sides; gray roof, doors and window inserts; maroon base.

	—	20	30	40

Signals and gates, old and new:

R. LaVoie Collection; B. Greenberg photograph

Top shelf: 2140 banjo signal, a postwar leftover piece; 2163 block signal with dark tan base; 2163 block signal, medium tan base, postwar leftover piece; 163 block signal, postwar production from 1969, for comparison.

Bottom shelf: 2152 crossing gate, postwar piece in a Fundimensions Type 1 box; postwar 252x crossing gate from 1952 for reference — these gates are mechanically identical, the visual difference is due to the aging of 252x piece; 2162 crossing gate and signal, a postwar piece in Fundimensions box, the earliest known modern era packaging of modern era accessory; 2162 crossing gate and signal, in double re-labeled Hagerstown postwar box (see text for an unusual story on this piece).

	GD	VG	EXC	MT

2115 DWARF SIGNAL: 1984-87; gray body; black twin-light lens hood; uses pin-type bulbs; Type III box. Note that this accessory is operated by a 153C contactor, while the postwar version was manually operated by a special switch.

| | — | — | 11 | 13 |

2117 BLOCK TARGET SIGNAL: 1985-87; black base; silver pole; red ladder; black two-light lens hood. C. Rohlfing Collection.

| | — | — | 17 | 21 |

2122 EXTENSION BRIDGE: 1977-87; two gray plastic piers; plastic bridge; requires assembly; 24" long by 5" wide; piers 7" high; overall height with piers is 11-3/4". Lionel's use of bridge terms is often muddled. This is an overhead truss bridge.
(A) Brown sides and top.

| | — | 20 | 30 | 40 |

(B) Brown sides and maroon top. P. Piker Collection.

| | — | 20 | 30 | 40 |

2125 WHISTLING FREIGHT SHED: 1971; white shed body; bright red door, window inserts and toolshed lid; green roof (slight variations of the green shade exist); dark brown base; postwar-type motor; Type I box; mint condition requires presence of box. Roof, window and door inserts, and base are Fundimensions products; shed parts and motor are postwar carry-overs. Has 12-volt automotive-type light connected to clips; light only works when whistle is blown. Instruction sheet shows that this operation was deliberately designed, not an engineering error.

	GD	VG	EXC	MT

Came with leftover No. 90 controller. Very hard to find, especially with original Type I box, which is very fragile.
(A) Green roof, as described above. G. Halverson and R. LaVoie Collections.

| | 40 | 50 | 60 | 75 |

(B) Same as (A), but extra wiring posts added to base to control whistle motor; main clips activate light only. Reader comments invited; appears to be a Service Station post-factory alteration. R. LaVoie Collection.

| | 40 | 50 | 60 | 75 |

(C) Same as (A), but maroon roof; same as postwar 125 model. Authenticated from original box; probable use of leftover roof. C. Rohlfing Collection.

| | 40 | 50 | 60 | 75 |

2126 WHISTLING FREIGHT SHED: 1976-87; dark brown plastic base; light yellow shed; green door and windows; opaque window in non-opening door; green toolshed lid; lighter brown plastic roof; diode-activated whistle motor. Found with two types of doors: one type has two large windows (1976-77); the other has 12 smaller windows (1978-87).
(A) Brown plastic roof. C. Rohlfing Collection.

| | 15 | 20 | 25 | 35 |

(B) Same as (A), but green plastic roof; possibly leftover roof from 2125 production. J. Cusumano Collection.

| | 15 | 20 | 25 | 35 |

2127 DIESEL HORN SHED: 1976-87; height 4-7/8"; base 6" x 6"; battery-operated by nine-volt transistor battery, not included; diesel horn remote-controlled; light tan plastic base; red

Bridges: The short girder bridges have been a good seller over many years. Consequently, several firms have produced competitive bridges.

Top shelf: Bridge made by Colber Corp. in 1952, note general similarity of size and construction to its Lionel counterpart on right; Lionel 214 from 1958.

Middle shelf: 2214 girder bridge second production run, note MPC logo; earliest production of 2214 girder bridge.

Bottom shelf: 12770 arch-under bridge from 1990.

	GD	VG	EXC	MT

building; white toolshed lid; white door; frosted window; gray roof; same door variation as 2126 above. **15 20 25 35**

2128 AUTOMATIC SWITCHMAN: 1983-85; animated blue switchman waves flag as train approaches; gray-painted metal base with green cardboard bottom; red tanks. Reissue of 1047 from 1959-61. Somewhat difficult to find. C. Rohlfing Collection. **— 25 30 40**

2129 FREIGHT STATION: 1983-85; brick red platform; tan building with brown windows and door; green roof; black picket fence with billboards reading "Cheerios", "Wheaties", and "Gold Medal"; several wall posters, illuminated by one interior bulb; catalogue shows station with white walls; 15" long, 5" wide, and 5-1/2" high. Reissue of 256 from 1950-53, except for colors and stickers instead of metal signs. Foster observation. **— 20 30 35**

2133 FREIGHT STATION: 1972-83; maroon plastic base; white plastic sides; box at one time made by Stone Container Corporation, Detroit, Michigan; white corrugated box with picture of station on lid (except version (A) below). Reissue of 133 from 1957-66. Earliest versions use metal clip-on bayonet-based light socket, rather than the postwar version, in which the light socket is riveted to the bracket. Later Fundimensions stations have

plastic clip-on socket using a 12-volt automotive-type bulb. T. Rollo comment.

(A) First production, 1972; white Stone Container Corp. box with no picture on lid (though space is there for it); example has bright metal crosspiece for bulb clip, small red and gold station end signs and bright green roof; quarter-sized hole in floor, last seen in 1966 version of 133, is retained. R. LaVoie Collection. **20 25 30 40**

(B) Later production, 1972; Stone Container Corp. box with black and white picture of accessory; medium green roof (less bright than (A)), door and window inserts; quarter-sized hole in base; green chimney secured by circular speed nut; black metal interior crossbar; bayonet-based metal light socket clips to bar. R. LaVoie Collection. **20 25 30 40**

(C) Same as (B), but has red chimney instead of green. Probable use of leftover postwar part. G. Halverson Collection. **20 25 30 40**

(D) Later production, 1973-75; Stone Container Corp. box has color picture of accessory; pea green roof, chimney, doors and window inserts; maroon base; previous hole in base is filled; chimney secured by rectangular speed nut; black metal interior crossbar; plastic light socket taking automotive-type bulb clips onto crossbar. T. Rollo and G. Halverson Collections. **12 15 20 30**

2133 freight stations

R. LaVoie Collection; B. Greenberg photograph

Top shelf: **Early 1972 with round clipped bulb socket; box has no paste-on picture.**

Bottom shelf: **Late 1972-74, round clip light bulb, black and white picture on box; Penn Central from 1976 and up: green roof, darker green windows, plastic square bulb clip, hole in bottom now plugged, age restriction now listed on box.**

Variations on a gateman:

R. LaVoie Collection; B. Greenberg photograph

Top shelf: **2145 (1972) box with cellophane window; 2145 (1973-1977).**

Bottom: **12735 diesel horn shed; 12713 gateman from 1987-88, new colors, but same general design.**

	GD	VG	EXC	MT

(E) Latest production, 1976-83; same as (D), but dull Penn Central green roof, chimney, doors and window inserts; red-brown base; gray metal crossbar inside station. R. LaVoie Collection.

| | 12 | 15 | 20 | 30 |

2140 AUTOMATIC BANJO SIGNAL: 1970-83; as train approaches, red light turns on, "stop" arm swings, die-cast construction; 7-1/2" high.

(A) "LIONEL CORPORATION" stamped on underside of base; postwar carry-over; came in Type I Fundimensions box. G. Halverson Collection.

| | 15 | 25 | 30 | 35 |

(B) Same as (A), but Type II box; accessory with postwar markings. C. Rohlfing Collection.

| | 15 | 20 | 25 | 30 |

(C) MPC logo on base; Type II Fundimensions box. G. Halverson Collection.

| | 15 | 20 | 25 | 30 |

2145 AUTOMATIC GATEMAN: 1970-84; 1985 marked the 50th anniversary of the most famous and long-lived of all Lionel accessories. This little shed was first offered in 1935 as the No. 45 for Standard Gauge and the 045 for O Gauge (differing only in the type of special insulated track or contactor included with the accessory). In 1946, its number changed to 45N, and in 1950 it was substantially revised and changed to the 145. Its spectacular market success reflects its great play value. The gateman, who is really a watchman, rushes from his lighted shed as the train approaches. He warns pedestrians and vehicles with his swinging lantern and returns to the shed after the train passes. The accessory came with a pressure contactor and a lockon. Refer to prewar and postwar Guides for further history of this accessory.

	GD	VG	EXC	MT

(A) 1970-71; green metal base; white shed with brown door and window; frosted plastic window inserts; maroon roof and toolshed lid. Mint value must have the Fundimensions Type I box. This accessory was actually a postwar 145 piece in the new Fundimensions packaging. G. Halverson Collection.

| | 20 | 30 | 40 | 50 |

(B) 1972; same as (A), but brown roof and toolshed lid; darker green base; Type II rectangular box with window; accessory packed horizontally. G. Halverson and R. LaVoie Collections.

| | 15 | 25 | 30 | 40 |

(C) 1973-75; same as (B), but packed in rectangular Type II box without window.

| | 10 | 20 | 25 | 30 |

(D) 1976-84, medium light green base; white shack; maroon doors, windows, toolbox lid and roof; Type III box. In 1978, door changes from two-paned variety to 12-pane variety. C. Rohlfing Collection.

| | 10 | 20 | 25 | 30 |

2151 SEMAPHORE: 1978-83; medium brown plastic base; black pole; yellow- and black-striped semaphore arm; red ladder; red and green jewel lights; raises as train approaches. Different design from postwar 151, which had die-cast construction and which lowered semaphore arm instead of raising it. C. Rohlfing Collection.

| | 10 | 20 | 25 | 30 |

2152 AUTOMATIC CROSSING GATE: 1972-86; black plastic base; white plastic gate with gray weights; on bottom "#252 Crossing Gate", with pressure contactor. Fundimensions version can be distinguished from its postwar 252 counterpart by the presence of a black plastic gate rest at the end of the gate arm

	GD	VG	EXC	MT

rather than the metal one used in the postwar version. Many postwar examples were repacked into Fundimensions Type I and Type II boxes. Some examples were sold in Type III rolling stock boxes with black print; "6-2152/AUTOMATIC CROSSING GATE" on the ends. R. LaVoie comment; G. Halverson Collection.

(A) Type I box; postwar leftover. **10 20 30 40**
(B) Type II box; postwar leftover or Fundimensions production.
10 15 25 35
(C) Type III box. **10 15 25 35**

2154 AUTOMATIC HIGHWAY FLASHER: 1970-87; red light blinks alternately as train passes; 8-3/4" high with special track clip, the 154C contactor. This device clamps over the track and has two thin metal plates which are insulated from the rail. The device is wired so that the train wheels run across the metal flanges, completing the circuit to each of the two bulbs in turn. Thus the left light goes on and off as the wheels pass over the left plate, and the right light goes on and off with the right plate, giving the flashing appearance of the accessory. This clever contactor first appeared in 1940 with the first versions of the 154. Modern era production has been observed in several colors. Reader comments are needed with the specific examples.

(A) White plastic crossbuck with raised black lettering; gray unpainted post with chrome finial cap. Postwar 154 packaged in a Type I Fundimensions box. G. Halverson Collection.
10 15 20 30
(B) Same as (A), except post is installed in black base from leftover 151 semaphore. Verified from photographs. In the 1971 catalogue, the 2154 is shown in the form of a 2162 top piece somehow installed into the base of a 2163 block signal. Other odd combinations of parts may exist; reader comments requested. L. Jagelski Collection. **— — — 30**
(C) Black crossbuck with raised white lettering; black finial cap; MPC logo stamped on underside of base. G. Halverson Collection.
10 15 20 30
(D) Black finial cap; white crossbuck; MPC logo on base; pink "STOP"; Type II box. Unusual combination of postwar and MPC parts. C. Rohlfing Collection. **10 15 20 30**

2156 STATION PLATFORM: 1971; rerun of 156 with 157 roof; new metal roof supports; pea green plastic base modeled after 156; medium red roof; lighted with two large prewar acorn light bulbs; underside of base reads "CAT. NO. 2156 STATION PLATFORM" and "LIONEL MT. CLEMENS MICH. MADE IN USA". Mint value must have original light bulbs and Type I box. Hard to find with original light bulbs. See 1985 edition of *Greenberg's Guide to Lionel-Fundimensions Trains, 1970-1985*, for Tom Rollo's article on this accessory. Grossano, G. Halverson, R. LaVoie, and T. Rollo Collections. **— 25 35 50**

2162 AUTOMATIC CROSSING GATE AND SIGNAL: 1970-87; black plastic base; black crossbuck with white lettering and simulated bell at top; white gate; red bulbs with pins; pressure contactor; lockon. This gate was made from the postwar 252 crossing gate and signal. It is stamped on the underside "NO. (blanked out) CROSSING GATE/MADE IN U.S. OF AMERICA/THE LIONEL CORPORATION, N.Y." The number 252 was deleted from the die when the base was reused for the 2162. I. D. Smith observation.

(A) Red-painted diagonal stripes; metal support rod on gate; Type I box; postwar markings on base. G. Halverson Collection.
10 12 20 30
(B) Same as (A), but black diagonal stripes instead of red. Postwar carry-over in Fundimensions box. R. LaVoie Collection.
10 12 20 30

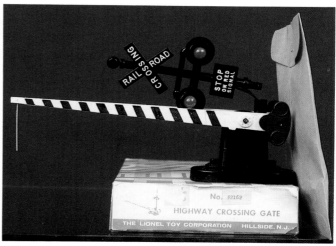

R. LaVoie Collection; B. Greenberg photograph

2162 highway crossing gate: Typewritten label over label, disassembled piece.

	GD	VG	EXC	MT

(C) Same as (A), but black-painted diagonal stripes; black plastic support rod on gate; Type II box; postwar markings on base blanked out. G. Halverson Collection. **10 12 20 25**

2163 AUTO BLOCK TARGET SIGNAL: 1970-78; green light switches to red as train approaches; 7-1/2" high; contactor, L-19R red bulb, L-19G green bulb, both with pins. Some early examples may have come in leftover plain white boxes with black printing on only one end; reader comments requested. This accessory was known to come in plain white boxes in the last year of postwar production. Early examples came with a single target lens, as in postwar production, but 1972 and later examples frequently had a two-lens head (they are interchangeable). See also version (D) below.

(A) Light tan base; Type I or Type II box.
8 10 20 25
(B) Medium tan base; Type II box. R. LaVoie Collection.
8 10 20 25
(C) Dark tan base; brass-colored wire thumbscrews instead of nickel; box type not known. G. Halverson Collection.
8 10 20 25
(D) Same as (B), but leftover postwar 163 repackaged in Type I box labeled "Automatic Single Block Signal" (Type II boxes were labeled "Automatic Block Target Signal"); both this box and the original postwar 163 box are mislabeled "9" high", but the signal itself is only 7-1/2" high; the Type II box corrects that error. Very unusual piece and packaging. M. Solly and R. LaVoie comments; M. Favale Collection. **NRS**

2170 STREET LAMPS: 1970-87; three per package. Earliest versions carry postwar stamping on underside of base but are packaged in Type I shrink-wrapped or Type I boxes. Later versions have Lionel MPC markings and come in Type I or Type II boxes.

(A) 1970; dark green pole; dark green pole top; cream globe; clear pin-type bulbs; same bulb was used for postwar 76 lamp post. G. Halverson and T. Rollo Collections. **7 10 20 25**
(B) 1971, early; light green pole; mismatched dark green pole top; white globe; small foreign-made midget bulb with screw base (note that a midget lamp is any lamp less than 1/4"-diameter). G. Cole comment; G. Halverson Collection. **10 15 20 25**

A bevy of station platforms, similar yet unique.   R. LaVoie Collection; B. Greenberg photograph
Top shelf: **2256** TCA special issue from 1975; **2256** probably 1972-73, unusual Stone Container Corp. box.
Bottom shelf: **2256** station platform, with leftover 2156 base, 1972 common variation; **2156** station platform, 1971 only, light bulbs are prewar leftover round or acorn shaped.

	GD	VG	EXC	MT

(C) 1971, later; Type I box dated 1971; lamps with light green base, pole and cap base; translucent white globes; embossed on bottom "MADE IN U.S.A./LIONEL MPC/MT. CLEMENS/ MICH."; MPC logo on top part of base; hand-etched "76-3" part number on bottom; foreign-made 8010-24 subminiature screw-based bulb. G. Cole and R. LaVoie Collections.

	10	15	20	25

(D) 1972-87; light green pole and pole top; white globe; midget screw-based bulb; Type II shrink-wrap packaging (earlier) or Type II box (later). G. Halverson Collection.　**7　10　15　20**

2171 GOOSE NECK LAMPS: 1980-83; set of two lamps in Type III box; black plastic base and lamp structure mounted to metal pole; frosted pin-based bulbs; reissue of postwar versions from 1961-63.

(A) Mt. Clemens production: solid black plastic light shields.
　　　　　　　　　　　　　8　10　20　30

(B) Mexico production: translucent black plastic light shields — light shines through them; "Mexico" adhesive sticker on bottom of each lamp post, white background with black lettering. Somewhat rare and difficult to find.　　　　　**NRS**

2175 SANDY ANDY: 1976-79; mechanically-operated gravel loader; light brown structure; dark brown roof and base; gray plastic girders; light brown ore cart; top of silo is loaded with coal; cart is attached to string with weight. When lever holding weight is released, weight brings cart to top of incline, where it pushes against lever which uncovers hole releasing coal into cart. When weight of coal overcomes brass weight on line attached to cart, cart travels down girders and is tripped into chute which unloads coal into waiting car or bin. Cycle then begins again. Difficult to

adjust properly, but action is delightful when accessory work properly. Plastic kit. Reissued in 1987 with new colors. Hard t find in intact, working condition. R. LaVoie comments.
　　　　　　　　　　　10　20　30　5

2180 ROAD SIGN SET: 1977-87; plastic one-piece signs.
　　　　　　　　　　　　　—　—　3

2181 TELEPHONE POLES: 1977-87; 10 light brown poles each 7" high.　　　　　　　　**—　—　3**

2195 FLOODLIGHT TOWER: 1970-72; eight lights; un painted gray tower, light bracket and reflectors; takes older two pin clear bulbs; tan base; "LIONEL" on two tabs near top of tower transitional hybrid; unpainted gray plastic tower structure wit unpainted gray "LIONEL" signs (postwar version has silver painted tower structure, red-painted "LIONEL"); postwa microwave relay top on tower; postwar markings on base; Type box. Very hard to find. B. Thomas, R. LaVoie, and G. Halverso Collections.　　　　　　**—　30　45　6**

2199 MICROWAVE TOWER: 1972-75; black plastic base unpainted dark gray plastic tower; black plastic top with thre operating blinking light tips; postwar markings on base; Type I box. The gray color of the tower structure is significantly darke than that of the postwar version, and the "LIONEL" plates on th side of the tower are not painted red. The radar dishes ar different as well: the postwar 199 has somewhat brittle whit plastic dishes, while this version has more flexible translucen plastic radar dishes. Very hard to find. R. LaVoie Collection.
　　　　　　　　　　　10　20　40　6

R. LaVoie Collection; B. Greenberg photograph

Top shelf: **2115** operating dwarf signal; **5025** manumatic uncoupler; **9550** box of two Standard O die-cast wheel sets (boxed pairs are seldom found today).
Middle shelf: Scarce **2260** plastic bumper from 1970-71; **2283** die-cast bumper from 1984-85; Lionel playing cards, part of a large number of peripheral items produced for Lionel's 75th anniversary in 1975; **2290** lighted bumper from 1974-85.
Bottom shelf: **2783** freight station from 1981-83; **2300** American Flyer oil drum loader from 1983.

	GD	VG	EXC	MT

2214 GIRDER BRIDGE: 1970-87; metal base, black- or brown-painted or brown-anodized; dark or light gray plastic side embossed "LIONEL"; comes knocked down or assembled. If knocked down, plastic sides must be screwed on with eight Phillips-head screws (but see earlier version below); 10" long, 4-1/2" wide.
(A) 1970-early 1971; flat black girder sides; white-outlined Lionel lettering; black-anodized base; comes assembled in larger Type I box; leftover 214 with postwar markings repackaged into a Type I Fundimensions box. C. Rohlfing and R. LaVoie Collections.
— 5 10 15
(B) 1971-72; smaller Type I box; knocked down assembly; dark gray plastic sides; outlined "LIONEL" with MPC logo to left; black-anodized metal base faintly embossed "No. 2214 BRIDGE/BY LIONEL MPC/Mt. CLEMENS, MICH./MADE IN U.S.A." Method of attaching base differs from later versions: girders fit into base by means of slots molded into girder sides and have no screws for assembly, snap-together. Hard to find. G. Halverson and R. LaVoie Collections. — 8 15 25

(C) 1973, early: light gray girders; comes assembled in unusual Stone Container Corp. box similar to that found on examples of 2256 station platform; dated as early 1973 based upon that example; very unusual packaging. F. S. Davis Collection. **NRS**
(D) 1973-87; Type II box; light gray girders; earliest production pieces still retain MPC logo; later ones omit it; screws provided for assembly; girders revert to postwar construction.
— 5 8 10

2256 STATION PLATFORM: 1973-81; green plastic base; metal posts; black plastic center fence; red unpainted plastic roof; not lighted.
(A) As described above. 8 10 15 20
(B) TCA special issue: Penn Central green base; lighter red roof than regular issue; overprint heat-stamped in white; "21 TCA National Convention, Orlando, Florida, June 19-26, 1975". G. Halverson and R. LaVoie Collections. — 15 25 35
(C) Same as (A), but has leftover 2156 light green base; fairly common variation. R. LaVoie Collection. 8 10 15 25

R. LaVoie Collection; B. Greenberg photograph

All four of these early Fundimensions towers are hard to find.
2314 all-black searchlight tower, usually found in red and black; 2313(A)
floodlight tower, hybrid metal leftover lenses instead of plastic; 2195
floodlight tower from 1971; 2199 microwave tower from 1972.

	GD	VG	EXC	MT

(D) Same as (A), but came in unusual Stone Container Corp. corrugated box with red and black wraparound label on one side and both ends. R. LaVoie Collection. **10 15 25 35**

2260 BUMPER: 1970-73; same mold used as for postwar 26 and 260 die-cast bumpers, but black plastic body; four screws at corners; translucent red cap (as opposed to bright solid red color); takes 14-volt bayonet-based bulb; may have come in Type I box (reader confirmation requested) or Type II shrink-wrap packaging. This bumper was originally designed as a less expensive replacement for the metal 260; it had been issued to fit Super O track in the late 1950s. Somewhat hard to find.
(A) Bottom fiber plate marked "NO. 260/THE LIONEL CORPORATION" in white; hex nut holds plate to chassis; identical to late postwar Hagerstown production except for the translucent lens cap; some Hagerstown versions also had translucent caps and cannot be distinguished from this version. G. Halverson Collection. **10 15 25 40**
(B) Same as (A), but later production; no lettering on bottom fiber plate. R. LaVoie Collection. **10 15 25 40**
(C) Unlighted version; no bottom plate or electrical connections. Came in 1972 Pioneer Dockside Switcher set. R. LaVoie Collection. **10 15 20 30**

2280 BUMPERS: 1973-80, 1983.

	GD	VG	EXC	MT

(A) 1973-75; three to a package; early version with open area on top just behind bumper plate; Type I box. **— 1 3 5**

(B) 1974-80, 1983; later version with closed area. **— — 3 5**

2282 BUMPER: 1983; uncatalogued black die-cast body which attaches to the track with screws; black plastic shock absorber; red illuminated jewel atop body; reissue of 260 bumper from the 1950s with a color change; Type V box. Illustrated in the 1983 Fall Collector's brochure. R. LaVoie comment. Price per pair. **— — 25 35**

2283 BUMPER: 1984-85; tuscan-painted die-cast body identical in construction to 2282 above. Made in Hong Kong and sold as part of Traditional Series in pairs in Type III boxes. Price per pair. **— — 10 15**

2290 LIGHTED BUMPERS: 1974-85; similar in construction to 2280, but with copper contact and small screw-based red bulbs; Type III box. Price per pair. **6 8 10 12**

2292 STATION PLATFORM: 1985-87; dark red base; black plastic roof supports; black fencing; dark green roof; chromed acorn nut roof fasteners; unlighted. **— 4 6 10**

2300 OIL DRUM LOADER: 1983; reissue of 779 American Flyer accessory from 1955-56. Colors differ and black striping on building of original 779 is not present, but mechanism is essentially identical. This reissue is more sensitive to voltage changes than its predecessor and requires more careful operation, although it works well. Listed here, as well as in our American Flyer book, because it appeared in a Fundimensions catalogue and will be found with Lionel trains. Very hard to find. **— — 95 125**

2301 OPERATING SAWMILL: 1981-83; dark gray plastic base; white mill building; red door; gray shed; red lettering on window facing track; white crane; simulates the transformation of logs into dressed lumber; vibrator mechanism moves lumber; length 10-1/2", width 6", height 6". Reissue of 464 from 1956-60. T. Baptist comment. Getting scarce. J. Kouba comment. **— — 95 125**

2302 U.P. GANTRY CRANE: 1981-82; maroon crane housing and boom; black platform spans track and runs on its own wheels; manually-operated; reproduction of 282 from 1954 but without motor and remote control. **— — 20 30**

2303 SANTA FE GANTRY CRANE: 1980-81; manually operated gantry crane; dark blue plastic cab; yellow boom and lettering; gray superstructure. Came as kit in 1072 Cross Country Express set. **— — 20 30**

2305 OIL DERRICK: 1981-83; walking beam rocks up and down; bubbling pipe simulates oil flow; hand-operated winch; ladder; barrels; red-painted sheet metal base; small brass identification plate with adhesive backing; reissue of 455 from 1950-54 but with Getty signs instead of Sunoco; slightly darker green tower structure; Type V box lacks gloss coating of most such boxes. Somewhat hard to find in last few years. R. LaVoie and C. Lang comments. **— 75 100 145**

2306 OPERATING ICE STATION: 1982-83; red roof; white chute; sold with 6700 refrigerator car; reissue of 352 from 1955-57. Lately, this accessory has become hard to find. Price includes car. C. O'Dell comments. **— 145 195 235**

2307 BILLBOARD LIGHT: 1983-84; black die-cast post; hooded black light casting attaches to base of billboard and blinks

Three of Lionel's most intriguing accessories.   *R. LaVoie Collection; B. Greenberg photograph*
Top shelf: **2318** control tower with red roof, made in Mexico (also produced in Mt. Clemens with maroon roof); **2494** rotary beacon from 1972, reissued 16 years later as **12720**.
Bottom shelf: **2317** drawbridge, an excellent operating piece.

	GD	VG	EXC	MT

by thermostatic control. Reissue of 410 model of 1956-58. I. D. Smith comment.   — 10 15 25

2308 ANIMATED NEWSSTAND: 1982-83; reissue of 128 from 1957-60; newsboy hands paper to dealer; dog circles fire hydrant. Somewhat hard to find.   — — 120 145

2309 MECHANICAL CROSSING GATE: 1982-87; operated by weight of train.   — — 2 4

2310 MECHANICAL CROSSING GATE AND SIGNAL: 1973-75; activated by weight of train; black and white plastic; requires assembly.   — 2 3 5

2311 MECHANICAL SEMAPHORE: 1982-87; operated by weight of train.   — — 2 4

2312 MECHANICAL SEMAPHORE: 1973-75; activated by weight of train; flag raises and green signal illuminates as train approaches; flag lowers and red signal illuminates after train passes contact track.   — 3 5 6

	GD	VG	EXC	MT

2313 OPERATING FLOODLIGHT TOWER: 1975-83; black plastic base; red plastic tower; black plastic top; gray light bar; eight miniature lights; two binding posts on bottom.
(A) Early hybrid; takes miniature plastic-based lamps, but reflectors remain metal. The postwar light bar has a metal frame running around its rear which provides contact for the lights; beginning with this version, the metal frame is absent and two wires come down from the mounting holes of the light bar to make electrical contact and carry power internally to the bulbs. This hybrid version has the later light bar; came in Type II box with the word "GAUGE" misspelled as "GUAGE" on front label. In view of its unusual nature, this version is surprisingly common. R. LaVoie Collection.   10 15 25 35
(B) Same as (A), but regular production; light reflectors are chromed plastic instead of metal; "GAUGE" is spelled correctly on box. C. Rohlfing Collection.   7 10 20 25

2314 OPERATING SEARCHLIGHT TOWER: 1975-83.

	GD	VG	EXC	MT

(A) Unpainted light gray plastic tower and dark gray base; two black searchlight hoods; rare. Shown this way in 1975-77 catalogues; further reader confirmation of existence in these colors requested. G. Halverson Collection. — — 125 160

(B) Black plastic tower, base, and tower top; two black searchlight hoods. Somewhat hard to find. C. Rohlfing, R. LaVoie, J. Kovach, C. O'Dell and G. Halverson Collections. 15 20 35 50

(C) Same as (A), but red tower; black base; red tower top. W. Eddins Collection. 7 10 20 30

(D) Same as (C), but black tower top. R. Sage Collection. 10 15 25 35

2315 COALING STATION: 1984-85; reissue of 497 from 1953-58. Originally scheduled for number 2324, but that number was used later for the revival of the postwar 445 operating switch tower. Dark red metal structure; gray support base; black pillars; red coal tray; gray roof (postwar version had maroon coal tray and green roof, and color of paint was lighter red). This version uses the new Fundimensions can motor instead of the postwar motor, so it runs more quietly at lower voltage. — — 90 120

2316 NORFOLK & WESTERN GANTRY CRANE: 1983-84; remote-control version; similar to the postwar 282R, but with several important construction changes. Dark maroon cab; gold lettering and cab base; maroon boom; gray superstructure; does not have electromagnet found on the 282R; the single motor and gearing of the 282R has been replaced by two Fundimensions can motors mounted under the superstructure, one for each operation of the crane (swiveling of body and hook operation). Compared to the 282R, this crane is not as strong a lifting device, but it operates much more quietly than the 282R on much lower voltage. The line for the lifting hook has a tendency to tangle and stall the lifting action; crane must be disassembled for rewinding of line. Generally neglected since Erie magnetic version was issued, but somewhat scarce. R. LaVoie Collection. — — 110 125

2317 DRAWBRIDGE: 1975-81; tan base; dark brown plastic piers; dark gray span; gray supports; five pressure binding posts visible on right side of illustration; olive green tender house with light brown roof; dark brown door and steps; with one full length of O27 track and two half sections. Very complex to wire, but excellent operating action. Wiring patterned after that of legendary 313 bascule bridge, but this is a Fundimensions original in every way. Difficult to find in mint, boxed condition. R. LaVoie and C. Rohlfing Collections. — 40 60 75

2318 CONTROL TOWER: 1983-84; yellow building; black superstructure; gray base (postwar 192 predecessor had orange and green colors); red ladders; two men move in circles around the building interior, powered by vibrator motor. Caution: many examples of both the postwar accessory and this version have damaged roofs caused by heat from the light bulb. The socket cannot be bent down, since the men pass under it. To prevent roof damage, replace the 14-volt light bulb supplied with the accessory with an 18-volt bayonet bulb or a 24-volt GE lamp. Fasten aluminum foil, shiny side out, to the underside of the roof just above the light bulb. Reissued in new colors and new number in 1987. R. LaVoie comments.

(A) Red tower roof; Mexican production; possibly scarcer than (B), but more reader confirmation needed. R. LaVoie Collection. — — 55 75

(B) Maroon tower roof; Mount Clemens production. — — 55 75

2319 WATCHTOWER: 1975-80; lighted non-operating version of postwar 445 switch tower; white body; maroon base and staircase; Penn Central green roof; red chimney; green door and window inserts. — 15 20 30

2320 FLAG POLE KIT: 1983-87; reissue of No. 89 from 1956-58; fabric 50-star flag; blue pennant with white lettering; brown plastic base; four sponge corner plots (sponge is less dense than on postwar version); 11" high; embossed on underside: "PART NO. 00-0089-003/LIONEL CORPORATION/1983 CPG." I. D. Smith comments. A version of this flagpole was made for LOTS in 1984. — 5 10 15

2321 SAWMILL: 1984-85; reissue of American Flyer accessory of late 1950s; dark red base; light tan house structures; dark green roofs; black metal lumber pickup mechanism; light tan simulated sawdust pile; gray circular saw blade; yellow lumber cart. When accessory is activated, lumber cart goes by saw blade, simulating cutting of log. Finished lumber plank emerges from compartment in house, where it is picked up by mechanism and lifted into waiting trackside gondola or flatcar. Very hard to find. — — 95 125

2323 OPERATING FREIGHT STATION: 1984-85; similar to postwar 356; dark red base; black baggage cart pathway; light tan housing; dark green roof; two green luggage carts; stick-on billboards; black fence with poster ads (postwar 356 model had metal signs, while this model has modified fence to accommodate stick-on posters); baggage carts move around station in alternation, both carts are dark green and have reinforcement pieces added to top rod which retains cart in station, where it is released by trip device. Earliest production suffered from warped bases. These will still operate properly with careful adjustment of base retaining screws. — — 60 75

2324 OPERATING SWITCH TOWER: 1984-85; similar to postwar 445; dark red base, steps, and upper doorway; tan building with dark brown door and window inserts; brown balcony; dark green roof with red chimney; one man runs into station house, other man comes down stairs; illuminated. Postwar man on stairs carries lantern in left hand; this version has a right-handed man. Some examples observed with left-handed man; probable use of postwar leftover figure, even this late after postwar years. Somewhat neglected recently because of issue of "burning" variety, but this version is scarcer than generally thought. R. Sigurdson and R. LaVoie observations. — — 55 65

2494 ROTARY BEACON: 1972-74; red sheet metal tower with revolving beacon powered by vibrator motor; beacon projects red and green illumination; over 11-1/2" high; red-stamped metal base 5" x 5"; black ladder; black-lettered aluminized foil nameplate on base; two clips on underside of base for wires; construction of light hood differs from postwar 494, black plastic light hood rotates on circular metal collar which is frequently missing from used examples. Box at one time made by Stone Container Corp.; some have glue-on paper overlay with black and white picture of accessory, while other boxes lack this picture. This is one of the scarcest of all the Fundimensions accessories. Some versions are known to have been issued with leftover postwar beacon tops instead of new assemblies. G. Cole, G. Halverson, and R. LaVoie comments; G. Halverson, C. Kruelle, and R. LaVoie Collections.

(A) Silver beacon heads. 20 30 40 50

(B) Black beacon heads. 20 30 50 75

2709 RICO STATION: 1981-85; large plastic kit; 22" long x 9" wide; different versions were reportedly made; the 2797 from 1976

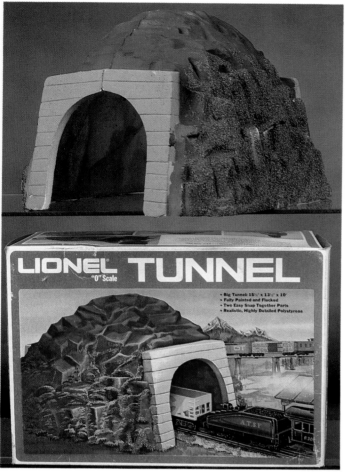

R. LaVoie Collection; B. Greenberg photograph

2714 styrofoam tunnel with box — no identifying Lionel marks, hard to find with box.

	GD	VG	EXC	MT

was made in different colors — reader comments about specific colors appreciated. Very large station which looks good because of its detail. Although all versions in all colors have been popular, the 2797 version is the most prized by collectors. This version comes in Type III packaging. — 10 20 30

2710 BILLBOARDS: 1970-84; five plastic frames in box with strip of five billboards; earliest cardstock billboards have lavender bordering instead of dark green used on most postwar examples, but these are still late postwar billboards; light green frames have "STANDARD" in oval on ribbed bottom; inside of frames stamped "2710 BILL BOARD MT. CLEMENS, MICH./MADE IN U.S.A." and Lionel logo.

(A) Type I box dated 8-70; five dark green leftover postwar frames with 310 markings; strip of five public service and other billboards: U.S. Bonds (2), Education (2), and "Get A Dodge." (1). J. R. Hunt and R. LaVoie Collections. 3 4 5 6

(B) Same as (A), but billboards differ: Sheraton, MPC, Kenner, Parker Brothers, and Lionel. R. LaVoie Collection. 3 4 5 6

(C) 1970-72; same as (A), but light green frames; MPC logo on inside of frame; Type I box. One sample observed had one dark

green postwar and four Fundimensions frames. J. R. Hunt, R. LaVoie, and G. Halverson Collections. 3 4 5 6

(D) 1973-84; slightly darker green frames; Type II or Type III box; Lionel logo on inside of frame. 1 2 3 4

2714 TUNNEL: 1975-77; 15-1/2" x 13-1/2" x 10"; two-piece construction; came in very large Type II box; no Lionel identification of any kind on tunnel and extremely hard to find in original box, which is virtually the only way the tunnel can be identified as a Lionel product! Both Excellent and Like New values require original box to establish both identity and values cited.
 — 5 40 50

2717 SHORT EXTENSION BRIDGE: 1977-83; 10" x 6-1/2" x 4-1/2"; plastic kit; maroon structure. Included as part of many lower-priced sets. This is actually a small truss bridge.
 — 2 3 5

2718 BARREL PLATFORM: 1977-83; plastic kit includes figure, barrels, tools, lamp, ladder and building; 4" x 4" x 3-1/2".
 — 1 2 4

2719 SIGNAL TOWER: 1977-83; described as "Watchman Shanty" in catalogue; 7" high, 4" x 4-1/2"; plastic kit.
 — 1 2 4

2720 LUMBER SHED: 1977-83; plastic kit includes workman, shed, table, lumber, tools and ladder; 4" high x 6" long x 3-1/2" wide. — 1 2 4

2721 LOG LOADING MILL: 1979; red plastic kit; manual operation; pressing a lever causes plastic log to be released and roll down ramp; part of inexpensive "Workin' On The Railroad" sets. — — 3 5

2722 BARREL LOADER: 1979; green plastic kit; manual operation; workman pushes barrel down a chute; part of inexpensive "Workin' On The Railroad" sets. — — 3 5

2723 BARREL LOADER: 1984; brown plastic kit; manual operation; workman pushes barrel down chute; part of 1403 Redwood Valley Express set. — — 3 5

2729 WATER TOWER BUILDING KIT: 1985; orange-brown pump house with gray door and window insert; light tan base; gray ladder; green tower support frame; light tan tank; gray spout; green tank roof. Pictured in the 1985 Traditional catalogue, but canceled from dealer order sheets in September 1985. Water tower kit in same colors released in 1987 as 12711.
Not Manufactured

2783 FREIGHT STATION KIT: 1981-85; light brown sides; dark brown platform; doors and windows; light gray roof; brick red chimney. Reissued later in different colors.
 — — 7 10

2784 FREIGHT PLATFORM: 1981-87; snap-together realistic O Scale plastic kit with opening door.
 2 3 6 9

2785 ENGINE HOUSE: 1974-77; plastic kit. Very similar kits have been produced in the past few years, both in single- and double-track versions, by Pola, IHC and others. This single-track kit is very hard to find. Reissued in 1987 as 12710.
 — 20 30 40

2786 FREIGHT PLATFORM: 1974-77; freight shed with platform; plastic kit. — 3 4 7

2787 FREIGHT STATION: 1974-77, 1983; highly detailed O Scale plastic kit. 3 5 7 10

GD VG EXC MT

2788 COALING STATION: 1975-77; plastic kit; coal may be mechanically dumped. Hard to find. Reissued in 1988 as 12736 in different colors. **5 10 20 40**

2789 WATER TOWER: 1975-80; water tower on brick structure; plastic kit. **— 3 7 10**

2790 BUILDING KIT ASSORTMENT: 1979-84; consists of four each for 2718, 2719 and 2720. L. Bohn comment. **NRS**

2791 CROSS COUNTRY SET: 1970-71; Type I box; five telephone poles; 12 railroad signs; watchman's shanty with crossing gate; 17-1/4" black bridge; contents wrapped in brown paper inside box. Hard to find in unused condition. This set and its corresponding 2792 and 2793 sets featured Plasticville pieces supplied to Fundimensions by Bachmann. Often the components can be found in reversed color schemes from the standard Plasticville production, and sometimes they are made of "marbled" plastic. G. Halverson Collection; R. LaVoie comments.
— 10 25 35

2792 LAYOUT STARTER PAK: 1980-83; snap-together bridge kit; barrel platform kit; lumber shed kit; 10 telephone poles; 14 road signs; five billboards; Track Layout Book.
— — 10 25

2792 WHISTLE STOP SET: 1970-71; contains signal bridge, watchman's shanty with crossing gate, freight loading platform with baggage accessories and five telephone poles. C. Rohlfing, T. Rollo and R. LaVoie Collections. **— 10 25 35**

2793 ALAMO JUNCTION SET: 1970-71; contains water tank with gray base, framework and roof; brown tank; switch tower with brown base, steps, roof and doors; gray sides; watchman shanty with gray base, roof and windows; brown building; black and white crossing gate; five light brown telephone poles. R. LaVoie Collection. **— — 25 35**

2796 GRAIN ELEVATOR: 1977; 16" high x 16" long x 13" wide; plastic kit. Very hard to find. Reissued in 1988 as 12726 in different colors. **— 40 60 75**

2797 RICO STATION: 1976; large plastic kit 22" x 9" x 9" high; modeled after Rico, Colorado station. Somewhat hard to find. See also 2709. **— 20 30 45**

2900 LOCKON: 1970-85; can be found in Type I, II or III shrink-wrap packaging. **.20 .50 1 1.25**

2901 TRACK CLIPS: 1970-85; 12-pack; Type I, II or III box.
— 1 2 5

2905 LOCKON AND WIRE: 1972-85; Type II or III blister pack. **— .70 .85 1.50**

2909 SMOKE FLUID: 1977-85; for locomotives made after 1970; comes in small plastic bottle with red or blue lettering; later smoke formulation made after 1989 by LTI is much more effective. **1 1.50 3**

2910-1 CONTACTOR: Probably 1984-91; reissue of postwar OTC contactor which was probably first reissued with 9224 Louisville horse car of 1984 or 9290 Union Pacific barrel car of 1983.
— — — 7

2911 SMOKE PELLETS: 1970-72; leftover supply of Hillside postwar production; came in postwar bottles of 50 pellets marked "SP LIONEL SMOKE PELLETS"; Type I shrink-wrap or pillbox. R. Hutchinson, R. Paris and T. Klaassen Collections.
— — 10 15

R. LaVoie Collection; B. Greenberg photograph

Some old Lionel favorites — one with a new twist.
Top shelf: 12703 operating icing station.
Middle shelf: 2324 operating switch tower; 12768 burning switch tower features a flickering light simulating fire, scorch marks, and a smoke unit spouting copious amounts of smoke.
Bottom shelf: 2301 operating sawmill — a remake of the 464 postwar favorite.

GD VG EXC MT

2927 MAINTENANCE KIT: 1970-71, 1977-87; consists of lubricant; oiler; track cleaning fluid; track cleaner; rubber eraser; all mounted on a piece of cardboard and shrink-wrapped.
(A) Type I packaging (same scheme as Type I box); oil; lubricant; eraser-type track cleaner; liquid track cleaner; materials are leftover postwar production with Hillside, New Jersey factory address. G. Halverson and R. LaVoie Collections.
— — 10 15
(B) Type II or III packaging; Fundimensions-produced materials.
— — 5 7

2951 TRACK LAYOUT BOOK: 1976-80, 1983; several editions have been issued; see listings in *Greenberg's Guide to Lionel Paper and Collectibles* by Robert Osterhoff for full information.
— .50 .75 2

2952 TRACK ACCESSORY MANUAL: See listings as noted above. **— — .75 1**

2953 TRAIN AND ACCESSORY MANUAL: 1977-85; several editions have been issued; see listings as noted above.
— — 1.25 2

2960 LIONEL 75TH ANNIVERSARY BOOK: 1975; blue cover with 75th Anniversary logo. See listings as noted in 2951 entry. **— 6 8 10**

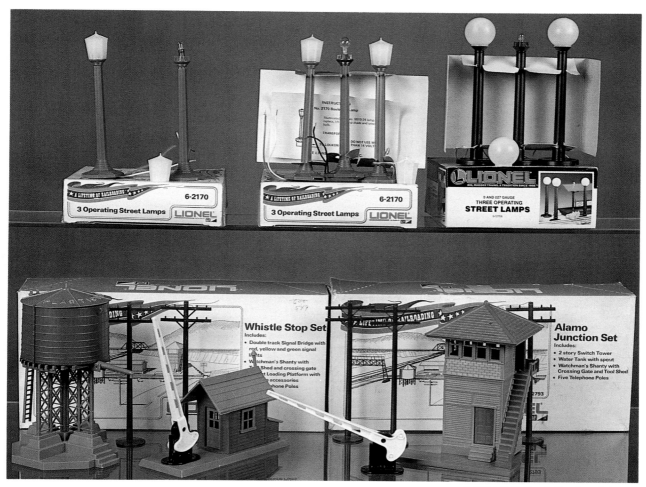

R. LaVoie Collection; B. Greenberg photograph

Top shelf: **2170 street lamps from 1971 and later; very unusual 2170 lamp — the MPC logo is molded into the base of this example, proving its modern era production; 12708 street lamps from 1988 — base is now circular, but the same screw-based bulb is used with a much larger nylon globe.**

Bottom shelf: **Two early Lionel building sets from 1971 — the 2792 whistle stop set and the 2793 Alamo Junction set.**

	GD	VG	EXC	MT

2980 MAGNETIC CONVERSION COUPLER: 1971, 1979 and probably other years as well; kit for replacing other types of couplers with magnetic operating couplers. Consists of plate assembly and either a Delrin plastic coupler with integrally molded leaf spring mounted with a chromed rivet, or a die-cast knuckle coupler, knuckle spring and chromed rivet. The 1971 version came with instructions marked on the envelope rather than on a separate sheet inside the envelope. Reader comments requested as to differences between 1971 kit and late postwar examples. I. D. Smith and R. Paris comments.

	—	—	1	2

2985 LIONEL TRAIN BOOK: 1986; See listings in *Greenberg's Guide to Lionel Paper And Collectibles* by Robert Osterhoff. Lionel's most ambitious effort to date to provide a recent "starter" book for operators.   — — 7 10

5031 TRAIN ACCESSORY KIT/FORD MARKETING CORPORATION: 1971; brown corrugated carton with three 2170 street lamps; set of five 2710 billboards, three of which (Play-Doh, MPC Model Kits and Lionel) are regular production; but two special billboards (Autolite Small Engine Spark Plugs and Motorcraft: We've Canned It) are also included; 2152 crossing gate and a yellow business reply card, "Wholesale Parts Salesmen/...WIN AN/ALL AMERICAN/VACATION!". G. Shewmake comments. We would still like to hear from any former Ford parts salespeople who know the details of this promotion.   **NRS**

8190 DIESEL HORN: 1981; electronic package that can be adapted to engines or rolling stock; operated by whistle button on older transformer; Type V box includes circuit board, speaker, two double-sided adhesive pads and instructions. Roller pickup assembly must be purchased separately if it is needed; unit can be installed with existing roller pickups. Price for unused unit only; such units are very hard to find.   — — — 40

8251-50 HORN/WHISTLE CONTROLLER: 1972-74; rectangular push-button box for early Fundimensions horns and whistles. Easily burned out if contacts stick in closed position, as they often did. Came in black or red case with matching push button. Additional instruction sheet cautions against holding down button only part way; this is apparently what burned out so many of these units. R. LaVoie comment; G. Halverson Collection.   — — 2 3

12700 MAGNETIC GANTRY CRANE: 1987, Erie-Lackawanna; black gantry frame and platform with white-outlined

Cranes and derricks from the sublime to the ridiculous.   *R. LaVoie Collection; B. Greenberg photograph*
12700 Erie magnetic gantry crane from 1987, value has escalated sharply in last two years because it possesses a magnet and was produced
in limited quantities; 2305 oil derrick from 1981-86; 2316 Norfolk & Western gantry crane from 1984.

	GD	VG	EXC	MT

"LIONEL"; gray crane body and boom; yellow cab base and gear; maroon crane cab roof; black magnet picks up loads as did predecessor from postwar years, 282R; motor changed from postwar type to new can-type which operates quietly. Hard to find recently and appreciating in value.   — **150   175   225**

12701 DIESEL FUELING STATION: 1987; dark blue housing on gray base; gray roof; orange sand tower stand and pipe base; black piping; black sand tank with yellow "DIESEL SAND"; light gray man with flesh-colored face appears to come from house to fuel hose when button is pressed. Similar to postwar 415 accessory, including its slow sales record.   —   —   **75   90**

12702 OPERATING CONTROL TOWER: 1987; see 2318 entries for earlier versions. This version operates the same but has new colors: red tower house with black roof and platform; black base; red ladders; gray superstructure with red "LIONEL"; white arrow and weathervane atop roof. Unlike 2318 version, has aluminum shield to prevent roof damage.

     —   —   **50   65**

12703 ICING STATION: 1988-89; orange housing and steps; red roof; dark gray superstructure with white lettering; black stamped-steel base. This version of the icing station was changed significantly from both its postwar and its modern era predecessors. Instead of the solenoid-operated mechanism, this version uses a can motor and a gear system to produce a much smoother

operation. It was sold without the special car, which was available separately in New York Central, Reading and Great Northern configurations. Both this accessory and the cars have sold very well.   —   —   **75   100**

12704 DWARF SIGNAL: 1988-91; maroon signal body; black lens hood; red and green lights operate by means of 153C contactor (unlike postwar design, which was manually operated).   **CP**

12705 LUMBER SHED: 1988-91; black shed structure; black base; dark tan awnings; light tan roof supports; light tan simulated lumber stacks; unpainted gray man.   **CP**

12706 BARREL LOADER BUILDING: 1987-91; all-gray platform, barrels, man, barrel chute and shack; manual turn of lever sends barrel out chute into car. Sold in kit form.   **CP**

12707 BILLBOARD SET: 1987-91; three large white plastic frames in a new design supplied with three double-sided billboards. Frames fit into white plastic bases, and billboard sheet is folded in half and slid into slot in frame. Pegs which fit into base are very fragile and easily broken. Includes instruction sheet 71-2707-250. Type VI box. R. LaVoie Collection. A special version of this billboard was made for LOTS in 1988.   **CP**

12708 STREET LAMPS: 1988-91; new design; black base and pole; white opaque rounded globe atop pole. Sold in sets of three.   **CP**

12712 ore loader with box.

R. LaVoie Collection; B. Greenberg photograph

	GD	VG	EXC	MT

2709 OPERATING BANJO SIGNAL: 1987-91; same design and operation as 2140, but die-cast frame painted tuscan instead of black. **CP**

2710 ENGINE HOUSE: 1987-91; revival of 2285 from 1975-6; brick red building; black doors and windows; gray roof; measures 20-1/2" x 6-1/8" x 7-1/8". **CP**

2711 WATER TOWER KIT: 1987-91; revival of 2789; identical in catalogue appearance to 2729 which appeared in 1985 catalogue but was never produced. **CP**

2712 AUTOMATIC ORE LOADER: 1987-88; revival of 175 Sandy Andy ore loader in new colors; bright blue base, roofs and chute roof; yellow elevator tower and structure; gray tower supports; yellow ore cart tracks; gray ore cart. Comes with ore and gray dumping bin. — — — 20

2713 AUTOMATIC GATEMAN: 1987-88; the longest-lived of all Lionel accessories returned in new colors after a two-year absence; light tan base; green cardboard base bottom (we would like to know if some earlier 2145 versions also have this base); door stop bump designed into metal base; bright yellow shack; red roof and toolbox lid; light gray man with red lantern; white crossbuck with black lettering and metal base. Still illuminated by 431 large-based bayonet bulb present with this accessory since 1950, but cardboard shield added to this version to prevent translucence. Variation without cardboard shield said to exist. J. Kouba comment. — — — 35

2714 AUTOMATIC CROSSING GATE: 1987-91; same design as 2152, but new colors: gray base; red safety stripes; brown plastic gate stop rod; Type VI box. **CP**

2715 ILLUMINATED BUMPERS: 1987-91; two per package; Type VI box. Same design as 2290, but tuscan in color. **CP**

	GD	VG	EXC	MT

12716 SEARCHLIGHT TOWER: 1987-91; same design as 2314, but new colors: light gray base and tower platform; bright orange tower structure; black searchlight hoods. **CP**

12717 BUMPERS: 1987-91; non-illuminated. Same design as 2280, but tuscan in color. Three per package. **CP**

12718 BARREL SHED KIT: 1987-91; light tan base and platform; black platform supports; tan man; white barrels; white house with black roof and door. Catalogue illustration shows custom-painted example; comes in all-tan kit. **CP**

12719 ANIMATED REFRESHMENT STAND: 1988-89; redesign of animated newsstand; light gray base; white shed; light green roof; red and white lettering; checkerboard countertop; white-clad attendant moves to front, painted boy and girl figures rotate, and giant ice cream cone spins. Very popular accessory which sold well. — — — 75

12720 ROTARY BEACON: 1988-89; similar to 2494, but has black tower top piece instead of all-red design. — — — 40

12721 ILLUMINATED EXTENSION BRIDGE WITH ROCK PIERS: 1989; medium brown bridge structure; gray rock piers; arched top segment with red light at top; stamped-steel base. Similar to 2122 model except for added light. Technically, this is a truss bridge. — — — 25

12722 ROADSIDE DINER WITH SMOKE: 1988-89; 9500-type passenger car body mounted on gray base; light tan body; red roof; black chimneys; black sign with white "LIONELVILLE DINER" lettering; illuminated; smoke from largest chimney; silhouettes in windows. Has been a popular addition to many layouts. — — — 40

12723 MICROWAVE RELAY TOWER: 1988-90; dark gray base; bright orange tower structure; white radar dish; light blinks

Recent action accessories, all well-received.

R. LaVoie Collection; B. Greenberg photograph

Top shelf: **12763** single signal bridge; **12724** two-track signal bridge.
Bottom shelf: **12729** mail pickup set; **12727** semaphore; **12760** highway flasher with new diode-activated flashing system instead of the track contactor.

	GD	VG	EXC	MT

thermostatically; remake of scarce 2199 model of 1972, but in new colors. — — — **20**

12724 SIGNAL BRIDGE: 1988-90; black metal girder structure; light gray plastic bases; two black plastic two-light lens hoods; die-cast metal bulb housings. Similar to postwar 450 model. — — — **40**

12725 LIONEL TRACTOR AND TRAILER: 1989; bright orange tractor unit with blue stripe and lettering; chromed plastic bumper, grille and exhaust stack; bright orange trailer with white-outlined lettering "LIONEL" and Lionel logo; metal undercarriage which can be separated from trailer; rubber wheels with chromed hubcaps. This was the first of a very popular series of road vehicles made in Macao to Lionel specifications. Their fine detail and attractive price have made them good sellers, especially since the intermodal cranes to handle the trailers were issued. — — **10** **14**

12726 GRAIN ELEVATOR: 1988-91; pale yellow building sides; dark gray roof pieces; tan platform. Remake of the scarce 2796 grain elevator kit of 1976-77 in different colors. **CP**

12727 OPERATING SEMAPHORE: 1989-91; dark maroon base; black pole; yellow arm. Similar to 2151 model of 1978-84. **CP**

12728 ILLUMINATED FREIGHT STATION: 1989; yellow-brown building with dark brown base and light brown roof, windows and doors; illuminated. Similar to 2133 model except for colors. — — — **25**

	GD	VG	EXC	MT

12729 MAIL PICKUP SET: 1988-90; black base; red pole semaphore arm and swinging arm; large red magnetic mailbag Similar to scarce 161 model of 1961-63. — — — **18**

12730 PLATE GIRDER BRIDGE: 1988-91; black plastic sides; white-outlined "LIONEL" lettering; chemically blackened metal base. Sold knocked down to be assembled by purchaser. Nearly a direct remake of the postwar 214 model. **CP**

12731 STATION PLATFORM: 1988-91; red roof; dark green base; black roof supports; signs on fence include Coca-Cola, Lionel Inc.; three chromed acorn nuts fasten supports to roof. **CP**

12732 COAL BAG: 1988-91; four ounces of plastic coal pieces packed in white sack with red lettering and logo and string tie Similar to postwar 206 coal sack. **CP**

12733 WATCHMAN'S SHANTY: 1988-91; dark red-brown house; black roof; light gray steps and stairway; light gray base. **CP**

12734 PASSENGER/FREIGHT STATION: 1989-91; building kit with light brown building; brick-red roof; gray chimney gray base; light green window and door inserts. Similar to previous 2783 except for colors. **CP**

12735 DIESEL HORN SHED: 1988-91; uses design of postwar 114 newsstand with horn; light tan house; dark brown roof and window edging; dark brown base; frosted window inserts illuminated. **CP**

12736 COALING STATION KIT: 1988-91; red-brown lower tower; medium tan upper housing; black roof; dark blue tipple structure and housing. **CP**

Some of Lionel's most recent accessories.
Top shelf: 12728 passenger and freight station; 12722 roadside diner with smoke.
Bottom shelf: 12720 rotary beacon, same as the earlier 2494 but with a black tower top; 12723 microwave tower, a reissue of earlier 2199; 12749 radar antenna.

R. LaVoie Collection; B. Greenberg photograph

	GD	VG	EXC	MT

12737 WHISTLING FREIGHT SHED: 1988-91; uses design of postwar 118 newsstand with whistle; dark maroon building; white window edging; black roof, door and base; illuminated.
CP

12739 LIONEL GAS CO. TRACTOR AND TANKER: 1989; blue tractor with orange markings; chromed bumper, grille and exhaust stack; gray tank trailer with white lettering and chrome trim. See 12725 entry for background.
— — — 11

12740 LOG PACKAGE: 1988-91; set of three real wood logs with bark to retrofit log dump cars and to supply flatcar loads.
CP

12741 UNION PACIFIC MI-JACK INTERMODAL CRANE: 1989-90; very large yellow crane structure with black Mi-Jack lettering and red, white and blue Union Pacific shield logo; black simulated spotlights atop crane structure. The crane makes use of Lionel's TOFC flatcars and new tractor/trailer models. This crane is capable of its own forward and reverse motion; it will also swing right or left, and its carrying jaws will open and shut, grasp a trailer, lift it (Lionel recommends lifting no more than seven ounces) and move it right or left. All this action is accomplished by a complex arrangement of string-driven motions powered by two can motors mounted within a rooftop structure. The device works through a five-lever controller whose levers can work either singly or in combination. Lionel also supplied a 12-page instruction book with an impressively-written history of the prototype. Both this and a second Norfolk & Western model have been somewhat discounted in some areas because the accessory is too large for some operator layouts. However, it represents an ambitious modern direction for Lionel and the accessory works well, providing the operator considerable entertainment. R. LaVoie Collection and comments.
— — 200 225

12742 GOOSE NECK STREET LAMPS: 1989-91; black lamp structure and base; frosted pin bulb. Sold in pairs and essentially identical to 2171 model of 1980-84. **CP**

12744 ROCK PIERS: 1989-91; two large 4-3/4" gray plastic simulated rock piles which support bridges as part of elevated layouts. Identical to those supplied with late-model extension bridges.
CP

12745 BARREL PACK: 1989-91; six dark brown- varnished barrels to a package. Operators of barrel car and/or ramp should

Lionel makes good looking trucks as well as trains. Top two shelves from "Workin' on the Railroad" sets:
Top shelf: No number Ryder tractor/trailer.
Second shelf: Santa Fe and Penn Central tractor/trailer.
Third shelf: 12725 Lionel; 12739 Lionel Gas Co.
Bottom shelf: 12777 Chevron; 12778 Conrail.

R. LaVoie Collection; B. Greenberg photograph

	GD	VG	EXC	MT

be aware that varnished barrels often are too slippery to be vibrated up the ramps of these accessories. **CP**

12748 ILLUMINATED STATION PLATFORM: 1989-91; light gray base; black plastic roof supports and fence; dark maroon roof; two hooded lamps resembling top part of goose-neck street lamps; press-on posters supplied for fence. **CP**

12749 ROTARY RADAR ANTENNA: 1989-91; gray tower structure; maroon tower base and top; silver radar antenna and black radio pole; vibrator motor makes antenna rotate. **CP**

12750 CRANE KIT: 1989-91; yellow crane and cab body; black crane and superstructure; swiveling cab and operating hook. Similar to crane which came with 9157 C & O flatcar. **CP**

12751 SHOVEL KIT: 1989-91; yellow cab; black shovel and superstructure; gray rubber treads. Shovel opens, closes, raises and lowers by hand. Similar to shovel which came with 9158 Penn Central flatcar. **CP**

12752 HISTORICAL LIONEL VIDEOTAPE: 1989-91; VHS format videotape of Lionel history. 1989 package features portrait of Joshua Lionel Cowen in catalogue, but production videos have brown cover with Santa Fe F-3 diesel and white lettering. **CP**

12753 ORE LOAD: 1989-91; red-brown simulated ore load in form of plastic shell which fits into Lionel ore cars. Sold in pairs. **CP**

12754 GRADUATED TRESTLE SET: 1989-91; set of 22 graduated trestle pieces in dark brown; fittings redesigned to work with O as well as O27 track. **CP**

12755 ELEVATED TRESTLE SET: 1989-91; set of 10 4-3/4" pieces to extend graduated trestle set listed above. **CP**

12756 A LIONEL TOUR: THE MAKING OF THE SCALE HUDSON: Videotape, 1991; VHS videotape showing the manufacturing process for the new version of the full-scale New York Central Hudson. Cover sleeve has photo of Hudson, red lettering and Lionel logo. **CP**

12759 FLOODLIGHT TOWER: 1990-91; light gray base and tower top; bright orange tower structure; chromed plastic reflectors; takes plastic-based lamps; 12" high. Similar to 2195 and 2313 predecessors. **CP**

12760 AUTOMATIC HIGHWAY FLASHER: 1990-91; modeled after 154 and 2154 predecessors, but has new electronic operating system which can employ 153C contactor or insulated track section instead of older 154C split-plate contactor. Flashing action is much more steady and prototypical. This version has tuscan base and crossbuck with white lettering. **CP**

12761 ANIMATED BILLBOARD: 1990-91; red-brown base; light gray casing; on-off switch in back. Billboard messages alternate between "WELCOME TO LIONELVILLE" and "JOCKO SPORTING GOODS". Billboards alternate about every 1-1/2 seconds under normal voltage. **CP**

12762 FREIGHT STATION WITH TRAIN CONTROL AND SOUNDS: Catalogued in 1990 and 1991, Book One, but not produced to date. Catalogue shows white building modeled after 2133 predecessor; light gray roof, doors and windows; black base; interior light; smoke and thermostat train-stop device. Three separate recordings are to announce arrivals and departures. If this accessory is ever produced, it will be interesting to observe the sound system employed. American Flyer and Noma both produced talking stations in the 1950s which worked by a

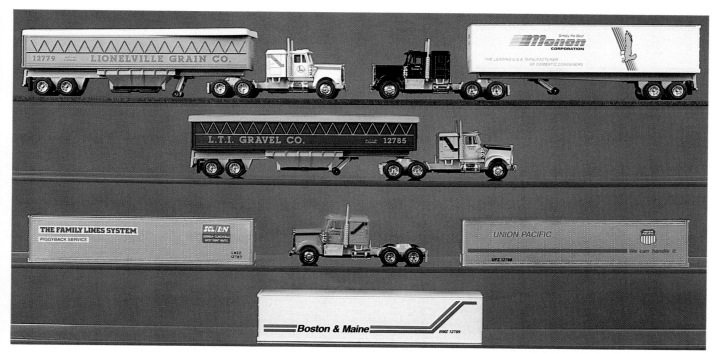

Top shelf: **12779** Lionelville Grain Co.; **12783** Monon.
Second shelf: **12785** L.T.I. Gravel.
Third shelf: **12787** The Family Lines System; **12794** Lionel tractor; **12788** Union Pacific.
Bottom shelf: **12789** Boston & Maine.

R. LaVoie Collection; B. Greenberg photograph

	GD	VG	EXC	MT

small plastic record played by a makeshift phonograph device which would be far too primitive for today's sophisticated electronics. **NRS**

12763 SINGLE SIGNAL BRIDGE: 1990-91; gray plastic base; black metal tower and gantry structure; twin-light plastic clip-on hood; die-cast bulb pockets. Essentially identical to very scarce 452 model of postwar years. **CP**

12765 DIE-CAST AUTO ASSORTMENT: 1990; six die-cast metal autos (catalogue states there are three Buicks and three Corvettes) similar to those provided with the 16208 Pennsylvania auto carrier of 1989. Announced but never made.
Not Manufactured

12768 BURNING SWITCH TOWER: 1990; modeled after the 445 and 2324 models, but there the resemblance stops. Light tan building with dark maroon window, door and deck trim; darker brown roof and black "scorch marks" weathered into plastic! The action of this accessory is clever and has made it a hot (excuse the term!) seller. When one button is pressed, two orange lamps light and start to blink in the bottom level of the tower (another in the top is constantly lit). A smoke generator is activated which pours copious quantities of smoke out of the top story, eerily simulating a fire. A second button sends two hand-painted figures into action: "Hector" (Lionel's name!) runs — rather foolishly — into the blazing building, while "Charles" scurries down the side steps, carrying a water bucket to fight the flames. Many operators combine this tower with a fire-fighting motorized car on a nearby track for sustained action. Lionel's new smoke formulation works extremely well in this accessory; so does LGB's smoke fluid because the smoke generator is a Seuthe-type

	GD	VG	EXC	MT

common in many Large Scale products. This is a somewhat melodramatic but very clever and popular accessory.
— — — **90**

12770 ARCH-UNDER BRIDGE: 1990-91; light gray plastic snap-together girders; black stamped-steel deck. Similar to scarce 332 model of postwar years. **CP**

12771 MOM'S ROADSIDE DINER: 1990-91; similar to 12722 Lionelville model, but with different colors: dark brown base; light yellow dining car; light gray roof; red lettering; silhouettes in windows; black stack issues smoke; interior light; dark brown sign with white "MOM'S" lettering. **CP**

12772 ILLUMINATED EXTENSION BRIDGE WITH ROCK PIERS: 1990-91; dark gray bridge structure with flat top segment (as opposed to arch of 2122 and 12721 models); stamped-steel base; gray rock piers; red light atop bridge structure. **CP**

12773 FREIGHT PLATFORM KIT: 1990-91; red base and building; light gray doors and windows; dark gray roof. Also in CSX set for 1990. **CP**

12774 LUMBER LOADER KIT: 1990-91; tan building structure; light tan roof; four logs which load into trackside car with flip of lever. **CP**

12777 CHEVRON TRACTOR AND TANKER: 1990-91; red tractor with chrome trim; white tank trailer with Chevron logo; chrome trim and red and black stripes at top of tank. **CP**

12778 CONRAIL TRACTOR AND TRAILER: 1990; blue tractor with chrome trim and white lettering; white trailer with blue lettering and Conrail logo. — — — **10**

GD   VG   EXC   MT

12779 LIONELVILLE GRAIN CO. TRACTOR AND GRAIN TRAILER: 1990; white tractor with chrome trim; gray striping and Lionel logo; dark gray trailer with red lettering and black simulated roping to hold down detachable light yellow plastic trailer top.　　　　—　　—　　—　　10

12781 NORFOLK & WESTERN INTERMODAL CRANE: 1990-91; nearly identical in function and appearance to 12741 Union Pacific model except for black "NW" lettering and logo on sides of superstructure and added floodlights. See 12741 entry for full operating details.　　**CP**

12782 OPERATING LIFT BRIDGE: Announced for 1991; extremely large (29-1/2" x 8" x 19-1/4") operating span corresponding to 213 model announced in early postwar years (1950) but never made; single motor lifts center span on command with bell and warning horn sounds and flashing warning lights; counterweights keep span raised while track sensors automatically stop train; lift works towers are both illuminated; yellow strobe aircraft warning lights and operating panel which connects to bridge's own self-contained separate power source. Expected to be in considerable demand despite its expense; will be the largest accessory ever produced by Lionel, dwarfing even the intermodal cranes. Structure is light gray with black ladders and catwalk detail.　**NRS**

12783 LIONEL/MONON TRACTOR AND TRAILER: 1991; black tractor with white lettering and chrome trim; white trailer with purple and black Monon lettering and gold eagle logo.　　**CP**

12784 THREE INTERMODAL CONTAINERS: 1991; three trailer bodies, each separately numbered, as follows: **12787** silver trailer, "THE FAMILY LINES SYSTEM" in blue with red, white and blue logo; **12788** silver trailer, "UNION PACIFIC" in red with blue stripe and lettering and Union Pacific shield logo; **12789** white trailer, "BOSTON & MAINE" in black with light and dark blue striping. These containers are designed for use with the Lionel intermodal cranes, but they can also be snapped onto the wheel structure of any current Lionel trailer for road use. Although they are numbered separately, all three containers are sold as one package.　　**CP**

12785 L.T.I. GRAVEL CO. TRACTOR AND TRAILER: 1991; silver tractor with chrome trim; blue striping and lettering; dark blue grain trailer with yellow lettering; white simulated roping to hold down detachable light gray roof.　　**CP**

12786 LIONELVILLE STEEL COMPANY TRACTOR AND TRAILER: 1991; red tractor with white stripe and lettering; red flat trailer with white fencing and silver simulated steel rod loads.　　**CP**

12787: See 12784.

12788: See 12784.

12789: See 12784.

12791 ANIMATED PASSENGER STATION: Announced for 1991; uses same mechanism as 12719 refreshment stand of 1989, but has red-brown base; raised light tan platform with black supports and light green open roof; cubic red cover to conceal motor; light tan freight truck; gray attendant with various pieces of baggage on dolly; black fencing and 2170 lamppost next to open shed. When button is pressed, man in blue suit moves back and forth, woman in brown overcoat revolves and looks both ways for train and attendant spins baggage cart around.　**NRS**

12794 LIONEL LINES DIE-CAST TRACTOR UNIT: 1991; orange tractor with chrome trim; dark blue stripe and

GD   VG   EXC   MT

lettering; appears to be identical to tractor unit supplied with 12725 tractor and trailer.　　**CP**

12795 TWO CABLE REELS: 1991; two light gray cable reels with black "LIONEL" lettering; similar to those which came with the postwar 6561 cable reel car and several other accessories and cars since then.　　**CP**

12797 CROSSING GATE AND SIGNAL: Catalogued in 1991 but delayed in production until 1992; catalogue shows silver base and superstructure; white crossbuck with black lettering; white gate with red striping and two sets of flashing lights; each with one amber and one red lens. Accessory is also to have warning bell when activated; exact nature of operating mechanism is not known at press time. This accessory is also to be made for Large Scale trains; it appears similar to a weight-activated unit made by LGB for several years.　**NRS**

12798 FORK LIFT LOADER STATION*: 1992; simulates loading a boxcar with pipes; on/off switch; 12-5/8" x 8-5/8" x 6-5/8".　CP

12805 THREE INTERMODAL CONTAINERS*: 1992; marked for American President Lines, "MAERSK", and "EVERGREEN" International; 8-1/4" long.　　**CP**

12806 LIONEL LUMBER TRUCK*: 1992.　　**CP**

12808 MOBIL TRACTOR AND TANKER*: 1992.　　**CP**

12811 ALKA SELTZER TRACTOR AND TRAILER*: 1992.　　**CP**

BILLBOARD LISTINGS

Unless otherwise stated, dates reflect catalogue period for a particular billboard. We welcome additions to this list, especially since we suspect that there are many more uncatalogued billboards in existence. In addition, descriptions of the color and lettering schemes are needed with some of the billboards. The examples listed are from the collections of I. D. Smith, G. Halverson, S. Hutchings, J. Sawruk, and R. LaVoie.

BUY U.S. SAVINGS BONDS: 1970-71; stack of $50 bonds wrapped in red, white, and blue flag wrapper on white background.

EDUCATION IS FOR THE BIRDS (The Birds Who Want To Get Ahead): 1970-71; uncatalogued; blue and red lettering on plain white background.

GET A DODGE: 1970-71; uncatalogued; cartoon figure of mule in brown tones; blue lettering on white background.

SHERATON HOTELS: 1970-71; blue and red rectangles; black lettering and black Sheraton logo.

BETTY CROCKER: 1970; blue script lettering on white background.

CHEERIOS: 1970; blue General Mills "G" and red lettering on white background.

LIONEL MPC: 1970-71; red "LIONEL" in modern typeface; red and blue lettering; red and blue MPC logo on white background.

AUTOLITE: 1971; uncatalogued; "Autolite Small Engine Spark Plugs For Work Or Play," in red, black and maroon lettering; green

A nearly complete history of modern era billboards.

R. LaVoie Collection; B. Greenberg photograph

Top shelf: **Three 2710 Type I boxes, with four different colors of billboard frames: dark green postwar frame repackaged in Type I box from 1970; earliest MPC billboard frame now marked 2710 with 1971 billboard; scarce 1971 Myco foam village packing billboard; scarce 1972 Ford Motorcraft special production billboard.**

Bottom shelf: **Perhaps the crowning irony of Lionel's use of billboards — an AF billboard on a Lionel product: 12707 billboard set with new frame designs and double sided billboards; 2307 operating billboard light which blinks thermostatically; 12761 animated billboard which changes signs from Jocko sporting goods (shown) to Welcome to Lionelville; 2710 billboard set in Type 2 box (also came in Type III boxes).**

	GD	VG	EXC	MT

and blue rectangles with lawn mower and motorcycle. Hard to find. Came in 1971 special version of the Allegheny set for Ford Motor Company promotion.

PLAY-DOH: 1970-71; uncatalogued; "America's Favorite" in blue; child in red pulls cans of Play-Doh on red wagon.

FOAM VILLAGE FOR LIONEL BY MYCO: 1971; uncatalogued; conveyor belt carries housing structures out of factory; black "Imagineering for Packaging & Material Handling Systems"; yellow background with black conveyor and green building with black "My-T-Veyor" lettering and logo; very hard to find.

LIONEL: 1972-84; picture of Santa Fe F-3 locomotive in red, silver, black and yellow; "LIONEL" in modern red typeface.

FAMOUS PARKER GAMES: 1971-76; dark orange background; black lettering and Parker Brothers "swirl" logo.

CRAFT MASTER: 1971-84; blue square at left with black and white Craft Master logo and white lettering; light brown portrait of mountain range at right.

MPC MODEL KITS: 1971-84; dark blue and white MPC logo; red lettering, cars, rocket and train on yellow and white background.

KENNER TOYS: 1972-76; yellow and red cartoon bird at right; white lettering on blue background.

SCHLITZ BEER: 1977-84; beer can and white lettering on red background.

BABY RUTH: 1977-84; picture of candy bar wrapper; red lettering on white background.

NIBCO WASHERLESS FAUCETS: 1982; uncatalogued; black Nibco logo, red lettering, and picture of faucet on white background. Came as part of a special Nibco Plumbing Products promotion in 1982 and is very hard to find.

RIDE THE NIBCO EXPRESS: 1982; uncatalogued; black and white lettering and script on dark red background. Came as part of set 1264, a special Nibco Plumbing Products promotion in 1982, and is very hard to find.

TAPPAN IS COOKING: 1982; white lettering on black background; "LIONEL" with red, silver and yellow Santa Fe set. Came with 7908 Tappan car as part of special promotional set. S. Hutchings and J. Sawruk Collections.

WE'VE CANNED IT! MOTORCRAFT: 1971; black and red lettering; picture of Motorcraft tune-up kit in can packaging with spark plugs, distributor cap, condenser and points. Came as part of special Ford Motor Company promotion in 1971; very difficult to find.

THIS BUD'S FOR YOU: 1989; uncatalogued; came with 11775 Anheuser-Busch set.

BILLBOARD: Double-sided billboard with 12707 frames. Side A: "Buy U.S. Savings Bonds" in black to left of American flag on white background. Side B: red "Adopt-A-Pet" and white "Support Your Local Humane Society" on blue background with picture of puppy and kitten.

BILLBOARD: Double-sided billboard with 12707 frames. Side A: large white "BUCKLE UP!" and black "For Safety's Sake" above black seat belt on medium green background. Side B: red

	GD	VG	EXC	MT

"Keep America Beautiful" atop dark, medium, and light blue and gray stylized mountain pass with white background.

BILLBOARD: Double-sided billboard with 12707 frames. Side A: black "READ...AND KNOW THE WORLD!" with multicolored balloon, airplane, Oriental child, locomotive, windmill, etc. on white background. Side B: black "Take The Train" below large red, white and blue "AMERICAN FLYER LINES" shield logo on white background.

> **NOTE:** *In 1976, the Train Collectors Association (TCA) produced six special billboards for its Bicentennial convention in Philadelphia, Pennsylvania. While these are desirable billboards from the collector's standpoint, they are not the products of Fundimensions. All are white with red and blue printing. They are listed here separately:*
>
> **TCA 1:** Blue "22nd NATIONAL CONVENTION", red "JUNE 23 to 26, 1976", blue "PHILADELPHIA, PENNSYLVANIA" with red TCA logo and star at left.
>
> **TCA 2:** Red "1976" with "9" and "6" in shape of couplers, blue "TRAIN COLLECTORS ASSOCIATION".
>
> **TCA 3:** Large red eagle, blue "Hosts To/22nd Annual Convention/Train Collectors Association Inc.", Delaware Valley Chapter logo in blue at upper left.
>
> **TCA 4:** Blue "22nd National Convention", red "TRAIN COLLECTORS ASSOCIATION", red 1976 coupler logo and blue TCA shield, blue "SHERATON HOTEL/ PHILADELPHIA, PENNSYLVANIA".
>
> **TCA 5:** Blue rectangular background, locomotive and tender in white, red "Train Collectors Association/22nd National Convention", blue "Philadelphia/June 23 to 26/1976".
>
> **TCA 6:** Blue "Hosts To The", large red "GREAT EVENT", red star and blue Delaware Valley TCA chapter logo at left.

TRANSFORMERS

Note: Lionel's transformers are often not identified by catalogue number or capacity. Precise data, including which ones were included in which sets, is sketchy. The following listings summarize the best available knowledge.

4044: 1970-71; 45-watt transformer; black and brown marbled plastic case; metal lever controls speed; two binding posts. H. Edmunds Collection. — — 3 5

4045 SAFETY TRANSFORMER: 1970-71; black case; variable AC output; lever controls speed; automatic circuit breaker; two binding posts with one serving as forward and reverse button; 45-watt output. G. Halverson Collection.
1 2 3 4

4050 SAFETY TRANSFORMER: 1972-79; can be found with either metal or plastic lever; circuit breaker 50 watts. Changed from 4045 due to compliance with safety regulations for toy transformers dictated by OSHA and the Canadian equivalent. Has flat-surfaced safety plug and reinforced strain-relief grommet where plug enters transformer. Inter-office correspondence reveals that Lionel had a very difficult time remanufacturing this transformer, the backbone of its starter sets. Once a successful design was approved, Lionel had trouble securing the electric cords and plugs needed. Until recent years, regulations prohibited Lionel from making transformers larger than its 90-watt 4090. However, in the last few years Lionel has won approval for larger transformers (as have other firms such as Right-Of-Way) as long as they are marketed for hobby use instead of toy use.
(A) Red case. 1 2 3 4
(B) Blue case. 1 2 3 4

4060 POWER MASTER: 1980-91; black case; AC or DC output; one lever, direction reverse switch; automatic circuit breaker. Used in both O Scale AC or DC sets, as well as Large Scale sets.
CP

4065 DC HOBBY TRANSFORMER: 1981-83; black plastic case; white lettering; red speed control lever; reversing switch; 0-18 V DC; 19V AC (5.5 VA). D. Anderson and C. Rohlfing Collections. — — 3 4

4090 POWER MASTER: 1970-81; 1983; AC output; right lever controls speed; left lever controls direction and whistle; fixed voltage taps; automatic circuit breaker; 0-16 V AC; 90 watts. Similar to 1044 model of postwar years.
10 25 40 55

4125 TRANSFORMER: 1972; 25 watts.
(A) Light blue case. C. Rohlfing Collection. 1 2 3 4
(B) Light maroon case. C. Rohlfing Collection. 1 2 3 4

4150 MULTIVOLT TOY TRANSFORMER: 1976-78; 50-watt AC output; blue plastic case; bright metal or black plastic speed control lever. D. Anderson Collection. — 3 6 12

4250 TRAIN MASTER TRANSFORMER: 45 watts. — 3 6 12

4651 TRAIN MASTER: 1978-79; lever controls speed; two posts with button on one post for forward and reverse; automatic circuit breaker. — — 2 3

4660 HOBBY TRANSFORMER: 1990; AC-DC power pack; 0-17 V DC with speed/reverse lever; 7 VA capacity. — — 4 6

4690 TYPE MW TRANSFORMER: 1987-89; black metal case; orange knobs and buttons; red, white and blue Lionel logo; white lettering; power-off switch (the first in any Lionel transformer); 0-17 VAC output; 50 VA capacity; variable accessory voltage knob can also be used to power a second train; solid state construction; variable intensity indicator lights for track and accessory lines; power-on light; horn-whistle; and directional buttons; two circuit breakers. This is Lionel's first truly modern transformer; it is somewhat like those which were issued by Model Power and Tech II some years ago. — — — 85

4851 TRANSFORMER: 1987-88; 15 VA; red case; black plastic handle. C. Rohlfing Collection. 1 2 3 4

	GD	VG	EXC	MT

4870 HOBBY TRANSFORMER AND THROTTLE CONTROL: 1977-78; consists of two pieces: a small black plastic wall-plug AC transformer and a red plastic throttle control. Transformer marked "Made In Taiwan", but throttle control marked "Mt. Clemens, Mich." Similar to arrangements found in racing car sets. D. Anderson Collection.

	GD	VG	EXC	MT
	—	—	3	4

5900 AC/DC CONVERTER: 1979-81, 1983.

| | — | — | 4 | 6 |

12780 RS-1 TRANSFORMER: 1990-91; similar to 4690 MW transformer listed above, but has RailSounds button added to activate new sound system and redesigned throttle knobs with handles. **CP**

12790 ZW II TRANSFORMER: Scheduled for early 1992 but catalogued in 1991; has all the features of postwar ZW transformer, but newer electronic practices replace older technology, including improved circuit breakers and diode-controlled whistle-horn switch instead of copper-oxide rectifier discs. Black casing is styled like original ZW, but RailSounds activation button has been added. Expected to be more expensive than currently available postwar ZW units on collector market. **CP**

15904 RAILSOUNDS HORN, WHISTLE & BELL SWITCH: 1990-91; for use with MW transformer only. **CP**

15906 RAILSOUNDS TRIGGER BUTTON: 1990-91; black case with gold lettering and logos; designed to operate RailSounds feature in locomotives and boxcars. Although all locomotives and cars equipped with RailSounds come with this button, extras may be needed for multiple tracks or insulated blocks. This button is for use with older Lionel transformers only, not the new. **CP**

O27 Track and Switches

5012 CURVED TRACK: 1970-91; four on card; shrink-wrapped packaging varies with production year. **CP**

5013 CURVED TRACK:

	GD	VG	EXC	MT
	.10	.30	.50	.55

5014 HALF-CURVED TRACK: 1980-83.

| | .20 | .40 | .50 | .75 |

5016 3-FOOT STRAIGHT SECTION: 1987.

| | — | — | — | 2.25 |

5017 STRAIGHT TRACK: 1980-83; four on card.

| | — | — | 3.50 | 3.50 |

5018 STRAIGHT TRACK:

| | .20 | .40 | .50 | .75 |

5019 HALF-STRAIGHT TRACK: 1986-88

| | .20 | .40 | .50 | .75 |

5020 90 DEGREE CROSSOVER: 1970-88

| | 1.50 | 3 | 3.50 | 4.75 |

5021 MANUAL SWITCH: 1986-88; left.

| | 4 | 7 | 8 | 13 |

5022 MANUAL SWITCH: 1986-88; right.

| | 4 | 7 | 8 | 13 |

5023 45 DEGREE CROSSOVER: 1970-88.

| | 1.50 | 3 | 4 | 6.50 |

5024 STRAIGHT TRACK: 35-inch.

| | — | — | — | 2.25 |

5025 MANUMATIC UNCOUPLER: 1971-75; small Type I box with three black plastic uncoupling devices which clamp to track. Pushing a button raises two extensions between the rails; these are supposed to catch the coupler discs and pull them down. As a rule, these uncouplers do not work very well. Packed three to a box; instructions printed on the box. G. Halverson and R. LaVoie Collections.

	GD	VG	EXC	MT
	—	—	1	2

5027 PAIR MANUAL SWITCHES:

| | 8 | 13 | 15 | 26 |

5030 TRACK EXPANDER SET: 1972 catalogue refers to this as "Switch Layout Expander Set"; Type I box; contains pair of manual switches, two sections of curved O27 track and six sections of straight O27 track. Made for distribution in Canada by Parker Brothers. See next entry for American production. G. Halverson Collection.

| | — | — | — | 25 |

5030 LAYOUT BUILDER SET: 1978-80, 1983; pair of manual switches; two curved, six straight track.

| | 10 | 14 | 17 | 25 |

5033 CURVED TRACK: 1986-88; bulk packed, but sold individually.

| | .10 | .20 | .30 | .75 |

5038 STRAIGHT TRACK: 1986-88; bulk packed, but sold individually.

| | .10 | .20 | .30 | .75 |

5041 O27 INSULATOR PINS: 1986-88; 12 per pack.

| | — | — | .50 | 1 |

5042 O27 STEEL PINS: 1986-88; 12 per pack.

| | — | — | .40 | .75 |

5044 O42 CURVED BALLAST: 1987-88; price per section.

| | — | — | — | 2.25 |

5045 O27 WIDE RADIUS BALLAST PIECE: 1987; molded gray flexible rubber ballast.

| | — | — | — | 2.25 |

5046 O27 CURVED TRACK BALLAST PIECE: 1987.

| | — | — | — | 2.25 |

5047 O27 STRAIGHT TRACK BALLAST PIECE: 1987.

| | — | — | — | 2.25 |

5049 O42 CURVED TRACK: Price per section.

| | — | — | — | 1.10 |

5090 THREE PAIR MANUAL SWITCHES: 1983.

| | — | — | 60 | 80 |

5113 O54 WIDE RADIUS TRACK: 1986-87; 16 sections make a 54-inch diameter circle; price per section.

| | — | — | 1.10 | 1.50 |

5121 REMOTE SWITCH: 1986-88; left.

| | 7 | 11 | 14 | 20 |

5122 REMOTE SWITCH: 1986-88; right.

| | 7 | 11 | 14 | 20 |

5125 PAIR REMOTE SWITCHES: 1986.

| | 14 | 20 | 28 | 40 |

5149 REMOTE UNCOUPLING TRACK: 1986-88.

| | — | 2.50 | 3.50 | 7.25 |

5167 O42 REMOTE SWITCH: Right.

| | — | — | — | 25 |

5168 O42 REMOTE SWITCH: Left.

| | — | — | — | 25 |

5823 45-DEGREE CROSSOVER: Type I or Type II shrink-wrapped packaging; comes in light brown or dark brown base. G. Halverson Collection.

| | — | — | 4 | 6 |

	GD	VG	EXC	MT

12746 O27 OPERATING/UNCOUPLING TRACK: 1989-91; similar to 6019 track of postwar years. Catalogue and box claim that O Gauge cars can be operated on this track, but in practice the track is too short for many O Gauge milk cars, barrel cars and the like. **CP**

O GAUGE TRACK, SWITCHES, AND UNCOUPLERS

550C CURVED TRACK: 1970; 10-7/8" long.

	GD	VG	EXC	MT
	.25	.30	.75	1.25

550S STRAIGHT TRACK: 1970; 10" long.

	.25	.30	.75	1.25

UCS REMOTE CONTROL TRACK: 1970; accessory rails; two-button controller; magnet.

	2	3	5	8

5132 REMOTE SWITCH, RIGHT: 1986-88; with controller.

	15	20	33	40

5133 REMOTE SWITCH, LEFT: 1986-88; with controller.

	15	20	33	40

5165 O72 WIDE RADIUS REMOTE SWITCH: 1987; left-hand, with controller. This and its right-hand version are revivals of the prewar 711 wide-radius Model Builder's switches and are expected to meet with great popularity among Lionel operators.

	—	—	50	60

5166 O72 WIDE RADIUS REMOTE SWITCH: 1987; right hand, with controller.

	—	—	—	50

5193 THREE PAIR REMOTE SWITCHES: 1983.

	—	—	90	110

5500 STRAIGHT TRACK: 1971; 10" long.

	—	.30	.75	1.25

5501 CURVED TRACK: 1971; 10-7/8" long.

	—	.30	.75	1.25

5502 REMOTE CONTROL TRACK: 1971-72; 10" long; postwar design.

	2	3	5	8

5504 HALF CURVED SECTION: 1983, 1985-88.

	—	—	—	1.05

5505 HALF STRAIGHT SECTION: 1983, 1985-88.

	—	—	—	1.05

5510 CURVED TRACK:

	—	.30	.75	1.25

5520 90-DEGREE CROSSOVER: 1971.

	2	3	5	7

5522 THREE-FOOT O GAUGE STRAIGHT TRACK SECTION: 1987.

	—	—	—	3.75

5523 EXTRA LONG STRAIGHT SECTION: 1988-91; 40".

				CP

5530 REMOTE UNCOUPLING SECTION: 1986-88; with controller.

	6	9	11	13

5540 90 DEGREE CROSSOVER: 1981-88.

	3	5	7	8

5543 INSULATOR PINS: 1970; 12 per pack.

	.25	.50	.75	1

	GD	VG	EXC	MT

5545 45 DEGREE CROSSOVER: 1982.

	—	—	—	13

5551 STEEL PINS: 1970; 12 per pack.

	.25	.50	.75	1

5560 WIDE RADIUS CURVED TRACK BALLAST PIECE: 1987.

	—	—	—	2.25

5561 CURVED TRACK BALLAST PIECE: 1987.

	—	—	—	2.25

5562 STRAIGHT TRACK BALLAST PIECE: 1987.

	—	—	—	2.25

5572 WIDE RADIUS CURVED TRACK: 1986-88; 16 sections make a circle with a 72"-diameter. Price per section.

	.50	.75	1.25	2

TRUTRACK SYSTEM ITEMS

In 1973 and 1974, Fundimensions attempted a major innovation in its operating system with the introduction of "Trutrack." Trutrack featured a realistic T-shaped rail made from aluminum, wood-grained plastic ties at relatively close intervals, wide-radius curves, and a thin, less conspicuous center rail. The track used a snap-lock assembly with rail joiners. The system featured separate pieces of flexible ballasted roadbed which snapped onto each track or switch piece. The ballasted roadbed is more plastic than rubber, but it is flexible. The 1973 catalogue listed remote and manual switches, switch roadbed and lockons, as well as the straight and curved track sections and their roadbed pieces. In 1973, the right manual switches caused derailments because they would not lock tightly, so in 1974 the mechanism was changed and improved for the manual switches. Unfortunately, aluminum track is not compatible with Magnetraction. Although some sources have stated that Fundimensions had problems with the switches, which were supposed to have been made in Italy, we suspect that the incompatibility with Magnetraction is the reason why the track was dropped from production after only small amounts were produced, since Magnetraction was more important to Lionel's operating system than an improved track appearance. We have updated our lists of Trutrack which actually reached production since the first edition of this Guide; more was actually produced than was first believed. F. Vergonet and G. Halverson comments.

5600 CURVED TRACK: 1973. F. Vergonet Collection.

	—	—	—	1.75

5601 CARD OF FOUR CURVED TRACK: 1973. F. Vergonet Collection.

	—	—	—	7

5602 CARD OF FOUR ROADBED BALLAST FOR CURVED TRACK: 1973-74; actually came fastened together with rubber band inside packaging. G. Halverson and F. Vergonet Collections.

	—	—	4	7

5605 STRAIGHT TRACK: 1973. F. Vergonet, R. LaVoie and G. Halverson Collections.

	—	—	1	2

22000 Lionel Double Crossing board game from 1989.

	GD	VG	EXC	MT

5606 CARD OF FOUR STRAIGHT TRACK: 1973; actually came fastened with rubber band inside packaging. F. Vergonet and G. Halverson Collections.
— — 4 8

5607 CARD OF FOUR ROADBED BALLAST FOR STRAIGHT TRACK: 1973; actually came fastened together with rubber band inside packaging; Type II packaging. F. Vergonet and G. Halverson Collections. — — 4 8

5620 LEFT MANUAL SWITCH: 1973-74; not distributed for sale, but some became available.
(A) First production; 1973. F. Vergonet Collection.
— — — 25

(B) Second production; 1974; redesigned mechanism. F. Vergonet Collection. — — — 30

5625 LEFT REMOTE SWITCH: 1973. F. Vergonet Collection.
NRS

5630 RIGHT MANUAL SWITCH: 1973-74.
(A) First production; 1973. F. Vergonet Collection.
— — — 25

(B) Second production; 1974; redesigned mechanism. F. Vergonet Collection. — — — 35

5635 RIGHT REMOTE SWITCH: 1973. F. Vergonet Collection. NRS

5640 CARD OF TWO LEFT SWITCH ROADBED PIECES: 1973. F. Vergonet Collection.
— — — 10

5650 CARD OF TWO RIGHT SWITCH ROADBED PIECES: 1973. F. Vergonet Collection.
— — — 8

	GD	VG	EXC	MT

5655 LOCKON: 1973. F. Vergonet Collection.
— — — 1.50

5660 CARD OF ONE TERMINAL TRACK WITH LOCK-ON: 1973. F. Vergonet Collection. — — — 3.50

PERIPHERAL ITEMS

JC-1 LIONEL JOHNNY CASH RECORD ALBUM: 33-1/3 speed. — 2 3 6

7-1100 HAPPY HUFF'N PUFF: 1975; train set; Fundimensions pre-school toy push train similar to those made by Fisher-Price and Playskool; whimsical old-fashioned four-wheel steamer and two gondolas embossed with two large squares on their sides. Train is made of plastic simulated to look like wood; wheels fastened with metal axles; locomotive has smiley-mouth and eye decorations; came with a circle of two-rail plastic track and a story booklet showing "how Happy Huff'n Puff got his name". L. Bohn and R. LaVoie comments. HUFF 'N PUFF BOOKLET also available in 1975, mint price $2.00. — 30 40 100

7-1200 GRAVEL GUS: 1975; three-piece road construction set consisting of a grader with a large squared head seated on the chassis (presumably Gus) and two side dump cars; grader has four large wheels and swivels in the center with a removable pusher blade; two cars each have one axle with two large wheels, with the first car resting on the grader and the second car resting on the

| | GD | VG | EXC | MT |

rear of the first car; set made from plastic simulated to resemble wood; came with a full-color story booklet. Weisblum comment.
— — 15 20

7-1300 GRAVEL GUS JUNIOR: 1975; appears to be identical to 7-1200 Gravel Gus, except has only one side dump car. L. Bohn comment.
— — 15 20

7-1400 HAPPY HUFF'N PUFF JUNIOR: 1975; similar to 7-1100 Happy Huff'n Puff, except does not include circle of track, locomotive has much thicker smokestack, and gondolas are not embossed with large squares. These four pre-school toys (7-1100 through 7-1400) were apparently offered only in 1975 through large toy outlets. Their success would have been an asset to Fundimensions, but they were launched into the teeth of a highly competitive pre-school market long dominated by giants such as Fisher-Price and Playskool. L. Bohn and R. LaVoie comments.
— — 40 65

6-1076 LIONEL CLOCK: 1976-77; made by American Sign and Advertising Services, Inc., 7430 Industrial Road, Industrial Park, Lawrence, Kentucky, 41042; 17" x 22" white dial with black hand; red second hand; black locomotive front in center of dial; red field on bottom with white "LIONEL"; available only to Service Stations for $20 to $25.
— — 200 300

2390 LIONEL MIRROR: 1982; old-fashioned mirror with dark walnut wood frame; gold, red and black decoration showing 1920-era picture of Lawrence Cowen with train set at base of antiqued gold archway; gold lettering, "LIONEL ELECTRIC TRAINS, THE STANDARD OF THE WORLD SINCE 1900"; also "COPYRIGHT 1981 GPC". Anderson and R. LaVoie Collections.
— — 50 100

22000 DOUBLE CROSSING: 1989, board game. NRS

NO NUMBER BELT BUCKLE: 1981; solid antique brass; Lionel logo. A. Passman Collection.
— — 15 20

NO NUMBER LIONEL PENNANT: Plastic; white background; black trim on edge; black "LIONEL"; left arrow red; right side arrow blue; "A LIFETIME INVESTMENT IN HAPPINESS" in black; 45" wide x 29-1/2" high.
— — 2 4

NO NUMBER BLACK CAVE VINYL PLAYMAT: 1982; 30" x 40"; from Black Cave Flyer set 1254.
— — — 10

NO NUMBER COMMANDO ASSAULT TRAIN PLAYMAT: 1983; 30" x 40"; from Commando Assault Train set 1355.
— — — 10

NO NUMBER ROCKY MOUNTAIN FREIGHT PLAYMAT: 1983; 36" x 54"; from Rocky Mountain Freight set 1352.
— — — 3

NO NUMBER CANNONBALL FREIGHT VINYL PLAYMAT: 1982; 36" x 54"; two-piece mat; from Cannonball Freight set 1155.
— — — 5

NO NUMBER L.A.S.E.R. VINYL PLAYMAT: 1982; 36" x 54"; from L.A.S.E.R. set 1150.
— — — 5

NO NUMBER LIONEL PLAYING CARDS: 1975; regulation poker deck; red and black diagonal "LIONEL" logo; head-on locomotive front against background in black; wrapped in cellophane and packaged in silver and black box. R. LaVoie Collection.
— — 1 10

NO NUMBER STATION PLATFORM: 1983; 23" x 3-1/2" x 5"; similar to 2256 station platform; details requested; part of set 1351.
— — — 10

| | GD | VG | EXC | MT |

NO NUMBER WRIST WATCH: 1986; special offer to Lionel Railroader Club members. Gold-plated case; gold dial face with circle of "track" around which a small "General"-type steam train revolves as it functions like the second hand; red, white and blue Lionel logo on dial face; alligator-style leather wrist band. Sold for $99.95, including shipping and handling.
— — — 120

SIDE TRACKS

The following items numbered in the 5800 series came as part of a brochure mailed by Lionel Trains, Inc. in 1987. Late in the previous year, Lionel had sent out letters to dealers requesting the cessation of any unauthorized use of Lionel's name and logos. The brochure, known as *Lionel Side Tracks*, illustrates that Lionel is using its own name and logos to begin its own peripheral marketing. This practice has continued in the last few years.

5800 BUMPER STICKER: Measures 3" x 14"; Lionel logo; black "Made In America" on white background with black locomotive pilot.
— — — 1.50

5801 LIGHTER: 1987-90; disposable white butane lighter with Lionel logo and black "Lines" lettering. — — — 3.50

5802 LAPEL PIN: 1987-91; enameled red, white and blue Lionel logo. CP

5803 LICENSE PLATE: 1987, 1991; white background; dark blue edges; red and blue lettering and Lionel logo; red and black freight train. CP

5804 EPOXY KEY CHAIN: 1987; red, white and blue Lionel logo screened and epoxied onto brass 24k gold-plated medallion attached to brass key ring. — — — 4.50

5805 ASH TRAY: 1987-90; triangular 3-1/2" glass ash tray with red, white and blue Lionel logo. — — — 6.50

5806 COFFEE MUG: 1987-90; 12-ounce black ironstone mug with gold rim and gold Lionel logo. — — — 7.50

5807 SPORT CAP: 1987; red cap with Lionel logo inside white rectangle. — — — 8

5808 BRASS KEY CHAIN: 1987-90; Lionel logo and steam engine boiler front stamped into brass-finished medallion.
— — — 8

5809 ENGINEER'S GLOVES: 1987; work gloves with gray cowhide palms, thumb, fingers and knuckle straps; blue denim collars and backs; black Lionel logo and lettering on glove collars.
— — — 8.50

5810 SLEEPING BOY POSTER: 1987; R. Tyrrell poster from 1980 catalogue; 21" x 27". — — — 9

5811 NICKEL PLATE SPECIAL POSTER: 1987; black border; painting of Nickel Plate Freight; "BIG, RUGGED TRAINS SINCE 1900"; 20" x 34". — — — 9

5812 RAIL BLAZER POSTER: 1987; red border; painting of Rail Blazer tank locomotive and freight train; "No Childhood Should Be Without A Train" lettering; 20" x 34".
— — — 9

| | GD | VG | EXC | MT |

5813 LIONEL T-SHIRT: 1987; blue shirt with rectangular red, white, and blue Lionel logo; size small.

— — — 11

5814 LIONEL T-SHIRT: 1987; blue shirt with rectangular red, white and blue Lionel logo; size medium.

— — — 11

5815 LIONEL T-SHIRT: 1987; blue shirt with rectangular red, white and blue Lionel logo; size large.

— — — 11

5816 LIONEL T-SHIRT: 1987; blue shirt with rectangular red, white and blue Lionel logo; size extra-large.

— — — 11

5817 PORTABLE TOOL KIT: 1987; 13-in-one ratchet-socket screwdriver folding set; black storage handle; red, blue and chrome Lionel logo; chromed attachment piece.

— — — 11.50

5818 MINI-MAG-LITE FLASHLIGHT: 1987; 5-1/2" long; engraved Lionel logo and steam engine boiler front on black metal flashlight body.

— — — 20

5819 PEN AND PENCIL SET: 1987-90; black matte barrels; chrome-trimmed, red, white and blue Lionel logo on cap ends; silver "LIONEL TRAINS" embossed into barrels.

— — — 20

5820 TRAVEL ALARM CLOCK: 1987; red plastic case; quartz movement; dial with circle of track and General train moving around track; red, white and blue Lionel logo.

— — — 20

5821 BEVERAGE COASTER SET: 1987; polished solid brass coasters with brown leather insert and central Lionel medallion; felt bottoms; oak holding tray. — — — 70

5822 WRIST WATCH: 1987; gold-plated case and band; black watch hands; dial has circle of track with SP Daylight engine and car moving around track to function as second hand; red, white and blue Lionel logo on dial face. — — — 110

5823 LIONEL THE LEGEND LIVES ON: 1989-90; bumper sticker; white background; gray photo of prewar train; red and blue lettering with Lionel logo. — — — 1.50

5824 LIONEL NOTE PADS: 1989-90; 3" x 5"; two pads; 100 sheets each; white paper with light lavender circle "L" logo and words "Official Lionel Enthusiast". — — — 2.50

5825 LIONEL FABRIC PATCH: 1989-91; 3"-diameter; red, white and blue circle "L" logo with black outlines. **CP**

5826 LIONEL PENNANT: 1989-91; red triangular pennant with white outline "LIONEL" and circle "L" logo. **CP**

5827 AMERICAN FLYER PENNANT: 1989-91; blue triangular pennant with white American Flyer in script. **CP**

5828 I BRAKE FOR LIONEL TRAINS! LICENSE PLATE: 1989-91; black background; white and red lettering; circle "L" logo; white- and red-striped crossing gate and signal. **CP**

5829 LIONEL CIRCLE L LAPEL PIN: 1989-91; brass pin with red and blue paint. **CP**

5830 AMERICAN FLYER LAPEL PIN: 1989-91; blue lettering on silver background. **CP**

5831 LIONEL POLYURETHANE FOAM BEVERAGE CAN HOLDERS: 1989-90; set of one red and one blue holder

ROLLING STOCK ASSORTMENTS

The following is a summary of Lionel's Rolling Stock Assortments in numerical order.

9090: 1978
(A) 9051 Firestone tank, 9016 Chessie hopper, 9035 Conrail boxcar, 9140 BN gondola.
(B) 9039 Mobilgas tank (red), 9016 Chessie hopper (blue), 9037 Conrail boxcar, 9049 Republic Steel gondola.

9191: 1976-77; 9133 BN TOFC, 9153 Chevron tank, 9157 C & O flat with crane, 9158 PC flat with shovel.

9194: 1978; 9280 Horse Transport car, 9148 Du Pont tank, 9146 Mogen-David vat.

9195: 1979-84, 1985-89
(A) 1979-82; 9036 Mobilgas tank (red), 9026 Republic Steel flat, 9011 GN hopper, 9140 BN gondola, 9019 PC flatcar, 9085 ATSF caboose.
(B) 1983-84; 9011 GN hopper, 7902 ATSF boxcar, 6308 Alaska tank, 9058 Lionel SP caboose, 9020 UP flat, 9340 ICG gondola.
(C) 1986; 6430 ATSF caboose, 6115 Southern hopper, 9339 GN boxcar, 6515 UP flat.
(D) 1987 and 1989; 6430 ATSF caboose, 9016 Chessie hopper, 9035 Conrail boxcar, 9140 BN gondola.
(E) 1988; same as (D), but 6137 Nickel Plate gondola replaces 9016 Chessie hopper.

9293: 1978; 9282 GN TOFC, 9279 Magnolia tank, 9157 C & O flat with crane, 9281 ATSF auto carrier.

9391: 1978
(A) 9302 L & N searchlight, 9303 UP log car, 9304 C & O coal dump car.
(B) 9312 Conrail searchlight, 9310 ATSF log car, 9311 UP coal dump car.

9394: 1979; 9333 SP TOFC, 9279 Magnolia tank, 9281 ATSF auto carrier, 9334 Humble tank.

9490: 1979; 9416 MD & W boxcar, 9414 Cotton Belt boxcar, 9413 Naperville boxcar, 9415 Providence & Worcester boxcar.

16999: 1990; 16222 GN Boxcar, 16111 Alaska tank, 16328 NKP gondola, 16521 PRR SP caboose.

| | GD | VG | EXC | MT |

with white "LIONEL" lettering and whited-outlined circle "L" logo. — — — 5.50

5832 LIONEL CARPENTER'S APRON: 1989-90; white canvas apron with red "LIONEL" lettering and circle "L" logo. — — — 7

5833 AMERICAN FLYER CARPENTER'S APRON: 1989-90; white canvas apron with blue "AMERICAN FLYER" script. — — — 7

	GD	VG	EXC	MT

5834 LIONEL BEVERAGE MUG: 1989-91; 13-ounce capacity glass mug with diesel and steam engines on either side of circle "L" logo and red "LIONEL" lettering.
(A) 1989-90; frosted glass mug. — — — **8.50**
(B) 1991; clear glass mug. **CP**

5835 LIONEL ENGINEER'S CAP: 1989-91; gray- and white-striped cap with red, white and blue circle "L" logo patch. **CP**

5836 through 5842 LIONEL T-SHIRTS: 1989-90; numbers between 5836 and 5842 refer to children and adult sizes. Children's shirts are blue with red, white and blue circle "L" logo; adults' shirts are white with same logo. — — — **11**

5843 POSTERS: 1989-90; set of three large posters: "Sleeping Boy" from R. J. Tyrrell drawing of 1980; "Nickel Plate Special" and "Rail Blazer". — — — **15**

5844 through 5846, 5849 through 5852 LIONEL SWEAT-SHIRT: 1989-90; red with Lionel lettering and logo. Numbers between 5844 and 5852 denote children and adult sizes. — — — **16**

5847 LIONEL TOTE BAG: 1989-91; bright red nylon bag with white-outlined "LIONEL" lettering and circle "L" logo. **CP**

5848 AMERICAN FLYER TOTE BAG: 1989-91; bright blue nylon bag with white "AMERICAN FLYER" script. **CP**

5853 LIONEL TIE: 1989-90; dark blue men's tie with small white circle "L" logos. — — — **22**

5854 LIONEL PERKY BOW WOMAN'S TIE: 1989-90; dark blue bow tie with white circle "L" logos. — — — **22**

5855 LIONEL SWISS ARMY KNIFE: 1989-91; black plastic handle; two knife blades; tweezers; toothpick and key ring; "LIONEL" lettering and circle "L" logo inlaid in nickel. **CP**

5856 LIONEL POCKET WATCH: 1989-90; nickel-plated case; engraving of "General" locomotive on back; white face with red "LIONEL" logo and black numerals. — — — **26**

5857 LIONEL WELCOME MAT: 1989-90; blue mat on black pad with red and white "LIONEL" lettering and circle "L" logo. — — — **30**

5858 LIONEL DIRECTOR'S CHAIR: 1989-91; varnished pine frame; white canvas seat and back; red "LIONEL" lettering and red and blue circle "L" logo on back. **CP**

5859 LIONEL ELECTRIC TRAINS PENNANT: 1991; orange triangular pennant with classic rectangular cream, orange and blue "LIONEL ELECTRIC TRAINS" logo. **CP**

5860 LIONEL ALL ABOARD COOKBOOK: 1991; 350 family recipes from Lionel Corporation employees; white front cover with red checkerboard border; blue lettering; gray place setting where dish is formed from red, white and blue circle "L" logo. **CP**

5861 through 5867 LIONEL TRAINS T-SHIRTS: 1991; numbers between 5861 and 5867 refer to children and adult sizes; white shirt with steam engine coming out of tunnel on front and SP-type caboose going into tunnel on back; back and front have red "LIONEL TRAINS" lettering and circle "L" logo. **CP**

5868 LIONEL BUMPER STICKER: 1991; black-outlined steam locomotive; red "LIONEL" lettering and circle "L" logo; American flag at right. **CP**

5869 LIONEL LIGHTED LOCOMOTIVE CHRISTMAS ORNAMENT: 1991; porcelain multicolored painted tank locomotive with white "LIONEL" and circle "L" logo. **CP**

5870 LIONEL LIGHTED CABOOSE CHRISTMAS ORNAMENT: 1991; porcelain multicolored wood-sided caboose with white "LIONEL" and circle "L" logo. **CP**

5871 LIONEL LIGHTED STATION CHRISTMAS ORNAMENT: 1991; porcelain multicolored freight and passenger station with white "LIONEL" and circle "L" logo. **CP**

5872 LIONEL ENGINEER FIGURE CHRISTMAS ORNAMENT: 1991; multicolored porcelain figure of boy-engineer holding lantern. **CP**

5873 OLD WORLD SANTA CHRISTMAS ORNAMENT: 1991; bearded Santa figure in multicolored porcelain holding toy locomotive. **CP**

5874 LIONEL CROSSING SIGNAL CHRISTMAS ORNAMENT: 1991; multicolored porcelain crossing warning signal with white "LIONEL" lettering. **CP**

5875 LIONEL STUFFED ANIMAL: 1991; "Lenny, The Lionel Lion"; 11"-tall lion doll dressed in blue- and white-striped engineer's cap and overalls; white gloves and red and white bandanna. **CP**

5876 LIONEL MEN'S TIE: 1991; same as 5853, except maroon instead of blue. **CP**

5877 LIONEL PERKY BOW WOMAN'S TIE: 1991; same as 5854, except maroon instead of blue. **CP**

5878 LIONEL SPORT CAP: 1991; dark blue cap and visor with white front; red "LIONEL" lettering and circle "L" logo. **CP**

FACTORY ERRORS & PROTOTYPES

CHAPTER 6

Thanks to our many readers who have notified us of their unique and interesting factory mistakes, we were able to substantially expand this chapter from the previous modern era Greenberg Guide.

Many collectors and dealers indiscriminately use, fail to use, or misuse the terms "prototype" and "factory error," and the many variations included therein. We hope to explain these terms in the next paragraphs.

PROTOTYPES

A *prototype* is a one-of-a-kind item, or one of an extremely small number of items, made by Lionel prior to mass production. This "pre-production" allowed the manufacturer or sponsor to see what a proposed item would look like, and to study the feasibility of mass producing it.

Prototypes were built for the purpose of making production and marketing decisions. Consequently, a prototype will have one or more of the following characteristics which will readily distinguish it from any similar mass-produced item:

(A) Numbers, lettering or logos will be hand-applied decals rather than other mass-production methods. It is also very possible that body color or text color will be different than on the regular-production piece, so that Lionel and/or a sponsor can get a feel for how the piece will appear.

(B) It might not be wired or otherwise assembled for operation. Very few of these prototypes have left the factory, although some of these are legitimate.

Perhaps the most intriguing aspect of prototypes is how *any* of them manage to leave the factory. Although Lionel's security and quality control have tightened considerably in recent years, we still have regular reports of such pieces showing up at train meets.

A number of so-called prototypes are fakes. Some counterfeit items have made their way into train meets, cleverly disguised with decals. Some people have made and sold prototypes manufactured outside of the factory. Therefore, it is always wise to ask an experienced collector if the piece is a valid variation or prototype. If the price is much over the regular price, is it worth the risk?

Some prototypes were never put into production, including: 9879 Kraft refrigerator car, 9237 United Parcel Service, and 9356 Pep-O-Mint tank car.

Color Variations

A color variation will, for all intents and purposes, be a production-run piece. It will not be amateurish or crude. It will be professionally clean and commercially sellable. Color variations fall into one of the following categories:

(A) One of an extremely small number of items. Examples are: 9703 CP Rail boxcar in dark green (five made), 9706 C & O boxcar in black (four made), and 9123 C & O auto carrier in yellow (10 made). In many instances these will be color samples (a form of a prototype), which reveal how a piece's color would look. That is the case for these three cars, which were pre-production Toy Fair samples.

(B) Color variation made in moderate amounts. Examples include: 9701 B & O auto boxcar in black (120 made), 9202 Santa Fe boxcar in orange (69 made), and 9207 Soo boxcar in white (24 exist). In some cases these are deliberate limited runs (the 9701 was made for a TCA convention), or they may be samples made when plastic of one color is purged from molding machines in preparation for the production run of another color. If these are made in sufficient quantities, they may be included in the first sets produced, rather than destroyed.

R. LaVoie Collection; B. Greenberg photograph

Differences in factory manufacturing processes. The 9135 N & W version without the stress mark was produced after the mold was changed in 1973; therefore, it is only found in the 1975 N & W Spirit of America set and is scarcer than the version with the stress mark. Please note: These are not factory errors or prototypes, but merely variations (see Volume I, page 246, for complete descriptions).
Top shelf: **Shows stress mark.**
Bottom shelf: **No stress mark.**

(C) Common color variations. Examples include: 9215 Norfolk & Western boxcar in royal blue (1000 made), 9730 CP Rail boxcar with white and black versions (about equal numbers of each exist), and the 9853 Cracker Jack refrigerator car, which has its own very complicated production history to tell (see Volume I). These changes occur for many reasons: the production team may not like the color combinations; complaints from collectors; production line limitations; need for matching colors of cars in a set; or changes made from year to year. In the early Fundimensions period, it was not always easy to match plastic colors from year to year.

Chemically-Altered Cars

Lionel produced many color variations from 1970 through 1988. Because of the high prices that legitimate color variations command, certain unscrupulous (or worse) elements of the train-collecting hobby have in the past few years attempted to "create" color variations using various techniques to sell at higher prices.

Charles Weber, a chemist and long-time train collector, has concluded that a number of cars which have surfaced in recent years have been chemically-altered after they left the factory and have been sold for much higher prices than "normal" examples would have brought. His observations are explained below.

During the period from the late 1970s to the mid-1980s, some Lionel cars were offered for sale at train meets in some very unusual colors. These cars had been subjected to a chemical process which altered the body color and/or the color of the lettering. They are not legitimate Lionel color variations.

Some cars are known to have been affected by such chemical processes. Several more may exist, so the collector is advised to exercise great care in the purchase of any car which is significantly different from regular mass-produced examples. Some legitimate color samples and cars with different colors of lettering exist as well, so the introduction of these chemically-altered cars has caused confusion in the marketplace. Good examples of this process are the 9447 Pullman Standard boxcar in gold and 9453 MPA boxcar in black, not blue.

Cars which were normally produced with yellow heat-stamped lettering have had the original yellow lettering chemically-altered to white or off-white. Examples are the 9427 Bay Line boxcar in white letters, and the 9403 Seaboard Coast Line boxcar with white lettering.

Chemically-altered cars are nothing but fakes and should be understood and treated as such. In the view of some authorities, these cars have no collectable value, yet others feel that they have modest to moderate value as conversation pieces. Fortunately, due to the publicity and expose engendered by the work of such experts as Charles Weber and Joe Algozzini, this practice has all but stopped in recent years.

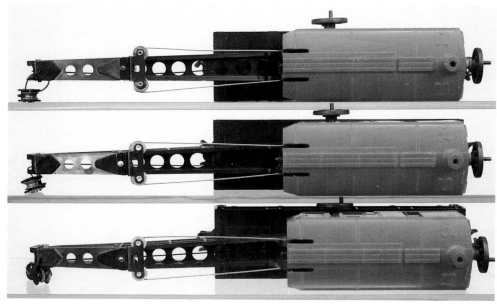

R. LaVoie Collection; B. Greenberg photograph

The only sure way to identify the 1971 version of the 6560 crane is to look at the boom fastening. Please note: These are not factory errors or prototypes, merely variations (see Volume I, page 211, for complete descriptions).

Top shelf: **Flathead screw, postwar Hillside production.**
Middle shelf: **Large chrome rivet, postwar Hagerstown production 1968-69.**
Bottom rivet **Small rivet with black washer, 1971 MPC production.**

Specially Requested Items

From time to time, the factory has created special products for train clubs such as the Lionel Collectors Club of America (LCCA), the Train Collectors Association (TCA), the Toy Train Operating Society (TTOS), and the Lionel Operating Train Society (LOTS). In addition, there are many other cases wherein a Lionel car is stripped, redecorated or overstamped to mark a special event or meet. These have been produced outside the Lionel factory by such professional redecorators as the Pleasant Valley Process Co. (PVP), and Nostalgia Train Works. Even though some serious collectors do not consider these pieces "true" Lionel, they are nonetheless based on original Lionel bodies, and this entire group is an important and growing area in the recent history of train collecting. (This Guide provides a complete rundown of these pieces in the Special Production chapter.)

It should be pointed out that there is a type of Lionel production which "overlaps" this definition — specially requested train pieces which Lionel *does* make entirely at its factory, for special customers. These include such uncatalogued special items as a unique 6464 boxcar made for Ohio dealer Glen Uhl, and a host of exclusive items made for department, hardware and retail stores through the years. However, since these cars do not meet our strict definition of "Special Production" (train club cars or pieces decorated outside the factory), they are considered a form of regular production (albeit uncatalogued) and their detailed listings are therefore included in Volume I of this Guide. They are not considered factory errors or prototypes because they were mass produced exactly as requested by the customer. See the Department Store Specials chapter for more information.

FACTORY ERRORS

The most common *factory errors* would have to be items with printing on one side only, or items in which one or more lines of text are missing. Those escaped detection during production and were shipped out unbeknownst to Lionel.

The next most common factory errors would be cars with no printing on either side. In some cases, these are items (usually without trucks) rejected by Lionel for one reason or another and picked up by employees or collectors and sold outside of the factory.

Perhaps the least common but most interesting type of factory error would be pieces missing parts or components. Since these are the easiest for Lionel's quality control to spot, they are the least-frequently reported. In a few cases entire trucks are missing!

It is important to distinguish a factory error from a variation. A *variation* is the result of an intended change in the production process. Some Lionel variations occurred because of an intentional decision to make the piece easier or less expensive to manufacture. Examples are the 9861-9863 refrigerator cars, which changed from metal door guides to plastic. Sometimes a variation exists because of a need to correct a defect in or make a change to an earlier version. An example is the infamous 9853 Cracker Jack refrigerator car, which has a maddening number of strange variations. Usually, variations exist in much greater numbers than factory errors.

Please be aware that *normal* production variations are included in the main listings in Volume I. This chapter describes only the principal factory errors and prototypes of which we have been made aware over the years.

With many pieces, we cannot be absolutely sure whether it is a prototype or an error, since in most cases we have little knowledge of the relative quantities made. Most of these items are errors. But, particularly on a piece without lettering or with irregular color variations, a case can be made for it being a prototype/color sample. We welcome readers comments in our endeavor to uncover the truth.

In general, many variations and errors are highly collectable and add great interest and complexity to the train-collecting hobby. Some collectors are willing to pay the much higher prices generally asked for Lionel items which differ significantly from those which were mass-produced in regular production runs. These collectors are involved in possibly the riskiest specialty of all.

FACTORY ERRORS LISTINGS

	GD	VG	EXC	MT

1776 NORFOLK & WESTERN: See 8559.

1776 SEABOARD: 1976, U-36 diesel; flag reversed (facing nose rather than rear). J. Dickerson Collection. **NRS**

2789 WATER TANK: White unpainted plastic water tank piece. D. Fleming Collection. **NRS**

3100 GREAT NORTHERN: 4-8-4 steam locomotive; same as regular issue, but missing GN logo from cylinder head pieces. R. Sigurdson and G. Romich Collections. **NRS**

5704 BUDWEISER: Turn-of-the-Century refrigerator car; came from factory with one door missing; authenticity established by presence of weathering on areas normally covered by door. R. E. Nelson Collection. **NRS**

5717 SANTA FE: Bunk car.
(A) No lettering or numbering on one side. R. Lord Collection. **NRS**
(B) No lettering or numbering on both sides. R. Lord Collection. **NRS**

5739 BALTIMORE & OHIO: 1986, tool car; no black lettering on one side. A. Jaworski Collection. **NRS**

6177 READING: Quad hopper.
(A) No lettering or numbering on either side. C. O'Dell Collection. **NRS**
(B) "R" in "READING" is missing on one side. C. Lang Collection. **NRS**

6405 AMTRAK: Pullman passenger car; one wood-beam passenger truck and one Symington-Wayne truck with extended coupler shank, like those on bay window cabooses. M. Sabatelle Collection. **NRS**

OBSERVATIONS

Roger Bartelt has made a number of observations which can be applied to any unusual item. His observations are in the form of questions which should be considered when any such items are being considered for purchase:

• Does the item make sense?

• Is there any discernible, rational reason why the particular set of components should have been combined to make this particular item?

• Are all of the materials used contemporary with, or prior to, the indicated date such an item was made?

• Are all of the components in the item from the manufacturer in question? It would be highly unlikely that Lionel would make a prototype using some other manufacturer's parts.

• Is there any evidence other than the item itself which indicates that the item is a genuine prototype such as, but not limited to, letters, factory engineering tags, or archives tags?

Due precisely to the fact that such items have commanded prices many times higher than similar items mass-produced in regular production runs, many examples of such items have appeared in the train-collecting markets during the last several years and are highly suspect. Great caution must be exercised when considering the purchase of one of these high-priced items.

Knowledge of the honesty, integrity, and reliability of the seller of any such item, coupled with insisting upon a written money-back guarantee if the item later proves to be a fake, are two steps in the right direction. Even these steps are not entirely satisfactory, however, because of the great difficulty in proving what is and what is not a fake and because of the diversity of opinion even among experienced collectors as to the authenticity of such items.

A full and unconditional money-back guarantee from the seller for return of the item is a good idea, but it is doubtful that many sellers (especially if they entertained any doubt about the authenticity of the item themselves) would be willing to give guarantees. These items are in such demand that other buyers might forego any guarantee. What it all comes down to in many cases is "you pay your money, and you take your chances."

	GD	VG	EXC	MT

6421 JOSHUA LIONEL COWEN: 1982, bay window caboose; missing black paper insert in bay window, so that center light bulb is visible. G. Romich Collection. **NRS**

6425 ERIE-LACKAWANNA: Bay window caboose.
(A) One arch bar truck and one Symington-Wayne truck. R. Conrad Collection. **NRS**
(B) Missing lettering. D. Aurand Collection. **NRS**

6427 BURLINGTON NORTHERN: Transfer caboose; no BN logo on one side of cab. G. Humbert Collection. **NRS**

6439 READING: 1984, bay window caboose; missing yellow lettering. R. Krenske Collection. **NRS**

6464-1971 TCA SPECIAL: Boxcar; Disneyland. Same as regular-issue, but Mickey Mouse logo shows half-smile rather than full smile on each side. R. M. Caplan Collection.
— — — **250**

6508 CANADIAN PACIFIC: Crane car; CP herald missing from both sides; only "CP" and "6508" stamped on each side. M. Sabatelle Collection. **NRS**

6567 IC GULF: 1986, LCCA crane car.
(A) Lettering missing on one side. V. Ingling Collection. **NRS**
(B) Missing two stripes on cab rear. M. Schmidt Collection. **NRS**

6905 NICKEL PLATE ROAD: Extended vision caboose; gray stripe and script lettering completely missing from one side. Other types of factory errors may also exist — reader comments invited. **NRS**

6920 BOSTON & ALBANY: Standard O wood-sided caboose, black-painted roof. C. O'Dell Collection. **NRS**

7216 BALTIMORE AND OHIO: 1983, General-style passenger coach; no white striping along windows. R. LaVoie observation. **NRS**

7303 ERIE: Stock car; lettering completely missing from one side. J. Grzyboski Collection. **NRS**

7304 SOUTHERN: 1983, stock car; painted dark green on one side only. J. Nowaczyk Collection. **NRS**

7515 DENVER: 1981, bullion car; one side has no lettering or numbers. P. Bauer Collection. **NRS**

8030 ILLINOIS CENTRAL: GP-9 diesel; Type II railings.
(A) Lettering and numbers missing from one side. G. Halverson Collection. **NRS**
(B) Gray plastic shell painted Milwaukee Road orange and dull chalk white, unpainted white brake unit, very deeply heat-stamped numbers and letters on side slightly raised, other side stamped normally. R. LaVoie Collection. **NRS**

8042 GRAND TRUNK WESTERN: 2-4-2 steam locomotive; tender printed on one side only. D. Fleming Collection. **NRS**

8050 DELAWARE & HUDSON: U-36C diesel; "Delaware & Hudson" and "8050" missing from one side. G. Halverson Collection. **NRS**

8104 UNION PACIFIC: 1981, 4-4-0, General-type locomotive; same as regular-issue, except tender has one arch bar truck on the front and one Symington-Wayne truck on the rear. Moyer Collection. — — **195 225**

8162 ONTARIO NORTHLAND: SD-18 diesel; stamped with "8162" on body shell, but "8163" on cab below windows. "Triple T" Collection. **NRS**

8304 PENNSYLVANIA: 1974, 4-4-2 steam engine; "8304" stamped on one side only. N. Smith Collection. **NRS**

8304 ROCK ISLAND: 1974, 4-4-2 steam locomotive; tender printed on one side only. D. Fleming Collection. **NRS**

8359 B & O: GM 50th Anniversary GP-7 diesel.
(A) Without "B & O" and "GM 50", but with nose decal. **NRS**
(B) No nose decal or numbers on sides, but "B & O" present. G. Halverson Collection. **NRS**

8363/8364 BALTIMORE & OHIO: F-3 AA-units; blue plastic body painted light blue; white and gray top; no lettering or decals. M. Sabatelle Collection. **NRS**

8371 NEW YORK CENTRAL: 1983, dummy F-3 B-unit; no lettering on one side; stripe is present. L. Yanoshik Collection. **NRS**

8378 WABASH: Fairbanks-Morse diesel; no flag logos on either side of cab, no Mexico paper sticker on battery box. D. Holst Collection. **NRS**

8380 LIONEL LINES: 1983, SD-28 diesel; "LIONEL LINES" missing from one side of the long hood. J. Koblan Collection. **NRS**

8404 PENNSYLVANIA: 6-8-6 S-2 turbine steam locomotive; number present on only one side of headlight. J. Sawruk Collection. **NRS**

8460 MKT: NW-2 switcher; deeper red than usual production; lettering missing from one side. G. Halverson Collection. **NRS**

8466 AMTRAK: F-3 A-unit; lettering, number and logo double-stamped on one side. M. Sabatelle Collection. **NRS**

8466/8467 AMTRAK: F-3 AA-units; no Amtrak logo or number on either unit. M. Sabatelle Collection. **NRS**

8474 RIO GRANDE: F-3 B-unit; lettering and stripes missing from one side. M. Sabatelle Collection. **NRS**

8477 NEW YORK CENTRAL: 1984, GP-9 diesel; printed on one side only. T. DeBord Collection. **NRS**

8550 JERSEY CENTRAL: 1975, GP-9 diesel; no number on one side. T. Ryan, T. Phelps Collection. **NRS**

8556 CHESSIE SYSTEM: NW-2 switcher.
(A) Chessie System lettering and logo missing from both sides. G. Halverson Collection. **NRS**
(B) "B & O/8556" missing from one cab side. R. Eskow Collection. **NRS**

8559 NORFOLK & WESTERN: Spirit of America GP-9 diesel; missing circle of stars from cab front on both ends. This is a well-known factory error. R. LaVoie Collection.
— — **120 145**

8587 WABASH: 1985, GP-9 diesel. In what must be one of the most amazing factory errors yet, Bob and Ron Hunley of Indiana report that they received this piece new in the box, opened the seal, and found the engine missing its power truck entirely! As they tell it: "No wheel marks on the styrofoam, no grease in the bag — no evidence that the motor had ever been installed at all. Someone was really asleep on this one!" R. and R. Hunley Collection. **NRS**

8630 WESTERN & ATLANTIC: 1986, 4-4-0 General-type steam locomotive; drawbar and coupler mounted to wrong ends of tender. D. Morse Collection. **NRS**

GD   VG   EXC   MT

8701 W & A: General 4-4-0 steam locomotive; yellow rectangle and "No. 3" omitted from one side of cab. R. Sage Collection. **NRS**

8702 CRESCENT LIMITED: 1977, 4-6-4 small Hudson steam locomotive; tender is missing "Southern" on left side only. J. Bonney Collection. **NRS**

8754 NEW HAVEN: Rectifier electric; engine numbers missing from cab sides. D. Fleming Collection. **NRS**

8759 ERIE-LACKAWANNA: GP-9 diesel; has maroon and yellow paint and stripe but no lettering either side. D. Fleming Collection. **NRS**

8764 BALTIMORE AND OHIO: Budd railcar; no lettering or numbering on either side. D. Fleming Collection. **NRS**

8801 THE BLUE COMET: 4-6-4 Hudson steam locomotive.
(A) Painted locomotive and tender, but no lettering. One known example. D. Fleming Collection. **NRS**
(B) Tender is dark and light blue; unpainted blue coal; lettered on only one side. D. Fleming Collection. **NRS**
(C) Tender painted dark blue only; blue coal; lettered only on one side. D. Fleming Collection. **NRS**
(D) Same as (C), but tender lettered on both sides. D. Fleming Collection. **NRS**
(E) Same as (C), but coal on tender three-quarters painted black. D. Fleming Collection. **NRS**
(F) "BLUE COMET" lettering missing on boiler front. T. Arpino Collection. **NRS**

8851 NEW HAVEN: F-3 A-unit; number missing from cab. D. Fleming Collection. **NRS**

8852 NEW HAVEN: F-3-unit; NH logo missing from nose of cab. D. Fleming Collection. **NRS**

8855 MILWAUKEE ROAD: F-3 unit; "8855" and Milwaukee logo missing from one side. D. Fleming Collection. **NRS**

8857 NORTHERN PACIFIC: U36B diesel; number and Monad logo missing from cab sides; one known example. D. Fleming Collection. **NRS**

8866 MINNEAPOLIS & ST. LOUIS: GP-9 diesel; lettered and numbered on one side only. G. Orffeo Collection. **NRS**

8868 AMTRAK: Budd railcar; painted stripe but no lettering. D. Fleming Collection. **NRS**

8869 AMTRAK: Budd railcar; painted stripe but no lettering. D. Fleming Collection. **NRS**

8872 SANTA FE: SD-18 diesel.
(A) Numbers missing from cab. D. Fleming Collection. **NRS**
(B) Painted, but no lettering. D. Fleming Collection. **NRS**

8900 ATSF: 4-6-4 Hudson steam locomotive.
(A) Boiler front in silver has feedwater heater; no evidence of removal or alteration. G. Parsons Collection.
— — — 320
(B) Tender missing "8900" on right side and gold FARR diamond logo on both sides. One example known. D. Fleming Collection. **NRS**

8951 SOUTHERN PACIFIC: Fairbanks-Morse; same as regular issue, but "SOUTHERN PACIFIC" missing from left side of diesel cab. Six examples reported to exist. N. Hussey observation, R. A. Hicks and J. Grzyboski Collections. **NRS**

8952/8953 PENNSYLVANIA: F-3 AA-units; power and dummy units with lettering and striping on one side only. D. Fleming Collection. **NRS**

8960 SOUTHERN PACIFIC: U36C diesel.
(A) Painted but lettered only on one side. D. Fleming Collection. **NRS**
(B) Painted but lettering missing from both sides. D. Fleming Collection. **NRS**

9010 GREAT NORTHERN: 1971, short hopper; lettering missing from one side. G. Halverson Collection. **NRS**

9017 WABASH: 1978-81, short gondola; no white lettering on either side. A. Jaworski Collection. **NRS**

9035 CONRAIL: Blue short boxcar; number printed on one side only. Two known examples. D. Fleming Collection. **NRS**

9037 CONRAIL: Brown short boxcar; lettering and number on one side only. D. Fleming Collection. **NRS**

9042 AUTOLITE: Short boxcar.
(A) Number printed on one side only. Three known examples. D. Fleming Collection. **NRS**
(B) Tuscan body with yellow lettering. C. O'Dell Collection. **NRS**

9045 TOYS 'R' US: Short boxcar; lettered and numbered on one side only. Two known examples. D. Fleming Collection. **NRS**

9058 LIONEL: SP caboose; some examples missing lettering due to improper stamping. D. Fleming comment. **NRS**

9090 MINI MAX: 1971, boxcar; dark blue roof and ends; "G" in fourth panel from left; missing "USLX 9090" lettering on lower left side. — — 50 60

9121 L & N: 1975, flatcar with dozer and scraper; brown flatcar body; white lettering on one side only. J. Breslin Collection. **NRS**

9128 HEINZ: 1974-76, vat car; medium yellow vats; no lettering. Purchaser should beware of switched vats; unlettered replacement vats are easily available. **NRS**

9134 VIRGINIAN: 1976-77, covered hopper; silver roof cover instead of blue. This is a legitimate factory error, not a switched cover, because the silver cover is painted over the normal blue unpainted cover. When the hatches are lifted, the blue shows through, and there are silver paint specks on the inside of the car, which is unpainted gray. Most likely, this car was run through the paint spray booth with the cover installed. R. LaVoie and C. Lang Collections. — — — 100

9136 REPUBLIC STEEL: Long gondola; lettered and numbered on one side only. M. Sabatelle Collection. **NRS**

9140 BURLINGTON: 1971, long gondola; flush-molded brakewheel; lettering on one side only. G. Halverson Collection. **NRS**

9141 BURLINGTON NORTHERN: 1973, long gondola; flush-molded brakewheel; lettering on one side only. G. Halverson Collection. **NRS**

9142 REPUBLIC STEEL: 1973, long gondola; lettering on one side only. G. Halverson Collection. **NRS**

9144 RIO GRANDE: Long gondola; recessed brakewheel molding; lettering on one side only. G. Halverson Collection. **NRS**

9160 ILLINOIS CENTRAL: Caboose; missing lettering on one side and white "ic" inside black circle logo on other side. D. Aurand Collection. **NRS**

D. Aurand Collection; B. Greenberg photograph

Top shelf: 9160 Illinois Central caboose without lettering on one side; 9160 Illinois Central caboose without white "ic" inside black logo circle.
Bottom shelf: 19703 Great Northern caboose without goat inside logo circle; 6425 Erie-Lackawanna bay window caboose missing lettering.

	GD	VG	EXC	MT

9203 UNION PACIFIC: 1971, boxcar; UP herald missing on one side. J. Michalak Collection.　　　**NRS**

9238 NORTHERN PACIFIC: 1984-85, log dump car; same as catalogued issue, but mirror-imaged lettering on both sides of car; electrocal was applied in reverse. G. Wilson Collection.
(A) As described above.　　—　—　—　75
(B) Lettering and numbers on both sides of car stamped upside down. M. Gural Collection.　　**NRS**

9239 LIONEL LINES: N5C caboose; one Symington-Wayne truck and one arch bar truck. A. Broderdorf Collection.　**NRS**

9271 MINNEAPOLIS & ST. LOUIS: Bay window caboose; no lettering or numbers on either side. D. Fleming Collection.　　**NRS**

9274 SANTA FE: Bay window caboose; red with black roof.
(A) Completely lettered, but with red unpainted roof; one known example. D. Fleming Collection.　　**NRS**
(B) Painted black roof but no lettering either side. Two known examples. D. Fleming Collection.　　**NRS**
(C) Red unpainted roof, no lettering either side. Four known examples. D. Fleming Collection.　　**NRS**

9276 PEABODY: Quad hopper; "PEABODY" double-stamped on one side. D. Fleming Collection.　　**NRS**

9279 MAGNOLIA: Three-dome tank car; letters "MA" missing from "MAGNOLIA" on both sides. D. Fleming Collection.　　**NRS**

9304 C & O: 1973-76, coal dump car; no lettering on either side.　　**NRS**

9306 ATSF: Flatcar with two horses; from 1053 James Gang set; one arch bar and one AAR truck. R. Grandison Collection.　　**NRS**

9307 ERIE: 1979-80, animated gondola; lettering and numbering completely absent from one side of car. Moss Collection.　　**NRS**

9320 FORT KNOX: Bullion car; clear unpainted bullion bar stacks. D. Fleming Collection. Though this is a legitimate factory error, purchasers should be aware that painted and unpainted bullion stacks are readily available from parts dealers.　**NRS**

9321 ATSF: Single-dome tank car; lettered correctly but unpainted (regular issue painted silver). D. Fleming Collection.　　**NRS**

9322 ATSF: Quad hopper; lettered and numbered on one side only. D. Fleming Collection.　　**NRS**

9323 ATSF: 1979, bay window caboose; diamond "FARR #1" emblem missing from one side. M. Finney Collection.　**NRS**

9352 CHICAGO & NORTH WESTERN: TOFC flatcar; no lettering on one trailer. J. Grzyboski Collection.　**NRS**

9401 GREAT NORTHERN: Boxcar; misprinted with additional electrocal Monad logos. D. Fleming Collection.　**NRS**

9449 GREAT NORTHERN: 1981, boxcar, FARR diamond logo missing on one side. J. Nowaczyk Collection.　**NRS**

9456 PENNSYLVANIA: Boxcar; PRR logo missing from keystones on both sides. J. Grzyboski Collection.　**NRS**

9525 BALTIMORE & OHIO: 1976, passenger coach; lettering and window trim paint missing on one side. D. and M. Taylor Collection.　　**NRS**

9532 SOUTHERN: 1978, "P.G.T. Beauregard" passenger car assembled as an observation car rather than the usual Pullman. See comments under 9534 below. W. Buschmeier Collection.　　**NRS**

9533 SOUTHERN: 1978, "Stonewall Jackson" Pullman passenger car; missing gold stripe above and below the windows. L. Fischer Collection.　　**NRS**

9534 SOUTHERN: 1978, "Robert E. Lee" passenger car assembled as a Pullman rather than an observation. This is possibly a post-factory alteration, since vestibules and platforms are

W. Buschmeier Collection; B. Greenberg photograph

"9532 P.G.T BEAUREGARD" on an observation chassis rather than a Pullman chassis, factory error.

	GD	VG	EXC	MT

removable pieces in the 9500-series passenger cars. P. Repka Collection. Later note: we have since discovered a 9532 "P.G.T. Beauregard" Southern car assembled as an observation rather than a Pullman. Possibly these cars were altered at the same time. See 9532 above. **NRS**

9537 HALLEY BLUE COMET: Combine; painted normally, but gold striping along windows missing from one side. R. LaVoie observation. **NRS**

9588 BURLINGTON: 1980, vista dome passenger car; "BURLINGTON" lettering missing above window. R. Kaptur Collection. **NRS**

95XX BALTIMORE & OHIO: 1975-76, Madison-style passenger car; number and car name below windows is missing on both sides, so this car could be any of the B & O Capitol Limited coaches. A. Jaworski Collection. **NRS**

9602 ATSF: 1977, hi-cube boxcar; all markings to right of door on both sides are missing. — — — 350

9669 BAMBI: Hi-cube boxcar; missing "Mickey Mouse" and "9669" markings from both sides. D. Fleming Collection. **NRS**

9703 CP RAIL: Boxcar; all "CP Rail" lettering stamped twice, once on each side of door. R. M. Caplan Collection. **NRS**

9708 U.S. MAIL: Boxcar.
(A) Reversed striping colors; blue on top and red on bottom. J. Grzyboski Collection. **NRS**
(B) No lettering or numbers on one side. Car is striped red, white and blue as usual. F. Jones Collection. **NRS**

9709 BAR STATE OF MAINE: Boxcar.
(A) No printing on the white areas of either side.
— — — 125
(B) Blue- and light red-painted gray body; blue- and red-painted gray doors; white- and black-painted lettering; number stamped on angle. — — — 100
(C) Blue- and dark red-painted gray body; blue- and red-painted gray door; white lettering, printed one side only in white areas; factory error. — — — 60

9729 CP RAIL: Boxcar; CP Rail logo is black with white only. D. Fleming Collection. **NRS**

9757 CENTRAL OF GEORGIA: Boxcar.
(A) Tuscan-painted brown body; silver-painted gray doors; number misprinted. **NRS**
(B) Lettering within central oval missing. **NRS**

9758 ALASKA: 1976-77, boxcar.
(A) Blue-painted white body; blue-painted white doors; white lettering, without "AT YOUR SERVICE". M. Blacet Collection.
— — — 325

	GD	VG	EXC	MT

(B) Blue-painted dark blue body and doors; yellow lettering, without "AT YOUR SERVICE". R. Vagner Collection.
— — — 350

9763 DENVER & RIO GRANDE: 1976, stock car; number and lettering double-stamped. M. Gural Collection.
— — — 95

9768 BOSTON & MAINE: Boxcar; BM logo and weights data missing from one side. R. Lord Collection. **NRS**

9772 GREAT NORTHERN: Boxcar.
(A) Missing number and "GN" on one side. We wish to learn how many of this variety are in collector hands. Reader comments are invited. J. Grzyboski Collection. **NRS**
(B) Same as (A), but completely missing GN logo on right. Black lettering and underscoring on left side is present, but has shifted downward so that the underscoring is through the yellow line. J. Breslin Collection. We wish to learn how many of this variety are in collector hands. Reader comments are invited. **NRS**

9776 SOUTHERN PACIFIC: Boxcar; black-painted body and black doors; white and gold lettering; double-stamped lettering and emblems. — — — 50

9784 ATSF: 1977-78, boxcar; dark maroon-painted body; flat black roof and ends; white lettering washed out with tinge of pinkish-maroon. Meisel comment; R. Vagner Collection. **NRS**

9801 BALTIMORE AND OHIO: 1975, Standard O boxcar.
(A) Dark blue lower stripe; B & O decal is misplaced on one side only. T. Klaassen Collection. **NRS**
(B) No lettering in upper left corner of one side. D. Newman Collection.
(C) Sentinel decal missing from one side. R. Moran Collection. **NRS**

9814 PERRIER: 1980 billboard refrigerator car; Perrier bottle missing from mountain spring electrocal. D. McCabe Collection. We do not know how rare this variety is. Reader comments requested. **NRS**

9856 OLD MILWAUKEE: 1975-76, refrigerator car; lettering (as measured by placement of gold scroll) shifted to the right on one side of the car and left on the other side. Borders on electrocals mis-stamped. W. Dyson Collection. **NRS**

9873 RALSTON: Refrigerator car; no checkerboard paint on one side; 10 known examples. D. Fleming Collection. **NRS**

9880 ATSF: Refrigerator car; numbering and lettering missing from one side. D. Fleming Collection. **NRS**

9887 FRUIT GROWERS EXPRESS: 1983, refrigerator car.
(A) Unpainted one side. J. Nowaczyk Collection. **NRS**
(B) Unpainted both sides. J. Nowaczyk Collection. **NRS**

16000 PENNSYLVANIA: 1987, vista dome passenger car; no lettering on one side. M. Konowich Collection. **NRS**

16018 NEW YORK CENTRAL: 1989, O27 passenger coach; missing light gray window stripe. R. LaVoie Collection. **NRS**

16023 AMTRAK: 1989, O27 passenger car; missing numbers on both sides. R. Beaulieu Collection. **NRS**

16107 SUNOCO: 1990, tank car; no lettering one side, but decal is there. J. Czelusta Collection. **NRS**

16214 DENVER & RIO GRANDE: 1990, enclosed auto carrier; missing all flatcar lettering on one side. W. Fuller Collection. **NRS**

16225 BUDWEISER: 1990, vat car; no lettering at all on car body. S. Competello Collection. **NRS**

	GD	VG	EXC	MT

16307 NICKEL PLATE ROAD: Flatcar with trailers; one trailer missing lettering on both sides. C. O'Dell Collection. **NRS**

16610 LIONEL: 1987, track maintenance car; incomplete heat-stamped lettering on one side of superstructure. C. Whiting Collection. **NRS**

16626 CSX: 1990, searchlight car; lettering missing from one side. J. Nowaczyk Collection. **NRS**

16801 LIONEL RAILROADER CLUB: Bunk car; no painting on one side. C. O'Dell Collection. **NRS**

17003 DUPONT ALATHON: 1990, two-bay ACF hopper; originally produced with "POLYTHYLENE RESIN" in black lettering on a white background on one side only. This was an error Lionel caught late in the production process. The factory relettered many of them "POLYETHYLENE RESIN" in white on a black background. Some cars with the error were released. G. Halverson and R. Feneran Collections. **NRS**

17402 SANTA FE: 1990, gondola; lettering only on one side. W. Cunningham Collection. **NRS**

17601 SOUTHERN: 1988, wood-side caboose; lettering missing on one side. J. Freeman Collection. **NRS**

17872 ANACONDA: 1988, ore car; no lettering on one side. D. Mareck Collection. **NRS**

18004 READING: 1989, 4-6-2 Pacific steam locomotive; "READING" missing from tender on both sides. Englehart Collection. **NRS**

18200 CONRAIL: 1987, SD-40 diesel; front marker boards read "8585", the number of the Burlington SD-40 produced in 1985; rear marker boards read the correct "18200". D. Finneyfrock Collection. **NRS**

18202 ERIE-LACKAWANNA: 1989, dummy SD-40 diesel; missing number and "Radio Equipped" lettering on one side. R. Weidinger Collection. **NRS**

18203 CP RAIL: 1989, SD-40 diesel; no graphics on either side of the locomotive. G. Carpenter Collection. **NRS**

18500 MILWAUKEE ROAD: 1987, GP-9 diesel; missing Milwaukee Road decal from one side; motor truck in this engine was not magnetized. When the owner received it back after repair at Lionel, the horn would not operate. It seems quality is hard to perfect even today. G. Ligon Collection. **NRS**

18702 VIRGINIA & TRUCKEE: 1988, 4-4-0 General-type locomotive; tender lettered on one side only. F. B. Collins, Jr. Collection. **NRS**

18806 NEW HAVEN: 1989, SD-18 diesel; no number on cab. R. Kaptur and F. Rudman Collections. **NRS**

18807 LEHIGH VALLEY: 1990, Alco RS-3 diesel; no steps mounted on front truck. **NRS**

19000 BLUE COMET: 1987, diner car; cream stripe between windows does not cover fully down to sills. J. Riemersma Collection. **NRS**

19208 SOUTHERN: 1988, boxcar; came from the box with two different trucks — one Symington-Wayne, one arch bar. While trucks can be changed easily, this appears to be a legitimate factory error. M. DiMonda and W. Howell Collections. **NRS**

19308 GREAT NORTHERN: 1989, ore car; no printing on one side. J. Lambert Collection. **NRS**

G. Halverson Collection; B. Greenberg photograph

17003 "DUPONT ALATHON" two-bay AFC hopper
Top shelf: **Shows correct spelling in white on black background.**
Bottom shelf: **Shows original production with "POLYTHYLENE RESIN" misspelled in black letters on white background.**

	GD	VG	EXC	MT

19703 GREAT NORTHERN: Caboose without goat inside logo circle. D. Aurand Collection. **NRS**

19706 UNION PACIFIC: 1989, extended vision caboose; missing red "UNION PACIFIC" lettering on one side. W. Fuller observation. **NRS**

19906 I LOVE PA: 1989, boxcar; missing red heart between "I" and "PA" on both sides of car. D. Best Collection. **NRS**

PROTOTYPES LISTINGS

665E JOHNNY CASH BLUE TRAIN: 1971, 4-6-2 Pacific steam engine. One-of-a-kind prototype. Dark gloss blue-painted Baldwin boiler; white stripe and "665E" below cab window; matching blue 2046 long streamlined tender lettered "JOHNNY CASH BLUE TRAIN" in white. Came with display case and plaque reading "PRESENTED TO JOHNNY CASH/BY THE MPC LIONEL PEOPLE NOVEMBER 1971". Photo appeared in Aug.-Sept. 1972 issue of *O-Scale Railroading Magazine*. I. D. Smith comment. **NRS**

4832 PENNSYLVANIA: Circa 1977, GG-1; chrome-finished; tuscan stripe. Pre-production sample. No Lionel GG-1s were made with this number. M. Levitt Collection. **NRS**

6403 GREAT NORTHERN: 1981, bay window caboose; prototype with red sides; black and white logo; gold FARR #3 logo; black roof; yellow heat-stamped lettering; Symington-Wayne trucks. Pre-production color sample. Regular-issue car was numbered "6438" and was orange and green. Note this number had previously been assigned to an Amtrak passenger car. R. Weidinger Collection. **NRS**

4832 GG-1 with tuscan stripe, pre-production sample.

M. Levitt Collection; B. Greenberg photograph

	GD	VG	EXC	MT

6464-1 WESTERN PACIFIC: Probably late 1969 or early 1970, boxcar; orange-painted orange body and door; white lettering; Type VII body with 9200 end plates; metal door guides; postwar bar-end metal trucks. Prototype for reissue of 6464-type boxcars by Fundimensions, but this version never produced; believed to be one of a kind. R. M. Caplan Collection. **NRS**

6464-50 MINNEAPOLIS & ST. LOUIS: Boxcar; tuscan (not red) body with white lettering; MPC logo. Possible prototype; two known to exist. H. Levine Collection. **NRS**

6464-1971 TCA SPECIAL: Boxcar; Disneyland convention.
(A) Red body; white, yellow and green heat-stamping; yellow doors; postwar bar-end trucks. Pre-production color sample. R. M. Caplan Collection. **NRS**
(B) Light blue body, white, yellow and green heat-stamping, yellow doors. Pre-production color sample. C. O'Dell Collection. **NRS**

7227-7232 WABASH: 1986, short Madison passenger cars; one side of all six cars painted and lettered in a silver/chrome color, not the usual gold. Possibly a color sample or prototype of the Wabash Fallen Flags #1 set. T. Ellison Collection. **NRS**

7404 JERSEY CENTRAL: 1986, boxcar; lettering is gold rather than usual cream; Symington-Wayne trucks instead of Standard O trucks. Could be a prototype. W. Sigmon Collection. **NRS**

7925 ERIE LACKAWANNA: 1986, short boxcar. Possible color sample. Car is bright orange with white lettering rather than the usual gray body with maroon lettering. Found in a factory-sealed set. Note: The small picture of the set in the 1989 catalogue shows this car. Roland and A. Russell Collections. **NRS**

8006 ATLANTIC COAST LINE: 1980, 4-6-4 Hudson; same as regular-issue, but no "LIONEL" cast into inside of boiler front; tender has four-wheel trucks; no Magnetraction. Possible prototype. R. Kuehnemund Collection. **NRS**

8066 TOLEDO, PEORIA & WESTERN: 1980, GP-20; red body with white lettering. Possible prototype. Reader comments invited. Eddins Collection. **NRS**

8140 SOUTHERN: 1971, 2-4-0 steam locomotive; dark green unpainted body darker than regular production; lacks black paint

on lower body half. Likely color sample or prototype. R. Weidinger Collection. **NRS**

8252 DELAWARE & HUDSON: Alco powered A-unit; factory prototype as shown in 1972 catalogue with lighter blue, almost powder blue, paint; numberboards read "8022"; D & H decal on side but road name and number not printed out; road name and number shown in 1972 catalogue are printer overlay; front coupler, side ladder steps do not line up with door. Believed to be one of a kind. P. Catalano Collection.
| — | — | — | 550 |

8253 DELAWARE & HUDSON: Dummy Alco; light blue, almost powder blue; yellow sticky strip along bottom; ladders do not line up with door; D & H decal but without number or name on side; 1972 catalogue shows prototype with name and number but these are printer overlay. P. Catalano Collection.
| — | — | — | 550 |

8268/8269 TEXAS & PACIFIC: 1982, powered and dummy Alco A-units. Powered unit has Type II integrated AC motor and mechanical E-unit, not the Type III can motor and electronic reverse as on the production units. Both 8268 and 8269 have silver eagle decal on the nose, not blue as in regular production. Dummy unit has a blue roof, as shown in catalogue. Regular production pieces had silver roofs. In addition, the 7200-7202 passenger cars which came with this set were decaled, not stamped. This is a possible prototype of the Quicksilver Express set. A. Adams Collection. **NRS**

8363/8365: F-3 A-unit postwar leftover shell; one side stamped for 8363 Baltimore & Ohio and the other for Canadian Pacific. Believed to be pre-production color sample. G. Halverson Collection. **NRS**

8464/8465: F-3 diesel shells.
(A) Shell has Amtrak paint scheme, but stamped with Rio Grande lettering on one side and Amtrak with decal number on the other. Believed to be pre-production color sample; reportedly, 10 exist. R. Shanfeld Collection. **NRS**
(B) Same as (A), but Rio Grande side numbered "8465" and Amtrak side numbered "8466". Two identical shells mounted on powered and dummy chassis. M. Sabatelle Collection. **NRS**
(C) Same as (B), but lettering, stripes and number double-stamped on both units. M. Sabatelle Collection. **NRS**

R. LaVoie and K. H. Miller Collections; B. Schwab photograph

Top shelf: 16323 Lionel Lines TOFC flatcar, nature of color of vans and different color decals makes it a possible prototype.
Bottom shelf: 16018 NYC passenger car missing light gray window stripe, factory error.

	GD	VG	EXC	MT

(D) Same as (B), but lettering, stripes and numbers missing from one side of both units. M. Sabatelle Collection. **NRS**

8763 NORFOLK & WESTERN: GP-9; black-painted plastic body with white lettering; red overspray inside cab painted over 8666 Northern Pacific cab; frame riveted instead of spot-welded. Prototype displayed at 1978 Toy Fair. G. Halverson Collection. **NRS**

9111 NORFOLK & WESTERN: 1971, quad hopper.
(A) Dark red body; white lettering; less than 40 reportedly produced. Probable trial run. A. Otten Collection. — — — 125
(B) Tuscan body; white decal lettering; prototype; rare. C. Lang comment. **NRS**

9123 C & O: 1973, open-style automobile carrier.
(A) Three-tier yellow body; blue lettering; "BLT 1-73"; "C & O" on upper boards only; Symington-Wayne trucks; "BLT 1-73"; Type II box; only 10 in existence. Probable color sample. Made for the 1973 Toy Fair and offered as door prize at 1973 TCA convention. Barbret Collection. — — 400 —

(B) Two-tier medium blue body; no "C & O" road name; white lettering; "BLT 1-73", "9123" and "TRAILER TRAIN"; Symington-Wayne trucks; Type II box; only six made. Color sample. Made for the 1973 Toy Fair and offered as door prize at 1973 TCA convention. Barbret Collection. — — 600 —

MX 9145 AUTOLITE: 1972 apparent prototype of 9042 Autolite short O27 boxcar. The lettering on the left side of the car is hand-lettered with a brush and a rapidograph-type pen. There are guide lines visible for the lettering. The words "AUTOLITE/SPARK PLUGS" are somewhat larger than those on the production 9042. The car does not have "MPC" or "9040" series embossed on the end plates. The body is embossed "Part No. 100 4-3" on the inside. The technical data on the right is simulated by rough writing. There is no "LIONEL" or "BLT. 1-71". The "MX" lettering may indicate "MOTORCRAFT EXPERIMENTAL". Symington-Wayne trucks, one operating and one dummy coupler. R. DuBeau Collection. **NRS**

	GD	VG	EXC	MT

9200 ILLINOIS CENTRAL: Boxcar; unpainted orange Type VI body; "IC" close; open AAR trucks; metal door guides; pre-production sample. G. Halverson Collection. **NRS**

9202 SANTA FE: Boxcar; orange-painted orange body; black-painted black door; black lettering; Type I door guides; AAR trucks; prototype, one of 69. "Triple T" Collection.
— — 800 900

9207 SOO: Boxcar; Type VII body; Type I frame.
(A) White-painted sides; black-painted roof on white plastic body; red-painted red door; black lettering; metal door guides; Symington-Wayne trucks; pre-production sample, one of 24.
— — — 225
(B) Same as (A), but all-white-painted car.
— — — 225

9301 U. S. MAIL: Operating boxcar; stamped "9301" on one side and "9708" on the other. Probable color sample. J. Grzyboski Collection. **NRS**

9307 ERIE: 1979-80 animated gondola; unpainted turquoise gondola body; unpainted tan crate load; no lettering or numbering. Possible prototype. A. Otten Collection. **NRS**

9308 AQUARIUM CAR: 1981-83; unpainted and unlettered clear plastic. Probably a prototype. A. Otten Collection. **NRS**

9309 TOLEDO, PEORIA & WESTERN: 1980; red body, not usual orange with silver roof. Possible pre-production color sample. W. Eddins Collection. **NRS**

9536 through 9540 THE BLUE COMET: Passenger cars; about 200 factory production samples were discarded but retrieved by collectors. These were sold in quantity to a dealer who advertised and sold them to the public. Some of these cars were repainted with circus designs. D. Fleming comments.
(A) Unpainted blue plastic. **NRS**
(B) Dark blue-painted blue plastic. **NRS**
(C) Dark blue-painted blue plastic with white window stripe, no gold stripes on edges. **NRS**

9576 through 9580 BURLINGTON: Aluminum passenger cars; cars have Amtrak markings instead of normal Burlington. Possible set of pre-production samples. J. R. Hunt Collection. **NRS**

9700 SERIES: Boxcar; true number unknown; white Type IX body; white doors; no letters, numbers or other markings on either side. Probably an early production test sample. M. Sabatelle Collection. **NRS**

9700 SOUTHERN: Boxcar; tuscan-painted tuscan Type IX body; tuscan-painted tuscan doors; Symington-Wayne trucks; Type II box. Possible pre-production sample for 9711 Southern boxcar, which was produced in this color. Two examples examined and known to exist. J. LaVoie Collection. **NRS**

9701 BALTIMORE & OHIO: Double-door boxcar.
(A) Black-painted sides; silver roof painted on blue plastic; yellow-painted yellow doors; yellow lettering; Type II frame; 12 made.
— — 400 —

(B) Black sides and silver roof painted on gray plastic body; light blue-painted light blue doors; light blue lettering; Type II frame. Pre-production sample. **NRS**
(C) Deep blue-painted deep blue plastic body; black-painted black doors; yellow lettering, printed on only one side; Type II frame; 12 in existence. Probable color sample. Offered as door prize at 1973 TCA convention. R. M. Caplan and E. Barbret Collections. **NRS**

GD   VG   EXC   MT

(D) Unpainted blue plastic body; yellow lettering, one side blank. R. M. Caplan Collection.   **NRS**

9703 CP RAIL: Boxcar.
(A) Dark green-painted light green body; dark green-painted light green doors; black lettering; Type II frame; one side blank. One of five pre-production samples. Offered as door prize at 1973 TCA national convention. E. Barbret Collection.
— — — **600**

9705 DENVER & RIO GRANDE: Boxcar.
(A) Silver-painted gray Type IX plastic body; red-painted red doors; Type I frame; red lettering; "BLT 1-72"; 11 made. The doors were factory installed. Pre-production sample, used as a door prize at the 1973 TCA national convention. E. Barbret Collection.
— — **400** —

(B) Silver-painted Type IX gray plastic body; orange lettering; Type II frame; 10 made. Pre-production sample.
— — **500** —

9706 C & O: Boxcar; black-painted gray plastic body; black-painted door; yellow lettering; Type II frame; four pre-production samples known. Offered as a door prize at the 1973 TCA national convention. E. Barbret Collection.   — — **700** —

9708-9709 U. S. MAIL/BAR: Boxcar; same color scheme on both sides, but one side is lettered for 9708 U. S. Mail car and one side for 9709 BAR State of Maine car. Probable pre-production sample. R. M. Caplan Collection.   **NRS**

9783 BALTIMORE & OHIO: 1977-78, boxcar.
(A) Shell only with no lettering or decals. Reportedly 48 test shot prototypes were made. These were available from the factory as shells only, not as complete cars. G. Halverson Collection. **NRS**
(B) Missing lettering and logo. J. Wojnar Collection.   **NRS**

9802 MILLER HIGH LIFE: Standard O refrigerator car; gray plastic body; red doors and lettering; "BLT 1-73"; red plastic snap-on walkway; die-cast sprung trucks; disc-operating couplers; the "2" in 9802 is slightly higher than "980". Probable prototypes, five known to exist. Offered as door prizes at the 1973 TCA convention. E. Barbret Collection.   — — **700** —

9820 WABASH: 1973-74, Standard O gondola; gray body; white lettering; simulated coal load; Standard O die-cast sprung trucks; only two in existence. Pre-production sample, one offered as a door prize at 1973 TCA convention. E. Barbret Collection.
— — **800** —

9821 SOUTHERN PACIFIC: 1973-74, Standard O gondola; black body; white lettering; "BLT 1-73"; Southern Pacific decal; no brakewheel but hole for brakewheel; only three known. Pre-production sample. Offered as a door prize at the 1973 TCA national convention. E. Barbret Collection.
— — **800** —

9830 JOHNNIE WALKER: Favorite Spirits refrigerator car; possible pre-production sample; logo is less defined than regular production and differs in the following ways: hat is less black,

J. Wojnar Collection; B. Greenberg photograph

Comparison of 9783 boxcar — top car missing orange paint on door; bottom car missing lettering and logo.

GD   VG   EXC   MT

face is flesh-colored instead of gold, ascot and buttons are white instead of gold, top of cane is a mallet instead of a ball with loops, solid black pocket flap, white trim on boots instead of yellow, blue-shaded white pants, and trademark next to left foot. Reader comments invited. W. Cunningham Collection.   **NRS**

16323 LIONEL LINES: 1989, TOFC flatcar; one normally marked van; one lighter blue van with gold "LIONEL LINES" heat-stamped on one side and white "LIONEL LINES" stamped on the other; round Lionel logo missing on both sides; possible prototype. K. H. Miller Collection.   **NRS**

MCFARLAND SET: 1974, one-of-a-kind boxcar set made by Fundimensions to honor James P. McFarland, Chairman of the Board of General Mills, upon his retirement in 1974. This set, currently in the collection of J. A. Fisher, is a unique prototype set consisting of a single powered F-3 A-unit diesel, 12 classic-style boxcars, and an N5C caboose. The F-3 is decorated in yellow, silver and green very similar to the Rio Grande F-3 Service Station set engines also made that year. It is lettered in black "THE JAMES P. McFARLAND" and is dated "1934-1974", marking the years of McFarland's career at General Mills. Each boxcar is a different color and depicts the many different General Mills products made at various periods in his career there. The N5C illuminated caboose matches the engine and is numbered "1974-?". While this set is not, strictly speaking, a collectible because it is one-of-a-kind, we include it here as an interesting prototype set and a classic example of specially-made individual products Lionel has sometimes created. In fact, this set is believed to be the first factory-produced train set made to honor an individual. Regular readers will find a picture of this set on pp. 180-181 of the second edition of *Greenberg's Guide to Lionel Trains, 1970-1988*.

MCHAPTER 7ODERN ERA BOXE S

ROLLING STOCK BOXES

Sometimes, especially with early production, it is important to know which type of box Fundimensions used for its rolling stock. A case in point is the rather limited distribution in early 1971 of the 6560 Bucyrus-Erie crane car. The Fundimensions box itself commands a substantial premium because it is critical to identifying the car. (For the full story of this mixed-up piece, see *Greenberg's Guide to Lionel Trains, 1970-1991, Volume I.*) Sometimes Fundimensions simply packaged postwar leftover stock into the new firm's boxes, as it did with many accessories. Each type of box has several variations, and of course the boxes differ according to the size and shape of the product. Special boxes have been made for, among other items, the Walt Disney series and the Bicentennial products. However, there are only six basic types of modern era Lionel boxes for rolling stock, as follows:

TYPE I: This box was used from the beginning until some time in early 1972. Its basic color is white. Unlike its successors, it has no inner divider. It features a banner done in red and blue with the lettering, "A LIFETIME OF RAILROADING", in white. It is the only box type displaying the MPC rectangle logo. Larger boxes have a paste-on label across the right edge of the box front extending down the end flap; this label both pictures and describes the product. The product description is usually in red. The smaller boxes have no such label; instead, one or both ends may be rubber stamped with the product description. One side of the box is blue, the other red. The back of the box has an elaborate banner with a central rectangle containing "LIONEL" in a modern, red typeface. Recently, we have observed early Fundimensions production in plain white boxes. These are leftover boxes from postwar Hillside production in 1969.

TYPE II: The production of this box began some time in early 1972. Much plainer than its predecessor, it has an inner divider and is thus larger and more rigid. The front of the box is red with "LIONEL" in a modern, white typeface. The product description on the ends may be rubber-stamped on a glued label or printed in black directly on the box. For the first time, these descriptions have the prefix "6" in front of the number. Part of the sides and all of the back portray line drawings of various Lionel accessories and products in black. A variation of this box, notably those labeled "Specialty Cars", has a third place for a product description on the lower right front of the box. The lower left of this particular Type II box has small white letters, "For Ages 8 To Adult". (I. D. Smith comment.) Some recent steam locomotives have come in large boxes with a Type II decorating scheme.

TYPE III: This box, which was first produced some time in 1975, was still in use for rolling stock in the Traditional Series as late as 1986. Its basic color is white. The front has "LIONEL O AND O27 GAUGE" in a modern, red typeface. The box ends follow the same pattern. The product description is either printed in black directly onto the box ends or printed onto a white label which is then glued to the box. Some of the front and all of the box sides and ends feature color photos of Lionel rolling stock, accessories and other equipment.

TYPE IV: This box was first used in 1978 for limited production sets; it was superseded by Type V in 1983. It is the most plain of all the rolling stock boxes. Its basic color is gold. The front has a black scrollwork logo and the wording "LIONEL LIMITED EDITION SERIES" within a black oval. There are no markings on the sides or back at all. The product description is either printed in black directly on the box or printed on a gold label affixed to the box ends.

TYPE V: First produced in 1983, this box is in current use for Collector Series products. It is a recreation of the older postwar box with some modern refinements. The basic color of the box is bright orange, as was postwar Lionel's basic box. Atop the front of the box is "LIONEL ELECTRIC TRAINS" in a dark blue, Art Deco typeface between two blue stripes on a cream or white background. The sides and ends of the box follow the same design, and the back of the box features a recreation of the old postwar Lionel rectangular logo in blue, orange and white. Collectors feel that this is an exceptionally handsome box, recalling as it does the glory days of the old Lionel Corporation. The product description is printed in black on a glossy orange sticker which is affixed to the box flap and matches the box color.

TYPE VI: This box was introduced during the brief Kenner-Parker management period in 1986, but its main marketing has been by Lionel Trains, Inc. within the Traditional Series. It represents some important new marketing strategies. The front of the box is white with a large black band running across the top edge. Within the black band is the new red, blue, white, and black Lionel lettering and logo, and blue lettering "Big, Rugged Trains./A Tradition Since 1900." At the lower right of the cellophane window is a diagonal cardboard band overscored by a red stripe and underscored by a blue one with black lettering, "Made In America". Just below the window is red lettering "O And O27 Gauge Rolling Stock". The ends of the box follow the same scheme, and the product within the box is named by a white sticker with black lettering and a Uniform Pricing Code. The sides of the box show black drawings of Lionel accessories and rolling stock much like those on Type II boxes, but the rear of the box has an interesting product pitch. To the right, there is a black line drawing of a large Lionel layout, and to the left a father and son are shown playing with a set of trains (where have we seen this before?). Within a bold black vertical band is white lettering, "LIONEL TRAINS TO GROW UP/WITH, NOT OUT OF".

TYPE 1986P: A short-lived prototype of a new box style was shown at the 1986 Toy Fair. This box style never made it to production, and appears to have been converted to the Type VI box. This box was a basic orange, with the car-display cellophane occupying the left three-quarters of the box front. The right side was a white rectangle within which was the wording "O And O27 Gauge Rolling Stock", as well as an odd blue circle logo with what appears to be a General-type engine. The modern, red "LIONEL" lettering, as it later appeared on the Type VI box, is overstamped on the blue circle, with "since 1900" at the bottom. Across the top of the box in black is Lionel's catch-phrase "More Than A Toy — A Tradition, Since 1900". The sides and back advertised Lionel products, as did earlier boxes.

BOX DATES

Mr. Thomas Rollo, a Milwaukee collector who has made many significant contributions to our books, has deciphered the dating process used on many modern era, prewar and postwar Lionel boxes. This is important because it helps establish the date when a particular piece was issued. Sometimes variations in production occur which can be dated by the box dates. For example, it is quite possible to have two 9200 Illinois Central boxcars in the same style of box. Suppose one of them has the "I. C." spread apart in the black logo and the other has the "I. C." close together; this is a legitimate varia-

tion. Which one was produced first? The box dates may tell you the exact manufacturing sequence!

On many Type I and some Type II Fundimensions boxes, one of the small flaps has a symbol which looks like a clock face numbered from 1 to 12. Two digits are inside the circle of numbers. To date these boxes, look at the circle of numbers; one of them will usually be missing. Then read the first of the two numbers inside the clock. The inside number designates the last digit of the year, and the missing number of the clock numerals indicates the month. So, if the number "4" is missing from the clock face and the numerals inside the clock are "01", the box was made in April of 1970! The inside numerals of the Type I boxes will usually be "01" or "12". On some boxes, the die apparently broke, and there is only an indeterminate squiggle inside the clock. We believe that this represents 1972 production. The early Type II boxes may show the same type of clock face, usually with "23" or just "3".

Specific examples of this clock face dating from my own collection include a 9110 B & O hopper in a Type I box from August 1970, a 9161 Canadian National N5C caboose in a Type I box with a smashed die, probably made in February, July, or September of that year (three numbers are missing from the clock), and a 9214 Northern Pacific boxcar in a Type II box dated August 1972. This last example is revealing because the 9214 car was first made the year before; thus, my particular car is a late production model.

Some of the later boxes can be dated in a similar fashion. There are some Type II and Type III boxes which just have two numbers on the flap — a single digit and a double digit. The single digit is the month and the double digit the year. Other boxes feature a variation of the clock face. There is a circle of numbers surrounding a company logo "P" with a dot in its middle. Below the clock face is the word "MENTOR" and a two-digit number corresponding to the year. Thus, I have a 9213 Minneapolis & Saint Louis hopper car whose box was made in January or February 1977. This car was not produced until 1978, so it follows that you cannot always date the car by its box.

Unfortunately, not all boxes can be dated. The Type II, III and IV boxes marked "STURGIS DIVISION" have no discernible dating method. However, even some of the latest boxes have date marks. My 7522 New Orleans mint car shows evidence of an entirely new dating system. On the flap of this box, there is a row of numbers from "2" to "12" to the left of a corporate symbol. Below that are the numbers "85 86 87". This box must be read differently from the clock types. The missing number of the series "1" to "12" gives the month of manufacture, while the number immediately before the listed years gives the year. Thus, the box for the 7522 was made in January 1984, sometime before the car came out in June 1985, but corresponding to the date stamp on the car! This raises an interesting question: Was the car made and then stored away for a year and a half before it was issued to dealers? That is not a likely scenario, given modern era Lionel's distaste for warehousing. More likely, it indicates that a stupendous number of boxes were printed at one printing and not used until much later. Remember that the product inside the boxes is identified with a pressure-sensitive label, not printed on the box itself, in this case. My 5724 Pennsylvania bunk car has an entirely different dating system. Below the word

Six Lionel boxes
Top shelf: **Type I; Type II.**
Middle shelf: **Type III; Type IV.**
Bottom shelf: **Type V; Type VI.**

M. Solly Collection; B Greenberg photograph

"FEDERAL" are two small numbers. One is "83", which should be the year the box was made. Just below it in microscopic print is "10", which should be the month. There is also a part number: "705713200". The presence of "5713" in that part number indicates that this box was first designed for wood-sided refrigerator car 5713, a Cotton Belt refrigerator car first made in 1983. It was also designed to accommodate successive cars in that series. Apparently, only the later Type V boxes have been dated in this fashion.

As a point of interest, it should be noted that the brown corrugated boxes used to pack many prewar and postwar Lionel accessories and locomotives can be dated just as precisely. Every one of these boxes has a circular testing seal. Beneath this seal, you may find a single digit, a double digit, or the entire year printed. (In the case of the single digit, it is not too hard to deduce the decade of manufacture!) The month dating can be done in one of two ways. There may be a row of numbers from "1" to "12" printed around the disc. Let us assume that you see the numbers "5" through "12". In that case, the box was made in the month preceding the earliest digit; "4" would correspond to April. The other method uses a series of dots or stars around the circle on either side of the date. Count them, and you will have the month. Eight dots would mean that the month of manufacture was August. I have seen transformer boxes dated in this way as early as 1921. Thanks to this information, I also know that my 1038 transformer was made in April 1940, my 2046 locomotive in August 1950, and my ZW transformer in March of 1954.

Perhaps box dating is a relatively small matter for now. However, further research might uncover more information about the manufacturing process used by Lionel and its

modern era successors, and even tell us about actual production figures. For that reason, we hope that many of you will add your own observations to this relatively new field for subsequent editions.

Julian Dating of Lionel's Boxes
Data Supplied by James Tomczyk and Tom Rollo

Observers of Lionel's packing boxes may have noticed a five-digit set of numbers rubber stamped in black on both outer cartons and individual boxes of Lionel's production beginning about late 1979. This is a box industry dating system known as the Julian Dating System, and it will enable Lionel owners to date their products more accurately than they have ever been dated before. In fact, by using the Julian System, the collector can determine the exact day the item was packed into its box, in addition to the month and the year.

The system works like this: The first number is usually a "1". Some recent boxes have a "2" prefix, which we have speculated to mean production outside the Lionel factory, or perhaps second-shift production. In any case, it is of little significance to the dating process. The next three digits represent the day of the year, and the last number is the last number of the particular year. As a practical example, we have data about a Jersey Central Fairbanks-Morse locomotive box with the number "11346" rubber stamped in black. This means that the locomotive was packed into its box on the 134th day of 1986, or May 14, 1986.

How do we know that all cars were not packed into the box with the same number, and that this five-digit number does not signify something else? A simple comparison shows that this cannot be true. Jim Tomczyk's 6908 Pennsylvania N5C caboose has the number "11655" stamped onto its box flap. This means that his caboose was packed into its box on June 14, 1985. My 6908 box bears the number 11685, which means that it was packed on June 17, 1985, three days later.

The significance of this dating system is not to be underestimated by the collector. The Julian Dating System can tell the collector about the relative scarcity of variations within the production of a particular piece. For example, the author has a 16303 Pennsylvania TOFC flatcar with dull gold lettering on the trailers; this box bears the number "10517". This translates to February 20, 1987. Later production of this flatcar has gold lettering on the trailer which is much brighter. Which version is scarcer? By finding the Julian date which is earliest and the latest Julian date, then determining the latest Julian date of the first version and the earliest Julian date of the second version, the collector can actually estimate the relative percentage of production for each version — and that will determine scarcity, all other factors being equal.

This is one case where seeing is believing. In a visit to the Lionel factory in Mount Clemens, Michigan on July 8, 1987, I observed the new Rail Blazer sets being assembled and packaged on a production line. At the end of the line, an employee was putting the sets into their packing boxes for shipment. I also saw him rubber stamping a number on the boxes. Managing a closer look, I saw that the number was "11897" — July 8, 1987.

The Julian Dating System may open up a new area for research by collectors. We would welcome reaction from our readers, and we will report on their conclusions in our next edition. For now, we are grateful to James Tomczyk for his fine analysis of the system and to Tom Rollo for his explanation of the system's significance to the packaging industry.

To convert the Julian number to the date of the year, use the following chart. The number represents the cumulative number of days in the year at the end of the month:

January	February	March	April
31	*59*	*90*	*120*
May	**June**	**July**	**August**
151	*181*	*212*	*243*
September	**October**	**November**	**December**
273	*304*	*334*	*365*

L IONEL CLASSIC S

CHAPTER 8

O AND STANDARD GAUGE

By Louis A. Bohn

*T*he Lionel "Classics" are faithful reissues of the enamel-finished sheet metal and metal castings originally used to manufacture the pre-World War II trains. Lionel began making (or remaking!) these old favorites in 1988, reproducing both O Gauge and Standard Gauge trains. No new Lionel Standard Gauge had been seen since 1939. Thus far, the emphasis has been the "Classics Era," circa 1923 through 1940, which featured brightly colored enamels and bright brass and nickel accents. Some of the most desired and collectable items have been reproduced, and more are sure to follow as the public's requests increase. Most are limited production (short run), and a complete collection necessitates a generous budget; but even a few pieces add to a collection's significance.

Some collectors of Classics wish to preserve their originals, so they run these reissues. Or, when the originals are not available to purchase, the modern era Classics offer the opportunity to purchase a near-exact remake of one of the finest trains ever made. Other people may have used originals which have lost their former brightness, and a newer, lustrous Classics is just the thing for a memory trip to the "good old days."

One of the most fascinating elements of both the new and old passenger coaches made by Lionel is that their roofs hinge open, revealing wonderfully detailed interiors containing swiveling seats, washrooms and restrooms with operating doors.

Lionel has remade several pre-1923 items, including the 200 trolley and 201 trolley trailer which were originally manufactured from 1910 to 1913. The 13803 racing automobiles from 1912 and the No. 7 steam locomotive from 1910 have also been released.

It is hard to beat the sight and sound of a Standard Gauge 400E or O Gauge 263E Blue Comet heading a passenger train, rumbling along under a holiday tree. A few accessories and a sprinkling of brightly wrapped presents complete the scene, creating a timeless setting for new and old memories.

So far, the Standard Gauge Classics pieces have been numbered in the 13000-series, and the O Gauge Classics numbers have appeared in the 51000-series.

REMAKING THE CLASSICS

An Interview with Mike Wolf

On June 13, 1991, Greenberg Publishing Company (GPC) visited Mike Wolf (MW), owner of *Mike's Train House* in Columbia, Maryland. Mr. Wolf graciously shared his time and knowledge of Lionel Classics with our interviewer, Dwayne Lindsay. Mr. Wolf also lent us his collection for the beautiful color photographs found in this chapter.

Mike's expertise in the Standard Gauge market is a direct result of his years spent manufacturing reproductions of original Lionel Standard Gauge items. Those items were marketed through his business, *Mike's Train House*, until he terminated the manufacturing operation in 1987 to act as a consultant for the Lionel Classics Line.

GPC: Who made the decision to reintroduce the prewar "Classics" trains to the Lionel line?

MW: Richard Kughn. One probable reason is because he likes and collects prewar trains, and has amassed an immense collection over the years. Another reason could be that he saw a continued market for the Classics as a result of the success of the reproduction market.

GPC: Did Lionel determine the product feasibility through any special marketing studies, or did Kughn basically rely on his intuition and experience?

MW: Basically, I think Mr. Kughn relied on his intuition and careful study of the competition, like *Mike's Train House* and *T-Reproductions*. Those competitors' dealers were wholesaling their reproductions through Lionel's dealer network, thus providing Kughn with a precedent of success on which he was sure he could capitalize.

GPC: How have the sales compared with Lionel's projection?

MW: I think that the sales since 1989 are what Lionel had expected. But in 1988, the first year of the Classics, many dealers and consumers looked at certain pieces and some of the earlier sets as future collectibles. This got the speculators involved early and drove the production numbers way above what anybody expected. But since that first year, the market has realistically stabilized.

GPC: So, you're seeing these Classics being purchased by collectors for display, or by operators for their layouts, rather than by the guy who's buying eight of them at a time and putting them up in his attic?

MW: Right.

GPC: How and who makes the decisions on what is to be made or reproduced?

MW: Lionel has marketing meetings to determine what is to be made, and then presents that decision to management. It's kind of like a group decision: many options are suggested, and then the best ones are chosen.

GPC: Are any production decisions based on customer suggestions?

MW: Yes, the warranty cards included in each Classics box provide a fair amount of positive feedback to Lionel.

GPC: How do the production methods differ from what Lionel originally did, in terms of tooling, machinery, assembly procedures, things of that nature.

MW: Well, the production method of the stamped-steel, modern era Classics is basically the same as that of the prewar die-cast pieces. One slight difference is that the tooling has been made with much more precision. This precision allows the modern era Classics to fit together with closer tolerances than the prewar Lionel pieces. For example, the roofs on the new pieces fit better, whereas a prewar roof might pop off. And the cuts on the prewar pieces were a little wavy; the cuts today are straight and more perfected. But the production of the stamped steel is basically the same — it's pierced and then formed.

GPC: These changes are basically due to improvements in machinery since the 1920s, right?

MW: Right. The machinery that makes the trains has closer tolerance levels than machinery used in the 1920s, resulting in a much better fit between the various parts on the train.

GPC: Is any of the original tooling still being used?

MW: Not for modern era pieces. What little tooling wasn't destroyed for the war was used in the 1950s.

GPC: How is the new tooling made?

MW: Unlike the development of the original tooling, today's toolmakers have the luxury of computer-assisted design techniques which result in extremely accurate dies. Because many of the parts used in the Classics items are developed from wire-cutting machines, lathes and stamping presses, the accuracy of the parts quality is determined by how these machines are set up. Using the computerized techniques, the exact specifications are keyed into the machines via computer keyboard and every part is produced according to those specifications.

The specifications are determined ahead of time, when the designers develop the plans to the items using Computer Assisted Design (CAD) programs on personal computers. Essentially, this eliminates almost all human error that could occur using the old-fashioned method of tooling design.

GPC: Is Lionel still using the old paint formulas?

MW: Because the original paint formulas are no longer available, Lionel uses a computerized matching system to achieve the original color. This involves taking paint samples from an original production model piece and analyzing it via a computer. Obviously, the condition of the sample must be excellent or the color analysis will be affected.

GPC: Is Lionel still using the same paint application and drying methods?

MW: Yes and no. The earliest items produced by Lionel were dipped in paint rather than sprayed because spraying had not yet been developed. The items were then baked in a baking oven to harden the finish. Today's items are all spray-painted in water filtration paint booths which are virtually dust-free. This not only ensures a clean paint finish, but the runs and drips which are common on dipped items are non-existent.

GPC: Is it true that some of the pieces have been made in colors not used on the original pieces? If so, why was this done?

MW: This was done to offer the collector more options. For example, a collector may have all the 500-series freight cars. By producing the new cars in different colors from the original, the collector can now expand his set.

GPC: Regarding the prewar pieces, there's been a tendency over the years toward zinc rot, such as wheel decay and things of that nature. What has Lionel done to prevent this from happening to its modern era pieces, say, 50 years down the road?

MW: Back in the 1920s and '30s, and possibly as far back as 1910, Lionel cast aluminum, zinc and other metals in the same machines. During the last 20 years, it's been found that when you mix aluminum and zinc, over time they react against each other and cause "exploding" or rot. Now this is standard knowledge in the casting industry; it is taboo to even consider using the same machine for more than one metal type. Separate machines are now used for zinc, aluminum, and white metal.

Another thing collectors should realize is that not every early Lionel train will suffer from zinc rot. For example, the 385 frames usually remain in good condition, possibly because they were manufactured in a factory that just cast zinc parts. The problem parts were most likely cast by subcontracting factories that produced parts in a variety of metals.

GPC: What sort of improvements have been made to the motors and electrical systems? The early ones had a tendency to overheat.

13001 Freight Express Set, Standard Gauge.
Top shelf: **1318E electric locomotive.**
Middle shelf: **5130 flatcar; 5140 refrigerator.**
Bottom shelf: **5150 tank car; 5160 caboose.**

M. Wolf Collection; B. Schwab photograph

MW: Lionel has studied that problem extensively. The engineers have gone through the old motors and re-timed them for optimum performance. Keep in mind that the original products were toys, and weren't required to be as exact a science as Lionel tries to make them now. The modern era motors are timed right and the commutators are improved — Lionel wraps the wires around the commutators and crimps them together so that under heavy loads they won't melt the soldering at the wire leads.

GPC: Is the intent to offer exact reproductions of the original Lionel pieces, or is it merely to capture the spirit of them?

MW: Well, I think those two objectives are the same. The incredible thing that intrigues me personally is that the prewar Classics were designed as *toys*. It's phenomenal to think that some engineer or designer sat down at his table and designed that 400E — the details he came up with, and the amount of work that Lionel put into making the 400E with the State cars and all those swivel seats...it's amazing! It's unbelievable that Lionel invested that much time in it. This is the spirit of Classics. And today Lionel is trying to capture it

by keeping it like the original. There may be a market for pieces not like the original — and it's being looked at. But the goal is to achieve that same design scheme of the 1920s, '30s and '40s.

GPC: Has Lionel incorporated any spotting or production differences to help the collector differentiate between a prewar and a modern era Classic?

MW: Yes. All the Classics are marked "LTI", or "Lionel Trains, Inc." with the copyright. You'll find it on the frames, on the motors, on the tender floors and inside every casting. Lionel doesn't want to promote or pass off the Classics as original prewar items. They are what they are, and Lionel is very pleased and proud to offer them to the market.

GPC: Compared to some of the other present-day toy trains being made, such as the Reading T-1 for example, are Lionel Classics difficult or complex to produce; or are they much easier to produce than, say, the die-cast pieces?

MW: The Classics are much harder because of the hand assembly required to produce the items. While the tooling for the T-1 or other die-cast steamers is very complicated, once it is completed each casting is the same. Assembly is relatively

M. Wolf Collection; B. Schwab photog.

Standard Gauge
Top shelf: **13100 locomotive and tender (No. 1390E).**
Middle shelf: **13400 Railway Mail baggage car (323); 13401 Pullman (324).**
Bottom shelf: **13402 observation (325).**

simple because these items have few outside parts. But the assembly on the Classics is another process altogether. Careful attention must be paid in order to prevent scratches and other defects from appearing while attaching the extra detail. For example, the 400E boiler must be assembled to the cab, painted, and then trimmed with the appropriate pipes, steam domes and such. One slip, and the paint is ruined and everything must be disassembled.

GPC: Interesting. I would have thought it would be the other way around.

MW: Well, that idea is common among enthusiasts because people tend to look at the detailed die-cast boiler and cars and assume that the development of those pieces is highly complicated. However, when Lionel's O Gauge line fully developed after World War II, many of the die-cast products used common parts to ease the company in assembly and manufacturing. Whether one is trying to manufacture toy trains or automobiles, it is best to design common parts that fit on a variety of items to relieve the burden on the manufacturing process. To develop the tooling and engineering for a small market, like that of the Classics, is expensive and complicated.

GPC: How do you think Lionel technology compared to that of its competitors in the 1920s and '30s; and how did Lionel's technology compare to state-of-the-art technology in general for that time period, for that type of metal-working and production?

MW: The way I see it, Lionel's advanced technology in the 1920s and '30s enabled it to produce a high-quality product. People like high quality; it sells. While Lionel marketed those products at higher prices than the competition, the items were considered advanced in design and function. Despite their higher price, Lionel trains were considered "the toy" of this time period. This was undoubtedly the obvious result of the time Lionel spent to achieve its quality — just look at the lines! The engineers who designed Lionel trains always made them so realistic looking. A few American Flyer and Ives sets — like the Presidential Set and the Circus Train — are really exciting. But for the most part, Lionel's look has been always better because it had advanced state-of-the-art technology at its disposal. Simply put, Lionel's metal-working and production technology was some of the most advanced of its day.

GPC: Do you know if there's any plan to broaden the Classics line in the future? Lionel, of course, owns the rights

Standard Gauge
Top shelf: **13101 locomotive and tender (1384E).**
Middle shelf: **13300 gondola (No. 1512); 13600 cattle car (No. 1513).**
Bottom shelf: **13200 searchlight car (No. 1520); 13700 caboose (No. 1517).**

to use the Ives and American Flyer names. As we discussed, these companies made some Standard Gauge pieces and prewar O Gauge pieces that are considered quite desirable. Is there any chance that any of these may become part of the line for the future?

MW: As far as expanding, I think it's a possibility that both American Flyer and Ives could be included in the tinplate Classics line. However, what you'll see in Classics will be a very limited product line, consisting of only a few pieces a year. This is the best way to keep it a viable product line with a long life span in the Lionel product mix. There are die-hard collectors whose lives revolve around Standard Gauge tinplate trains, and if there wasn't a Classics line, I don't know what they'd do. It doesn't take long to own everything Lionel has ever made — Lionel didn't make but five steam engines in Standard Gauge, so it doesn't take long to acquire every variation. We get letters all the time from people who just love the idea of recapturing some of their childhood memories, expressing their nostalgia, or simply acknowledging their appreciation of these pieces. They want to see the Classics.

GPC: Lionel has released a few pieces in O Gauge, both in the tinplate style and in the later die-cast styles. Do you know of any plan to expand that production and perhaps get in a reissue of double O or similar?

MW: Yes. Consumers seem to want more scale-oriented trains. As a competitor, Lionel must concede and give the customers what they want. I think since Kughn has taken over, Lionel is becoming a much more competitive company. Lionel is looking at what the *consumer* wants rather than what Lionel wants. It takes time to make these changes, but Kughn promises they are coming. Look for them coming on strong in the next couple of years.

GPC: Has there been any thought given to producing starter sets or something like Lionel used to have with the Standard Gauge pieces, or maybe some of the smaller pieces, like the No. 8 locomotive with two passenger cars, perhaps to compete with the LGB Christmas market? Something for people who want more for their children than the O27 plastic, something of heirloom quality? Or maybe even to entice

M. Wolf Collection; B. Schwab photograph

13102 locomotive with 13403 State Car Set and 13407 Illinois coach, Standard Gauge.
Top shelf: **13102 electric locomotive (1381E).**
Second shelf: **13404 California coach (1412).**
Third shelf: **13405 Colorado coach (1413).**
Fourth shelf: **13407 Illinois coach (1414).**
Bottom shelf: **13406 New York observation (1416).**

M. Wolf Collection; B. Schwab photograph

13103 locomotive and 13408 Blue Comet Passenger Cars, Standard Gauge.
Top shelf: **13103 locomotive and tender (No. 1-400E).**
Second shelf: **(1420) Pullman.**
Third shelf: **(1421) Pullman.**
Bottom shelf: **(1422) observation.**

operators to Standard Gauge rather than O, and expand the market that way?

MW: It would be nice to make a $200 or $300 train set in Standard Gauge. But it's very expensive and labor intensive to make a tool and to make the train set. You can make 100,000 of them and can still only drive your cost down to a certain point. The comparison I like to use is that a Lionel train set has always been equivalent to two-weeks' pay of a middle-class salary. This holds true since the 1920s and '30s. In some cases — like the State sets — they were a month's pay. Lionel trains have always been expensive. And as we discussed earlier, the reason they're expensive is because of their high quality. I think it's impossible to make a Standard Gauge train set for $200 to $500. Even the competitors don't offer $200 tinplate sets because it's just not feasible from a cost standpoint.

GPC: You've provided us with some great information, Mike. It seems to me that collectors of the Classics have a lot to look forward to in the hobby. Thanks.

STANDARD GAUGE CLASSICS LISTINGS

	GD	VG	EXC	MT

7E: See 13104.
200: See 13900.
201: See 13901.
323: See 13400.
324: See 13401.
325: See 13402.
1-384E: See 13101.
1-400E: See 13103.
2-400E: See 13108.
1-408-E: See 13107.
1217: See 13702.

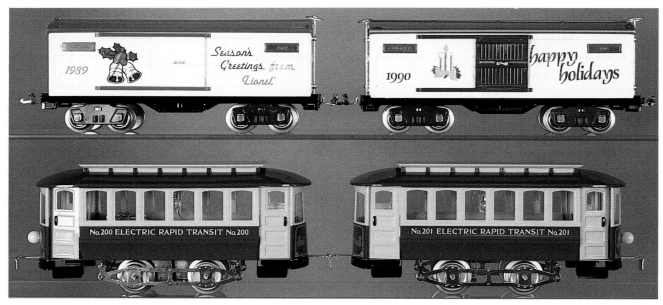

Standard Gauge

M. Wolf Collection; B. Schwab photograph

Top shelf: 13602 Christmas boxcar from 1989 (13601), erroneously catalogued as 13602; 13602 Season's Greetings boxcar from 1990.
Bottom shelf: 13900 trolley (No. 200); 13901 trailer (No. 201).

	GD	VG	EXC	MT

1381E: See 13102.

1390E: See 13100.

1423: See 13425.

1512: See 13300.

1513: See 13600.

1517: See 13700.

1520: See 13200.

13001 FREIGHT EXPRESS SET: 1990-91, 0-4-0 electric locomotive; green body, darker green roof; "1-318E" and "LIONEL"; black frame with Build-a-Loco motor; headlights reverse with direction; brass trim and nickel handrails; "5130" black flatcar with lumber load and nickel stakes; "5140" refrigerator car with ivory body, blue roof and brass trim, "LIONEL VENTILATED REFRIGERATOR" in black; "5150 SHELL" orange tank car with red decal and brass trim; "5160" caboose with red body, dark green roof, brass trim and operating light. All these 500-series cars have a black frame and nickel journals. Sold as a set only. **CP**

13002 FIREBALL EXPRESS SET: 1990, 2-4-2 steam locomotive and tender; bright red with maroon cab roof; "No. 2-390-E", catalogue number 13106; black frames; nickel trim, wheels, rods and journals; E-unit; Build-a-Loco motor; whistle; 13416 red "NEW JERSEY" "326" baggage car with maroon roof and cream inserts; matching 13417 "CONNECTICUT" "327" parlor car; matching 13418 "NEW YORK" "328" observation car. Brass steps and nickel journals on parlor and observation cars only, which are illuminated; "LIONEL LINES" and latch-style couplers on each piece. Sold as a set only. Shown only in 1989 Stocking Stuffers flyer. — — — **1100**

13100 LOCOMOTIVE AND TENDER: 1988, 2-4-2 steam locomotive and tender; black; "LIONEL LINES" and "No. 1390E"; brass and copper trim; nickel wheels, rods and journals; Build-a-Loco motor; operating headlight and whistle; E-unit; operates on

10 to 20 volts AC; 23-1/4" long. Shown in Lionel Classics flyer with 13400 baggage, 13401 Pullman and 13402 observation, but sold separately — see those listings in this section for more detail. — — — **550**

13101 LOCOMOTIVE AND TENDER: 1989, 2-4-0 steam locomotive and tender; two-tone gray body; blue-gray frame; maroon running board edge; "1-384E" and "LIONEL LINES"; nickel trim; operating headlight and whistle; Build-a-Loco motor; E-unit; operates on 10 to 20 volts AC; 22-1/2" long. Shown in flyer with 13200 searchlight, 13300 gondola, 13600 cattle car, and 13700 caboose, but sold separately — see those listings in this section for more detail. — — — **590**

13102 LOCOMOTIVE: 1989, 4-4-4 electric locomotive; state green body; light green edge accent; black frame; "1381E"; brass, copper and nickel trim; Build-a-Loco motor; operating headlights; red and green end marker lights; weighted for increased traction; working pantographs; E-unit; operates on 14 to 20 volts AC; 18-5/8" long. Shown only in flyer; matches 13403 State Car set and 13407 coach, but sold separately — see those listings in this section for more detail. Copy also sold by Mike's Train House and Williams Reproductions, circa 1981 and 1983. — — — **800**

13103 BLUE COMET: 1990, 4-4-4 locomotive and tender; two-tone Blue Comet blue; "No. 1-400E" on locomotive; "LIONEL LINES" on tender; nickel trim, wheels, rods and journals; red pilot and wheels spokes; firebox glow; Build-a-Loco motor; E-unit reverse; headlight; operates on 14 to 20 volts AC; 31" long. A remake of one of the most famous Lionel sets of all time — the Blue Comet. Shown in catalogue with 13408 Blue Comet passenger car set, but sold separately — see listing 13408 in this section for more detail. — — — **1300**

13104 OLD NO. 7: 1990, 4-4-0 steam locomotive and tender; polished brass; nickel trim and red edge stripe; "No. 7E" on locomotive; "LIONEL LINES" on tender; red pilot and drive

51001 Lionel Lines #44 Freight Special Set, O Gauge
Top shelf: 44E electric locomotive.
Middle shelf: 51500 hopper (8816); 51400 boxcar (8814).
Bottom shelf: 51800 searchlight car (8820); 51700 caboose (8817).

M. Wolf Collection; B. Schwab photograph

	GD	VG	EXC	MT

wheels; wood yoke; operating headlight; reversing unit; combination latch coupler on tender; operates on 10 to 20 volts AC; 23-1/2" long. Shown in catalogue with 13412 passenger car set, but sold separately — see listing 13412 in this section for more detail. Reissue of Standard Gauge locomotive from 1910.

	—	—	—	**800**

13106 LOCOMOTIVE AND TENDER: See 13002.

13107 LOCOMOTIVE: 1991, 0-4-4-0 electric locomotive; State brown body; dark brown roof; black frame; "1-408-E"; brass and nickel trim; dual Build-a-Loco motors; automatic reversing unit; directional headlights; red and green marker lights; operating pantographs; 17" long. Intended for use with 13420 State Car set, but sold separately — see listing 13420 in this section for more detail. Copy also sold by Williams Reproductions and Mike's Train House, circa 1975, 1980 and 1983. Remake of the 1928 engine that headed the famous "State Set." **CP**

13108 LOCOMOTIVE AND TENDER: 1991, 4-4-4 steam locomotive and tender; black; "2-400E"; nickel trim, wheels, rods and journals; red firebox glow; Build-a-Loco motor; whistle; headlight; E-unit reverse; Vanderbilt oil tender with six-wheel trucks; operates on 14 to 20 volts AC; 31" long. Shown in catalogue with 13702 caboose, but sold separately — see listing 13702 in this section for more detail. Copy also sold by Mike's Train House,

circa 1987. Remake of Standard Gauge 400E from 1931, one of the largest engines made by prewar Lionel. **CP**

13200 SEARCHLIGHT CAR: 1989, operating dual searchlight car with control switch; black frame; white "LIONEL LINES No. 1520"; nickel trim and journals; 11-1/2" long. Intended to be pulled by 13101 locomotive; shown in flyer with and matches 13101, 13300, 13600 and 13700, but sold separately.

	—	—	—	**145**

13300 GONDOLA: 1989, gondola; yellow body; black frame; "No. 1512"; nickel trim and journals; 11-1/2" long. Intended to be pulled by 13101 locomotive; shown in flyer with and matches 13101, 13200, 13600 and 13700, but sold separately.

	—	—	—	**102**

13400 BAGGAGE CAR: 1988, "RAILWAY MAIL"; red roof and body; cream inserts; "323"; brass steps; nickel journals; opening doors; illuminated; latch-style couplers; 13-1/4" long. Intended to be pulled by 13100 locomotive; shown in 1988 Classics flyer with and matches 13100, 13401 and 13402, but sold separately.

	—	—	—	**200**

13401 PULLMAN CAR: 1988, "PULLMAN"; red roof and body; cream inserts; "324"; brass steps; nickel journals; opening doors; illuminated; 13-1/4" long. Intended to be pulled by 13100

51004 Blue Comet Set, O Gauge
Top shelf: **1-263E locomotive and tender.**
Middle shelf: **1612 Pullman; 1614 Lionel Lines baggage car.**
Bottom shelf: **1615 observation; 1613 Pullman.**

M. Wolf Collection; B. Schwab photog

	GD	VG	EXC	MT

locomotive; shown in 1988 Classics flyer with and matches 13100, 13400 and 13402, but sold separately. — — — **200**

13402 OBSERVATION: 1988, "OBSERVATION"; red roof and body; cream inserts; "325"; brass steps and end platform; nickel journals; opening doors; illuminated; 13-1/4" long. Intended to be pulled by 13100 locomotive; shown in 1988 Classics flyer with and matches 13100, 13400 and 13401, but sold separately.
— — — **200**

13403 STATE CAR SET: 1989; consists of 13404 "CALIFOR-NIA" coach "1412", 13405 "COLORADO" coach "1413", and 13406 "NEW YORK" observation "1416". All cars feature State green bodies; cream window inserts; "LIONEL LINES"; brass nameplates, handrails, steps, end platforms, journals and air tank ends; opening doors and roofs; detailed interior with swivel seats; two washrooms; illuminated; 22" long. Matches 13102 locomotive and 13407 coach, but sold separately. Copy also sold by Williams Reproductions, circa 1980. — — — **2000**

13404: See 13403.

13405: See 13403.

13406: See 13403.

13407 ILLINOIS COACH: 1990, "ILLINOIS 1414"; additional car for above set. Shown only in 1989 Stocking Stuffers flyer;

matches 13102 locomotive and 13403 State Car set, but sold separately. Also sold by Mike's Train House and Williams Reproductions, circa 1981 and 1983. — — — **575**

13408 BLUE COMET PASSENGER CARS: 1990; consists of "1420 FAYE" Pullman, "1421 WESTPHAL" Pullman, and "1422 TEMPEL" observation. All feature two-tone Blue Comet blue bodies; cream window inserts; nickel trim and nameplates; six-wheel trucks with nickel journals; opening doors and roofs; detailed interior with swivel seats; two washrooms; illuminated. Shown with and matches 13103 locomotive, but sold as a set only. Remake of original prewar Blue Comet cars from the 1930s.
NRS

13412 PASSENGER CAR SET: 1990; consists of 13413 combination "PARLOR CAR" and "BAGGAGE" "183", 17-7/8" long; 13414 "PARLOR CAR" "184", 16" long; and 13415 "OBSERVATION CAR" "185", 17-7/8" long. All cars feature cream bodies; orange roofs; brass steps, trim and seats; frosted clerestory windows; opening doors; combination couplers; nickel trucks; wood air tanks; all pieces are lighted. Shown in catalogue and matches 13104 locomotive, but sold separately. The original cars first appeared in 1906. — — — **800**

13413: See 13412.

Back: **13802** runabout boat.
Front: **13805** boat (1-44).

M. Wolf Collection; B. Schwab photograph

	GD	VG	EXC	MT

13414: See 13412.

13415: See 13412.

13416: See 13002.

13417: See 13002.

13418: See 13002.

13420 STATE CAR SET: 1991; consists of "1412 CALIFORNIA" coach, "1413 COLORADO" coach, and "1416 NEW YORK" observation. All have brown bodies; dark brown roofs; cream window inserts; brass trim, steps and journals; opening doors and roofs; detailed interior with swivel seats; two washrooms; illuminated; 21" long. Matches 13107 locomotive, but sold separately. Copy also sold by Mike's Train House and Williams Reproductions, circa 1981 and 1983. Modern remake of 1929 "State Set." **CP**

13425 BLUE COMET PASSENGER CAR: 1991; two-tone blue; cream windows; black "BARNARD" and "1423" on car; nickel trim and journals; illuminated; detailed interior; swivel seats, two washrooms; 12" long. Made to match Blue Comet train. Offered in 1991 Stocking Stuffers flyer. **CP**

13600 CATTLE CAR: 1989; white body; blue roof; "No. 1513"; nickel trim and journals; sliding doors; 11-1/2" long. Intended to be pulled by 13101 locomotive; shown in flyer with and matches 13101, 13200, 13300 and 13700, but sold separately. — — — **120**

13602 CHRISTMAS BOXCAR: 1989; ivory body; red roof; "13601" and "1989" on car; brass trim; nickel journals; "Seasons/Greetings from/Lionel" with holly and bells decoration; 11-1/4" long. Erroneously listed in Holiday Collection flyer as 13602. — — — **100**

13602 SEASON'S GREETINGS BOXCAR: 1990; white body; gold roof; green door and door guides; "13602" and "1990" on car; brass trim; nickel journals; "happy holidays" with candle decoration; 11-1/4" long. Shown only in 1990 Stocking Stuffer flyer. — — — **170**

13604 SEASON'S GREETINGS BOXCAR: 1991, holiday boxcar; blue "Season's Greetings"; green "1991"; red "13604"; white body; red roof; brass-colored door; brass trim; nickel journals; decorated with candy canes, toy soldiers and a toy train on side; 12-1/4" long. Offered in 1991 Stocking Stuffers flyer. **CP**

13700 CABOOSE: 1989, red body; black frame; "No. 1517"; nickel trim and journals; illuminated platforms; 11-1/2" long. Intended to be pulled by 13101 locomotive; shown in flyer with and matches 13101, 13200, 13300 and 13600, but sold separately. — — — **138**

13702 CABOOSE: 1991; red body; black frame; "1217"; nickel trim; illuminated platforms; latch coupler; 12-1/2" long. Shown in catalogue with 13108 locomotive, but sold separately. Remake of prewar 200-series caboose. **CP**

13900 TROLLEY: 1989; blue and yellow body; "No. 200" and "ELECTRIC RAPID TRANSIT" on side; nickel truck frame and wheels; illuminated interior; operating headlight; opening doors; original style motor; E-unit; long hook coupler; operates on 8 to 12 volts AC. — — — **315**

13901 TRAILER: 1989; same as 13900 except no E-unit reverse or motor; "No. 201" and "ELECTRIC RAPID TRANSIT" on side. — — — **210**

19400: See 51701.

478039: See 51702.

13803 racing automobiles set.

M. Wolf Collection; B. Schwab photograph

	GD	VG	EXC	MT

O GAUGE CLASSICS LISTINGS

	GD	VG	EXC	MT

51000 HIAWATHA SET: 1988; "350-E" steam 4-4-2 locomotive and 350WX six-wheel tender; whistle and nickel trim; black roof; gray boiler; orange lower skirt, cab and car sides; maroon underbelly; lettered for Milwaukee Road and Lionel Lines; requires O72 curved track; "882" front coach with head end and lighted vestibule; "883" middle coach with lighted vestibule; "884" observation with boat tail, illuminated. Overall length nearly 6'. Sold as a set only. Copy also sold by Mike's Train House, Pride Lines and Williams Reproductions, circa 1988. This was LTI's first entry into the recreation of the prewar Classics.

— — — **900**

51001 #44 FREIGHT SPECIAL SET: 1989; electric 0-4-0 locomotive; orange body; "44E" and "LIONEL"; nickel trim; reversing headlights; original style motor; latch couplers; 51400 boxcar "8814" with cream body and doors, brown sides and ends, black frame, and nickel trim; 51500 hopper car "8816", black with nickel trim; 51800 searchlight car "8820", black with nickel trim, and lights with switch; 51700 caboose "8817", red with nickel trim and black frame. These cars have early box-style couplers, have "LIONEL LINES" on body, and are reproductions of the prewar 800-series cars. Sold as a set only. — — — **725**

51004 BLUE COMET SET: 1991; 2-4-2 steam locomotive and oil tender; two-tone blue; "1-263E"; E-unit reverse; headlight; firebox glow; consisted of "1612 PULLMAN"; "1613 PULLMAN"; "1614 LIONEL LINES" baggage car with doors that open; "1615

OBSERVATION", two-tone blue with cream inserts, nickel trim and journals. Cars have removable roofs and are illuminated. Set is 66" long. Sold as a set only. The original O Gauge "Baby Blue Comet" set was made between 1936 and 1939. **CP**

51201 RAIL CHIEF CAR SET: 1990; consists of 51202 combination car "892" with head end and lighted vestibules; 51203 coach "893" with lighted vestibules; 51204 coach "894" with lighted vestibules; 51205 observation car "895" with boat tail and lighted vestibules, maroon roof, red sides and underbelly; "LIONEL LINES" in black with car numbers under windows. Heavy metal construction. Four cars are about 5' long. A uniquely designed streamlined passenger train in which the vestibules actually ride on the trucks and the car bodies rest between them. The car bodies are a tight-tolerance fit to the vestibule piece, which is decorated the same way. The total effect is one of a single five-foot-long tubular car. Shown in catalogue with 18005 1-700E Hudson locomotive on O72 track, but sold separately. Copy also sold by Mike's Train House, Pride Lines and Williams Reproductions, circa 1988. Remake of prewar Rail Chief cars from 1937.

— — — **770**

51202: See 51201.
51203: See 51201.
51204: See 51201.
51205: See 51201.
51400: See 51001.
51500: See 51001.
51700: See 51001.
51800: See 51001.

51900 signal bridge and control panel.

M. Wolf Collection; B. Schwab photograph

ACCESSORIES LISTINGS

	GD	VG	EXC	MT

13800 PASSENGER STATION 1115: 1988; "LIONEL CITY"; red and cream; aluminum bulb sockets; original style train control; skylight; opening doors; illuminated. For O, Standard or G Gauges. — — — 195

13801 LIONELVILLE STATION 126: 1989; "LIONEL-VILLE"; cream walls; green roof and trim; mojave base and inserts; brass nameplates; size 10-1/8" L x 7-1/8" W x 7-1/4" H. — — — 100

13802 RUNABOUT BOAT: 1990; reproduction of No. 45; key-wound spring motor; cream body; red underhull; deck switch; adjustable rudder; two figures; two keys; opening hatches; 17" long. — — — 470

13803 RACING AUTOMOBILES: 1991; consists of two 1912-style cars, one orange with "9" on front, and one red with "8" on front; nickel trim; two figures in each; start/finish line banner; eight-piece inner and outer loop track sections, green and nickel; powered with AC transformer or proper DC power supply. Sold as a set only. **CP**

	GD	VG	EXC	MT

13804 TOWER: 1991; red base and doors; cream walls; orange roof; pea green windows; dark floor line; illuminated; 10-1/8" L x 8-7/8" W. Reissue of prewar No. 437 switch tower. For O and Standard Gauges. **CP**

13805 BOAT 1-44: 1991; "1-44"; key-wound spring motor; aluminum engine; brown deck; cream hull; green underhull; deck switch; adjustable rudder; two figures; 17" long. **CP**

13807 RACING STRAIGHT TRACK: 1991; extra section, for use with Racing Automobiles. **CP**

13808 RACING INNER RADIUS CURVE TRACK: 1991; extra section, for use with Racing Automobiles. **CP**

13809 RACING OUTER RADIUS CURVE TRACK: 1991; extra section, for use with Racing Automobiles. **CP**

51900 SIGNAL BRIDGE AND CONTROL PANEL: 1989; reincarnation of 440N from 1932 era. Consists of two-head signal bridge; red base and deck; black mounting panel, bridge and signals; brass trim; control panel with switches and "PANEL BOARD/No. 4400 C"; light and simulated meters. Bridge is 21" L x 5" W x 14-1/2" H; control panel is 7" L x 3-1/4" W x 8-1/2" H. Suitable for O and Standard Gauges. — — — 300

L ARGE SCAL E

• CHAPTER 9 •

L. Caponi Collection; B. Schwab photograph

81002 Frontier Freight Set
Top shelf: 85104 Santa Fe locomotive (5104).
Middle shelf: 87502 A.T. & S.F. flatcar (7502).
Bottom shelf: 87704 Santa Fe caboose (7704).

By Louis A. Bohn

Large Scale model trains originated in Europe in 1968 with the Lehmann Gross Bahn (LGB) company of Nürnberg, Germany. These rugged, over-sized, weatherproof trains, based upon one-meter Narrow Gauge, were modeled after the trains found in the mountains of Austria, Germany and Switzerland. LGB originally called this size "G Gauge," which has been interpreted to mean *Gross* (which means large in German) and *Garden* (because the layouts were often built outside in one's yard). Eventually, sales in the United States of LGB trains prompted it to offer a few American-style items for sale in the states and in Europe to collectors of United States railroad models. Lionel realized the market potential and began producing its own version of American-like G Gauge locomotives and cars in 1987, using the same track gauge, but incorporating knuckle couplers instead of the European hook-and-loop couplers. Lionel applied the term Large Scale to its trains.

Large Scale trains are approximately the same size as the cherished Standard Gauge, with several distinct advantages. They are non-rusting. The track rails are brass with plastic ties. The locomotives and rolling stock are high-grade plastic, brass and stainless steel, and are designed to shed rain. Motors are enclosed, so they can be run in rain or light snow! Great detail is molded into them, compared with their steel predecessors or their O Gauge counterparts, and the size makes elaborate decoration possible. DC power at about six to 18 volts provides more precise control. And since they are not metal, the cost of Large Scale items is much less than Standard Gauge. A whole new world of garden railways is blossoming. In fact, some say that Large Scale is the fastest growing gauge today in all of model railroading.

Lionel Large Scale offers models prototypical of older Narrow Gauge wood-style and more modern steel-style items. This choice includes small locomotives and sets suitable for holiday enjoyment or for short trains on large layouts. Lionel

L. Caponi Collection; B. Schwab photograph

81004 North Pole Railroad Set
Top shelf: **85114 locomotive (5114).**
Middle shelf: **87508 flatcar (7508) (packages not shown).**
Bottom shelf: **87716 caboose (7716).**

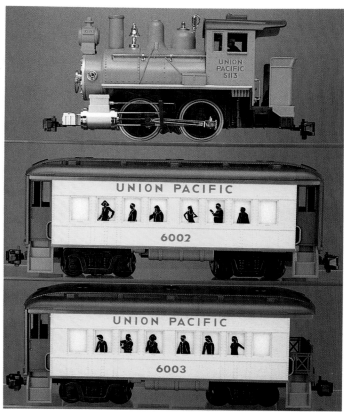

L. Caponi Collection; B. Schwab photograph

81006 Union Pacific Limited Set
Top shelf: **85113 locomotive (5113).**
Middle shelf: **86002 coach (6002).**
Bottom shelf: **86003 observation (6003).**

also produced the superb larger 4-4-2 Atlantic steamers and the two-motored GP-7 and GP-9 diesels for hauling long trains. In 1990, RailSounds was introduced and included with the magnificent Pennsylvania Railroad E6 Atlantic steamer and the General Purpose (GP) diesels. Because Large Scale items are of recent production, few appear used for resale, and a collection is possible at modest cost. The RailSounds items are most desirable, with the E6 Atlantic already disappearing from sales lists.

In regards to the DC power needed, the small 12 va (volt-ampere) power pack is adequate for the boxed sets, but not for the larger locomotives hauling long trains, especially large illuminated passenger cars. They experience drag caused by the electric collectors. Representative power required is charted below:

LOCOMOTIVE	LOCO ONLY	LOCO & 3 CARS	LONGER TRAIN
0-4-0 Steamer	400 ma	600 ma	—
0-4-0 Handcar	350 ma	—	—
0-6-0 Steamer	500 ma	1000 ma	1200 ma
4-4-2 Atlantic	600 ma	800 ma	1500 ma
4-4 GP 2-motor diesel	800 ma	1200 ma	1800 ma
4-4 GP 4-motor diesel	1600 ma	2400 ma	3600 ma

The No. 4060 power pack is rated at 12 va and will deliver 1200 ma (milliampere) maximum at 10 volts (slow moving train). At 15 volts, only 800 ma is available (faster or heavier train). Beyond there, the circuit breaker will open. More power can be obtained with the use of a larger AC-transformer such as a Lionel V or ZW, along with a full-wave bridge rectifier to convert AC to DC and a DPDT reversing switch. These are available from electronic supply houses such as Radio Shack. Lionel has also announced a new product that will perform this function. Remember, AC power will destroy DC motors.

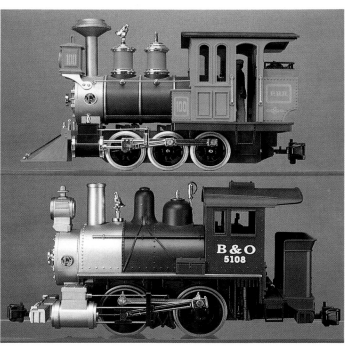

L. Caponi Collection; B. Schwab photograph

Top shelf: **85100 P.R.R. locomotive (100).**
Bottom shelf: **85108 B & O locomotive (5108).**

LARGE SCALE LISTINGS

> **Note:** *All Lionel Large Scale steam engines come with a black and gold "Lionel Large Scale" emblem prominently displayed. All Large Scale cars have two operating knuckle couplers and two-axle trucks, for a total of eight wheels. Bobber cabooses have two axles for a total of four wheels.*

3: See 81007.
100: See 85100.
700: See 87700.
2003: See 85003.
5000: See 85000.
5001: See 85001.
5102: See 85102.
5103: See 85103.
5106: See 85106.
5107: See 85107.
5108: See 85108.
5109: See 85109.
5110: See 85110.
7400: See 87400.
7402: See 87402.

	GD	VG	EXC	MT

7403: See 87403.
7405: See 87405.
7406: See 87406.
7407: See 87407.
7500: See 87500.
7501: See 87501.
7503: See 87503.
7504: See 87504.
7702: See 87702.
7703: See 87703.
7705: See 87705.
7706: See 87706.
7707: See 87707.
7708: See 87708.
7713: See 87713.
7800: See 87800.

55000 LIONEL LINES RAILSCOPE: 1988-90, steam 0-4-0 tank locomotive; slate and dark gray; white "LIONEL LINES/5000" on cab; headlight; DC can motor; fuel box with short straight stack. Contains miniature black and white television camera that can be viewed through any television receiver. Picture is transmitted whether locomotive is moving or stopped. Includes stack of lumber containing receiver, hook-up cable, matching transformer, two inductors and a capacitor; 13-5/8" long.
— — — **285**

81000 GOLD RUSH SPECIAL SET: 1987-90; 85101 D. & R.G. 0-6-0 steam locomotive with tuscan cab, metallic blue and black body, red headlight and pilot, gold lettering and trim, "101" on cab, fuel box behind cab, flared stack, brass wheel tires, headlight, DC can motor, 11-5/8" long, pictured in 1987 flyer and then in catalogue; 87401 Narrow Gauge wood-style gondola with tuscan body, black deck, white "401" on car, 11-1/2" long; 87701 Narrow Gauge wood-style caboose, red body with black roofwalks, white "DENVER & RIO GRANDE" and "701", sliding side door, illuminated by either two D-cell batteries (1987-90) or track-powered (1989-90); 12 curved tracks; lockon with wires; 64060 12VA AC-DC power pack; engineer figure.
— — — **80**

81001 THUNDER MOUNTAIN EXPRESS SET: 1988-89, Pennsylvania; 85105 0-4-0 tank steam locomotive with tuscan body, black boiler front and pilot, gold trim and "5105" on cab, fuel box, tall straight stack, headlight, DC can motor, 13-5/8" long; 86000 passenger coach with tuscan body and black roof, gold stripe and lettering, "6000" on car, passenger silhouettes in windows, illuminated; 86001 passenger observation with tuscan body and black roof, gold stripe and lettering, "6001" on car, passenger silhouettes in windows, illuminated; 12 curved tracks; lockon with wires; 64060 12 va AC-DC power pack; engineer, fireman and conductor figures.
— — — **185**

81002 FRONTIER FREIGHT SET: 1988-89; 85104 0-4-0 tank steam locomotive with red body, aluminum boiler front and pilot, white "Santa Fe" and "5104" on cab, fuel box, DC can motor, 13-5/8" long; 87502 Narrow Gauge wood-style flatcar with 10 stakes, black deck, white "A.T. & S.F." and "7502", 11-1/2" long; 87704 wood-style bobber caboose with red body and black roofwalks, yellow "Santa Fe" herald and "7704", not illuminated,

Top shelf: **85000 Seaboard GP-9 (5000).**
Bottom shelf: **85001 Conrail GP-7 (5001).**

L. Caponi Collection; B. Schwab photograph

GD VG EXC MT

12-1/4" long; 12 curved tracks; lockon with wires; 64060 12 va AC-DC power pack; engineer and fireman figures.

— — — 135

81003 GREAT NORTHERN SET: 1990.

Not Manufactured

81004 NORTH POLE RAILROAD SET: 1989-91, Merry Christmas Lines; 85114 0-4-0 tank steam locomotive with aluminum and green body, black undercarriage, lettered "North Pole R.R.", "5114" on headlight, fuel box, tall straight stack, headlight, DC can motor, 13-5/8" long; 87508 Narrow Gauge wood-style flatcar with 10 blue stakes and a white deck, six packages and three bows, with red "N.P. 7508" and "Merry Christmas Lines", 11-1/2" long; 87716 wood-style bobber caboose with red body and cupola, aluminum roof and black roofwalks, gold "Merry Christmas" and "7716", black "NORTH POLE R.R.", 12-1/4" long; 12 curved tracks; lockon with wires; 64060 12 va AC-DC power pack; Santa engineer figure. 1989 issue had loose tires which caused the locomotive to topple over on curves, easily fixed. An aluminum and red steam locomotive was announced for 1991, but not produced; excess stock of aluminum and green locomotives was shipped instead. **CP**

81006 UNION PACIFIC LIMITED SET: 1990-91; 85113 0-4-0 tank steam locomotive with aluminum boiler front, gray boiler and cab, black undercarriage, red "UNION PACIFIC" and "5113" on cab, headlight, fuel box, tall straight stack, DC can motor, 13-5/8" long; 86002 passenger coach with yellow sides, gray roof and red trim, red "UNION PACIFIC" and "6002", passenger silhouettes in windows, illuminated; 86003 passenger observation with yellow sides, gray roof and red trim, red "UNION PACIFIC" and "6003", passenger silhouettes in windows, illuminated; 12 curved and four straight track; lockon with wires; 64060 12 va AC-DC power pack; engineer, fireman and conductor figures. **CP**

81007 DISNEY MAGIC EXPRESS SET: 1990; Disneyland 35th Anniversary; 0-6-0 steam locomotive with black boiler front and undercarriage, green boiler and fuel box, red pilot and cab,

GD VG EXC MT

white "3" on sand dome and boiler front, white "DRR" logo, multicolor "Disneyland/35/YEARS OF MAGIC" herald, fuel box, brass accents, flared stack, headlight, DC can motor, puffing smoke; 87404 Narrow Gauge wood-style gondola with blue and green body, yellow "404" and multicolor "Disneyland/35/YEARS OF MAGIC" herald; 87709 Narrow Gauge wood-style caboose with red body and roof, green roofwalks, yellow "709" and multicolor "Disneyland/35/YEARS OF MAGIC" herald, sliding side door, illuminated, 10-1/4" long; 12 curved tracks; lockon with wires; 64060 12 va AC-DC power pack; Mickey Mouse engineer and Donald Duck conductor figures. Heralds issued differently than shown in catalogue. — — — 250

81008 WALT DISNEY WORLD SET: Announced in 1991, but not manufactured. **Not Manufactured**

85000 SEABOARD SYSTEMS: 1990-91, GP-9 diesel with RailSounds; gray body; white edge stripe; red and orange Seaboard logo; white "5000" on cab; front and rear directional headlights; cab light; detailed cab interior with engineer; two DC can motors; electronic horn, clanging bell and engine roar; trigger button; operating couplers; 21-1/2" long.
(A) 1990; as described above. — — — 340
(B) 1991; volume control added. **CP**

85001 CONRAIL: 1990-91, GP-7 diesel with RailSounds; blue body; white "CONRAIL" and "5001"; front and rear directional headlights; cab light; detailed cab interior with engineer; two DC can motors; electronic horn, clanging bell and engine roar; trigger button; operating couplers; 21-1/2" long.
(A) 1990; as described above. — — — 340
(B) 1991; volume control added. **CP**

85003 BURLINGTON NORTHERN: 1991, GP-20; green chassis and lower body; black upper body; white "BUR-LINGTON/NORTHERN", "BN" logo, and "2003"; diesel RailSounds; all-wheel drive; four heavy-duty DC motors; volume control; illuminated markers and cab; directional headlights; comes with cab engineer figure. **CP**

L. Caponi Collection; B. Schwab photograph

Top shelf: **85106 Chessie System locomotive (5106) and tender.**
Middle shelf: **85107 Great Northern locomotive (5107) and tender.**
Bottom shelf: **85110 Pennsylvania locomotive (5110) and tender.**

	GD	VG	EXC	MT

85100 P.R.R.: 1987, 0-6-0 steam locomotive; two-tone green, metallic blue, and black; gold "100" and "P.R.R."; fuel box; sunflower stack; brass wheel tires; headlight; DC can motor; engineer figure; brass accents; drawing illustrated only in flyer; 11-5/8" long. Available for separate-sale only.
— — — 110

85101: See 81000.

85102 NEW YORK CENTRAL: 1988, 4-4-2 Atlantic steam locomotive and tender; all black with white lettering; "5102" on cab; headlight in center of smokebox door; puffing smoke; DC can motor; engineer and fireman figures; operating couplers, but forward coupler does not swing; 31" long.
— — — 200

85103 A.T. & S.F.: 1988, 4-4-2 Atlantic steam locomotive and tender; all black with white lettering; "5103" on tender; headlight in center of smokebox door; puffing smoke; DC can motor; engineer and fireman figures; operating couplers, but forward coupler does not swing; 31" long.
— — — 225

85104: See 81002.

85105: See 81001.

85106 CHESSIE SYSTEM: 1989, 4-4-2 Atlantic steam locomotive and tender; black with yellow and orange trim; black "5106" on cab; gray smokebox; yellow running board stripe; bright yellow, orange and black tender with blue "Chessie System" logo; headlight in center of smokebox door; puffing smoke; DC can motor; engineer and fireman figures; operating couplers, but front coupler does not swing; 31" long.
— — — 250

85107 GREAT NORTHERN: 1989, 4-4-2 Atlantic steam locomotive and tender; graphite aluminum boiler front and smokebox; hunter green boiler, cab sides, tender, both ends and coal bunker; black pilot, undercarriage, tender sides, steam dome and sand dome; tuscan cab roof; white "5107" on cab; red, white and black "GREAT NORTHERN RAILWAY" logo on tender and cylinders; white running board edge stripe; headlight in center of smokebox door; puffing smoke; DC can motor with engineer and fireman figure; operating couplers, but front coupler does not swing; 31" long.
— — — 250

85108 B. & O.: 1989, 0-4-0 steam tank locomotive; aluminum and dark blue; white "5108" on cab; fuel box; tall straight stack; headlight; DC can motor; engineer and fireman figures; puffing smoke; 13-5/8" long. Available for separate-sale only.
— — — 120

85109 CANADIAN PACIFIC: 1989, 0-6-0 steam locomotive; tuscan cab, black and aluminum body; gold trim and lettering; "5109" on cab; fuel box; flared stack; headlight; DC can motor;

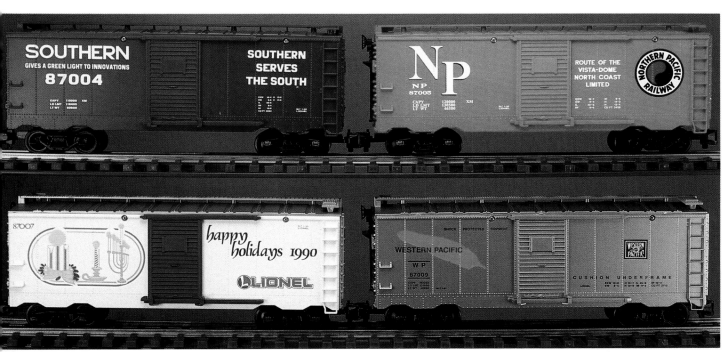

L. Caponi Collection; B. Schwab photograph

op shelf: **87004 Southern boxcar.**
econd shelf: **87005 Northern Pacific boxcar.**
hird shelf: **87007 Happy Holidays boxcar.**
ottom shelf: **87009 Western Pacific boxcar.**

	GD	VG	EXC	MT

engineer figure; puffing smoke; 13-5/8" long. Available for separate-sale only. — — — **140**

85110 PENNSYLVANIA: 1990, 4-4-2 E6 Atlantic steam locomotive with RailSounds; gray smokebox and boiler front; Brunswick green boiler, cab and tender body; red cab roof and tender deck; black pilot undercarriage and tender coal bunker; gold "5110" on cab; gold "PENNSYLVANIA" on tender; headlight at top of boiler front; DC can motor; electronic sounds: chuff, whistle and clanging bell with volume control, with activation buttons; engineer and fireman figures; puffing smoke; firebox glow; operating couplers, but front coupler does not swing. An excellent model of real PRR E6; 31" long. — — — **365**

85111 GREAT NORTHERN: 1990, 0-4-0 steam locomotive. **Not Manufactured**

85112 R.I. & P.: 1990, 0-6-0 steam locomotive. **Not Manufactured**

85113: See 81006.

85114: See 81004.

86000: See 81001.

86001: See 81001.

86002: See 81006.

86003: See 81006.

87000 N.Y.C.: 1989, standard steel boxcar; tuscan body; white "N.Y.C./87000"; yellow early bird herald; sliding doors; 15" long. — — — **50**

	GD	VG	EXC	MT

87001 PENNSYLVANIA: 1988, standard steel boxcar; tuscan body; white "P.R.R./87001"; red "PRR" keystone herald; sliding doors; 15" long. — — — **45**

87002 A.T.S.F.: 1988, standard steel boxcar; green body; yellow "A.T.S.F./87002", "Santa Fe" herald, and "The/Grand Canyon/Line"; sliding doors; 15" long. — — — **45**

87003 GREAT NORTHERN: 1989, standard steel boxcar; orange with green lower half of sides; green "GREAT NORTHERN", "DF", and "GREAT NORTHERN RAILWAY" circular herald; orange "G. N./87003"; sliding doors; 15" long. — — — **45**

87004 SOUTHERN: 1990, standard steel boxcar; tuscan body; white "SOUTHERN/GIVES A GREEN LIGHT TO INNOVATIONS/87004" and "SOUTHERN/SERVES/THE SOUTH"; sliding doors; 15" long. — — — **46**

87005 N.P.: 1990, standard steel boxcar; orange body; white "NP/87005" and "ROUTE OF THE/VISTA-DOME/NORTH COAST/LIMITED"; red, white and black "NORTHERN PACIFIC RAILWAY" monad herald; sliding doors; 15" long. — — — **46**

87006 SEASONS GREETINGS: 1989, standard steel boxcar; white body; green roof; red sliding doors; red, green and gold lettering; 15" long. Shown only in 1989 Holiday Collection flyer. — — — **70**

87007 HAPPY HOLIDAYS: 1990, standard steel boxcar; white sides; gold roof, ends and doors; green "87007" and "happy/holidays 1990"; red "LIONEL"; red, yellow, gold and green candle design; 15" long. Shown only in Stocking Stuffers flyer. — — — **75**

L. Caponi Collection; B. Schwab photograph

Top shelf: **87500** D. & R.G. flatcar (7500); **87501** Pennsylvania flatcar (7501).
Middle shelf: **87503** Illinois Central Gulf flatcar (7503); **87504** Union Pacific flatcar (7504).
Bottom shelf: **87505** Soo Line flatcar with logs.

	GD	VG	EXC	MT

87009 WESTERN PACIFIC: 1991, standard steel boxcar; aluminum; orange feather; black "WESTERN PACIFIC", "WP/87009", "SHOCK PROTECTED SHIPMENT", and "CUSHION UNDERFRAME"; square orange, white and black "WESTERN PACIFIC" herald; sliding doors; 15" long. **CP**

87100 PFE: 1988, standard steel refrigerator car; orange roof and sides; black ends; black "PACIFIC/FRUIT/EXPRESS", "PFE/87100", "UNION PACIFIC RAILROAD" herald, and round "SOUTHERN PACIFIC" herald; plug doors; 15" long.
— — — **52**

87101 PENNSYLVANIA: 1988, standard steel refrigerator car; tuscan body; yellow-gold "RAILWAY EXPRESS/AGEN-CY/REFRIGERATOR", and "PENNSYLVANIA/87101"; plug doors; 15" long. — — — **52**

87102 C & O: 1989, standard steel refrigerator car; yellow body; aluminum roof; black "C & O/87102", "INSULATED/REFRIGERATOR", "C &/O/FOR/PROGRESS"; plug doors; 15" long. — — — **50**

87103 TROPICANA: 1990, standard steel refrigerator car; orange body; green "TPIX/87103"; green and white "TROPICANA" emblem; plug doors; 15" long. — — — **52**

87104 GERBER: 1990, standard steel refrigerator car; green body; white roof; white "Gerber/Babies are our business..." and "87104"; white Gerber baby emblem; plug doors; 15" long.
— — — **52**

87105 SEABOARD: 1989, standard steel refrigerator car; dark green body; black roof; yellow-gold "SEABOARD/EXPRESS/REFRIGERATOR/87105" and "RAILWAY EXPRESS/AGEN-CY/87105"; plug doors; 15" long. — — — **50**

	GD	VG	EXC	M

87107 ATLANTIC & PACIFIC: 1991, standard stee refrigerator car; yellow sides; tuscan roof and ends; red and yellow "A & P/Where Economy Rules" logo; black "THE/GREAT/ATLAN TIC & PACIFIC/TEA/CO." and "UNION/REFRIGERATOR TRANSIT CO."; red "87107"; plug doors; 15" long. **C**

87200 LIONEL: 1989-90, handcar; tan body; black "87200" Buford and Roscoe track worker figures and loose tool set; DC ca motor; will pull a flatcar, but not intended as a switcher; operatin couplers; 8-1/2" long. — — — **6**

87201 THE MILWAUKEE ROAD: 1989, steel ore car; tus can body; white "MILW/87201" and "THE MILWAUKEE ROAD opening bottom; no load; 11-1/2" long. — — — **3**

87202 B & O: 1989, steel ore car; black body; yellow "Ches sie/System" and "B & O/87202"; yellow Chessie cat logo; openin bottom; no load; 11-1/2" long. — — — **3**

87203 SANTA AND SNOWMAN: 1990, handcar; aluminum with Santa and Snowman figures and loose tool set; metal wheel DC can motor; 8-1/2" long. — — — **7**

87204 NORTHERN PACIFIC: 1990, steel ore car; blac body; white "NORTHERN PACIFIC 87204"; opening bottom; n load; 11-1/2" long. — — — **3**

87205 PENNSYLVANIA: 1990, steel ore car; tuscan; whit lettering; opening bottom; no load; 11-1/2" long.
— — — **3**

87207 MICKEY AND DONALD: 1991, handcar; red; wit Mickey Mouse and Donald Duck figures and loose tool set; DC ca motor; "BLT 1-91"; 8-1/2" long. **C**

Top shelf: **87600 Alaska Railroad tank car; 87601 Santa Fe tank car.**
Middle shelf: **87602 Gulf tank car; 87603 Borden tank car.**
Bottom shelf: **87604 Shell tank car.**

L. Caponi Collection; B. Schwab photograph

	GD	VG	EXC	MT

87400 P.R.R.: 1987, Narrow Gauge wood style gondola; tuscan body; black deck; white lettering; "7400" on car; 11-1/2" long. Drawing shown in flyer only. — — — **36**

87401: See 81000.

87402 ATSF: 1988, Narrow Gauge wood-style gondola; black body and deck; yellow "ATSF/7402"; round black and white "Santa Fe" herald; 11-1/2" long. — — — **36**

87403 NYC: 1988; Narrow Gauge wood-style gondola; green body; black deck; white "NYC/7403"; number under- and over-scored; black "NEW YORK/CENTRAL/SYSTEM" herald; 11-1/2" long. — — — **36**

87404: See 81007.

87405 B & O: 1989, Narrow Gauge wood-style gondola; black body and deck; yellow "B & O/7405" and "Chessie/System"; yellow Chessie Cat logo; 11-1/2" long. — — — **35**

87406 SOUTHERN: 1989, Narrow Gauge wood-style gondola; tuscan body and black deck; white "SOUTHERN/7406" on car; 11-1/2" long. — — — **35**

87407 M-K-T: 1990, Narrow Gauge wood-style gondola; yellow body and black deck; black "M-K-T 7407" on car; 11-1/2" long. — — — **35**

	GD	VG	EXC	MT

87500 D. & R.G.: 1988, Narrow Gauge wood-style flatcar with 10 stakes; gray deck; black "D. & R.G 7500" on car; tall brakewheel post; 11-1/2" long. — — — **32**

87501 PENNSYLVANIA: 1988, Narrow Gauge wood-style flatcar with 10 stakes; tuscan deck; white "PENNSYLVANIA 7501" on car; tall brakewheel post; 11-1/2" long.

— — — **32**

87502: See 81002.

87503 ILLINOIS CENTRAL GULF: 1989, Narrow Gauge wood-style flatcar with 10 stakes; orange deck; black "ICG 7503" and "ILLINOIS CENTRAL GULF" on car; 11-1/2" long.

— — — **30**

87504 UNION PACIFIC: 1989, Narrow Gauge wood-style flatcar with 10 stakes; tuscan deck with yellow "UNION PACIFIC/UP 7504" and "ROAD OF The/Streamliners" on car; 11-1/2" long. — — — **30**

87505 SOO LINE: 1990, Narrow Gauge wood-style flatcar with 10 stakes and log load; tuscan deck with white "SOO LINE 87505" on car; 11-1/2" long. — — — **36**

87508: See 81004.

87600 ALASKA RAILROAD: 1989, single-dome tank car with platform and opening hatch; aluminum tank; black under-

L. Caponi Collection; B. Schwab photograph

Top shelf: **87700** Pennsylvania caboose (700); **87702** ATSF caboose (7702).
Middle shelf: **87703** NYC caboose (7703); **87705** Great Northern caboose (7705).
Bottom shelf: **87707** B & O caboose (7707); **87708** Canadian Pacific caboose (7708).

	GD	VG	EXC	MT

frame; black "ALASKA RAILROAD" and "ARR 87600"; 14-3/4" long. — — — **40**

87601 SANTA FE: 1989, single-dome tank car with platform and opening hatch; black tank and underframe; white "Santa Fe/A. T. S. F. 87601" on car; 14-3/4" long. — — — **40**

87602 GULF: 1990, single-dome tank car with platform and orange opening hatch; white tank sides, orange ends; large orange "Gulf" logo; black "WRNX/87602" on car; 14-3/4" long. — — — **43**

87603 BORDEN: 1990; single-dome tank car with platform and opening hatch; aluminum tank sides; black ends, hatch and underframe; red "BORDEN" emblem; black "IF IT'S BORDEN—IT'S/GOT TO BE GOOD/G. A. T. X/87603"; black and yellow Elsie cow emblem; 14-3/4" long. — — — **43**

87604 SHELL: 1991, single-dome tank car with platform and opening hatch; yellow side; black ends, hatch and underframe; red "SHELL"; black "SHELL OIL CO. INC." and "S. C. C. X. 87604" on car; 14-3/4" long. **CP**

87700 PENNSYLVANIA: 1987; Narrow Gauge wood-style caboose; red body and cupola; black roof; white "PENNSYL-

VANIA" and "700" on car; sliding side door; illumination provided by two D-cell batteries. Drawing shown only in flyer; 10-1/4" long. — — — **40**

87701: See 81000.

87702 ATSF: 1988, Narrow Gauge wood-style caboose; bright red with black roofwalks; white "7702"; yellow "Santa Fe" herald; brass trim; sliding side door; track-powered illumination; 10-1/4" long. — — — **40**

87703 NYC: 1988, Narrow Gauge wood-style caboose; brown with black roofwalks; white "NYC/7703" and "NEW YORK/CENTRAL/SYSTEM" herald; brass trim; sliding side door; track illuminated; 10-1/4" long. — — — **40**

87704: See 81002.

87705 GREAT NORTHERN: 1989, Narrow Gauge wood-style caboose; brown with black roof and roofwalks; yellow "GREAT NORTHERN" and "7705"; yellow, white and black "GREAT NORTHERN RAILWAY" herald; sliding side door; illuminated; 10-1/4" long. — — — **50**

87706 C & O: 1989, Narrow Gauge wood-style caboose; bright yellow; black roofwalks; blue "7706" on car; sliding side door; illuminated; 10-1/4" long. — — — **50**

	GD	VG	EXC	MT

87707 B & O: 1989, wood-style bobber caboose; red body and cupola; black roof and walks; yellow "B & O/7707" on car; not illuminated; 12-1/4" long. — — — 40

87708 CANADIAN PACIFIC: 1989, wood-style bobber caboose; brown body and cupola; black roofs and walks; white "Canadian Pacific/7708" on car; not illuminated; 12-1/4" long. — — — 40

87709: See 81007.

87712 ROCK ISLAND & PEORIA: 1990, Narrow Gauge wood-style caboose. **Not Manufactured**

87713 PENNSYLVANIA: 1990, Narrow Gauge wood-style caboose; tuscan with black roofwalks; yellow "PENNSYL-VANIA/7713" on car; sliding side door; illuminated; 10-1/4" long. — — — 50

87716: See 81004.

87800 NEW YORK CENTRAL: 1989-90, extension searchlight car; black deck; yellow generator; orange reel of gray wire; gray railings; track-powered large gray swiveling light is removable and can be placed up to five feet from the car; white "NEW YORK CENTRAL 7800"; 13" long. — — — 61

87802 CONRAIL: 1990-91, standard steel-style boxcar; brown car with white "CONRAIL" and "CR/87802" on car; sliding doors and End-of-Train Device (ETD); ETD is a red blinking light; requires nine-volt battery; 15-7/8" long. **CP**

87803 SEABOARD: 1990-91, standard steel-style boxcar; green with yellow lettering and multicolor herald; "87803" on car; sliding doors and End-of-Train Device (ETD); ETD is a red blinking light; requires nine-volt battery; 15-7/8" long. — — — 52

87806 RAILWAY EXPRESS AGENCY: 1991, standard steel-style boxcar. Announced for 1991, but not manufactured. **Not Manufactured**

TRACK AND ACCESSORIES LISTINGS

82000 STRAIGHT TRACK: 1987-91; 11-3/4" long; bulk; hollow brass rails; brass-plated steel pins; brown plastic ties; snap-fit together. **CP**

82001 CURVED TRACK: 1987-91; 13" long; bulk; 12 pieces to a 4.3-foot-diameter circle. **CP**

82002 STRAIGHT TRACK: 1987-91; 11-3/4" long; four in a carton; four brass rail joiners. **CP**

82003 CURVED TRACK: 1987-91; 13" long; four in a carton; four brass rail joiners. **CP**

82004 CURVED TRACK WIDE RADIUS: 1988-91; 15-1/4" long; 12 to a 5.3-foot-diameter circle. **CP**

	GD	VG	EXC	MT

82006 EXTRA LONG STRAIGHT TRACK: 1988-91; 35-1/4" long. **CP**

82007 REMOTE SWITCH, R. H.: 1989-91; with lighted remote control; lighted lantern; 3-3/8" high; solid brass rails; includes six rail joiners. **CP**

82008 REMOTE SWITCH, L. H.: 1989-91; with lighted remote control; lighted lantern; 3-3/8" high; solid brass rails; includes six rail joiners. **CP**

82101 LOCKON WITH WIRES: 1988-91; brass on plastic. **CP**

82102 RAIL JOINERS: 1988-91; brass; package of six; used to join tubular track with solid rail track, or solid rail to solid rail track. **CP**

82103 COUPLERS: 1988-91; pair of knuckle couplers to replace hook-and-loop couplers on other G Gauge stock. **CP**

82104 WATER TOWER: 1988-89; wood building kit to assemble and paint; 7-3/4" x 7-3/4" x 16-1/2" H. — — — 40

82105 ENGINE HOUSE: 1988-89; wood building kit to assemble and paint; 40-1/2" L x 10-1/2" W x 13-1/4" H. — — — 125

82106 WATCHMAN SHANTY: 1988-89; wood building kit to assemble and paint; 8" L x 7-1/4" W x 12-3/4" H. — — — 50

82107 PASSENGER AND FREIGHT STATION: 1988-89; wood building kit to assemble and paint; 21-1/2" L x 11-1/2" W x 9-1/2" H. — — — 90

82108 MANUAL UNCOUPLER: 1988-91; uncouples cars as they pass over it. **CP**

82109 BRASS PINS: 1988-91; brass-plated steel replacement pins; 12 per package. **CP**

82110 LUMBER SHED: 1989; wood building kit to assemble and paint; 13" L x 6-1/2" W x 6-1/4" H. — — — 35

82111 FREIGHT PLATFORM: 1989; wood building kit to assemble and paint; 17" L x 10-1/2" W x 8-1/2" H. — — — 75

82112 FIGURE SET: 1989-91; six-piece figure assortment of engineers, firemen, conductor and brakeman. **CP**

82115 WOODEN VEHICLE ASSORTMENT: 1989; vintage Ford vehicles in unfinished wood: two 82116 (1936) Pickups, two 82117 (1928) Model A Coupes, and two 82118 (1936) "Woody" Station Wagons. — — — 45

82115 RAILSOUNDS CONTROL: 1991; buttons for horn or whistle or bell. **CP**

82116 DC CONVERTER BOX: 1991; converts AC transformers to DC output for operating Large Scale trains. Includes forward-reverse control switch and a manual reset circuit breaker. Offered in 1991 Stocking Stuffers flyer. **CP**

82117 CROSSING GATE AND SIGNAL: 1991. **Production Delayed**

GLOSSARY

A-unit: Lead unit for certain diesel locomotive designs, such as F-3 units; has cab for crew.

AA: Combination of two A-unit diesel locomotives.

AB: Combination of an A- and B-unit.

ABA: Combination of an A-unit, a B-unit, and a second A-unit.

AC: Alternating Current. This term is used for the most common household electrical current; it changes polarity between positive and negative (or alternates) 60 times (or cycles) per second. Most Lionel motors are made to run on this current, although they also can run on direct current.

Advance catalogue: A catalogue for wholesale and retail distributors that indicates what would most likely be available for sale.

Airbrush: A small paint-spraying device which produces a very fine paint mist for detailed model painting.

Alco: An acronym for American Locomotive Company, manufacturer of locomotives for full-size railroads; made the FA units popularized in O27 by Lionel. Alco also made the RS-3 diesels.

Amperes: Usually abbreviated as *Amps*, this is a unit of measurement determining the strength of electrical flow within a circuit. The greater the amperage, the more forceful is the current passing through the circuit.

B-unit: Trailing unit for certain diesel locomotive designs, such as F-3 diesels; has no cab or windshield.

Bakelite: A trade name for a compression-molded plastic powder which, because of its resistance to heat, is used in appliances and stoves. Lionel has used compression-molded plastic for transformer casings and rolling stock.

Ballast tamper: A track installation machine used to tamp down the rock ballast used on real railroads to hold the ties in position on the roadbed. Lionel has made a model of this machine, which replaced laborers who tamped this rock down by hand.

Bay window caboose: Caboose with no cupola, but with extended side windows.

Bell wire: The name given to light-duty solid insulated wire often used in telephone applications or for household doorbells. It is usually 18- or 20-gauge in thickness and ideal for model railroad uses.

Benchwork: A generic term used to describe the structure supporting a train layout.

Big hook: A railroading nickname for a crane car used to lift cars and locomotives back onto the track after a wreck or derailment.

Blocks: The term used for sections of track in model railroading which are insulated electrically from other sections of track. The most common application of block circuitry is in the system known as cab control.

Box cab: Electric-outline locomotive with a rectangular body.

Brush: A critical component of the small electric motors Lionel uses. Usually cylindrical pieces of graphics which serve to conduct current to the rotating commutator.

Budd RDC: Self-propelled Rail Diesel Car; resembles a passenger car.

Builder's plate: A marker plate on an engine or rolling stock identifying the builder. It is usually rectangular.

Cab: (1) The location on an engine or rolling stock that is occupied by the crew. (2) The entire plastic shell of a diesel or caboose.

Cab control: A system for switching control of a series of blocks on a model railroad so that two or more throttles are capable of controlling those blocks, depending upon which engine is to use the blocks of track at any given time. By this system, the Lionel railroader can perform intricate switching maneuvers without fear of collisions.

Can motor: A small electric motor which is permanently sealed inside a cylinder, resembling a tin can. These motors are usually made to run on DC current, but Lionel has used them with rectifying circuits for AC applications quite successfully in recent years.

Catenary: A system of overhead wires suspended from girders to provide power for electrically-driven locomotives. Some model railroads feature elaborate hand-soldered catenary for an extremely realistic look.

Circuit breaker: An electrical trip switch which shuts off the flow of current to a circuit when there is a short circuit. It is usually tripped by excessive heat. This prevents damage to the transformer and wiring, which would otherwise overheat and melt. Most Lionel transformers are equipped with these devices.

Coach: a.k.a. Pullman. Specific type of passenger car originally designed by George Pullman; often used as a generic term for better-grade passenger cars.

Collector: Lionel's term for its more expensive, high-end, limited edition sets and rolling stock. Indicates larger and scale-sized equipment with added operating features. Contrasts to *Traditional*.

Combine: Car used in passenger trains with combination of uses, such as baggage-passenger combinations, or baggage-Railway Post Office combination.

Common ground: The use of one ground wire (or ground rail) from the track, to complete the circuit for operating many accessories. This one lead substitutes for many wires leading back to the transformer.

Commutator: The rotating part of a locomotive motor which contacts stationary carbon brushes and completes the circuit. There are flat types in most modern Lionel locomotive motors, but some of the older types had drum-type commutators.

Compression molding: A manufacturing process in which a plastic compound in the form of powder is subjected to